TWO
BLADES
OF GRASS

TWO BLADES OF GRASS

an Autobiography

John Spinks

John Spinks

Western Producer Prairie Books
Saskatoon, Saskatchewan

Printed and bound in Canada by Modern Press
Saskatoon, Saskatchewan

Western Producer Prairie Books publications are produced and
manufactured in the middle of Western Canada by a unique publishing
venture owned by a group of prairie farmers who are members of
Saskatchewan Wheat Pool. Our first book in 1954 was a reprint of a serial
originally carried in *The Western Producer*, a weekly newspaper serving
western Canadian farmers since 1923. We continue the tradition of
providing enjoyable and informative reading for all Canadians.

Cover design by John Luckhurst

Canadian Cataloguing in Publication Data

Spinks, J. W. T., 1908-
    Two blades of grass

    Bibliography: p. 219
    Includes index.
    ISBN 0-88833-57-X

    1. Spinks, J. W. T., 1908-
2. Chemists - Canada - Biography. 3. College.
presidents - Saskatchewan - Biography.
I. Title.
QD22.S65A3   540'.92'4   C80-091041-9

To Mary,

who took part in most of what follows,
as loving companion and as sage adviser

Contents

FOREWORD
PREFACE
I EARLY LIFE
    1. A Norfolk Dumpling   3
    2. "Loyaute Me Oblige"   8
    3. Undergraduate: King's College   14
    4. Research Student: King's College   20
    5. London to Saskatoon   28
    6. Dirty Thirties   31
    7. Darmstadt, Germany   36
    8. Prewar University and Marriage   42

II SCIENTIST IN WAR AND PEACE
    9. World War II   53
    10. Atoms in Wartime   63
    11. Atoms in Saskatchewan   68
    12. Atoms for Peace   77

III POSTWAR UNIVERSITY
    13. Graduate Studies   89
    14. Dumpling to President   94

15. Blue Spruce   103
16. Travel within Canada   108
17. "Da" and "Niet"   113
18. Poland, Jamaica, and Geneva   123
19. Alice in Ceylonland   128
20. Northern Lights   135
21. Decade of Change; 1959–1969   140
22. Humpty-Dumpty   144

IV   A SYSTEMS APPROACH TO SCIENCE
23. The Infrastructure   153
24. Two Blades of Grass   162

V   A SCIENTIST'S PHILOSOPHY
25. Science, Language, and Truth   175
26. Science and Creativity   184
27. Epilogue: Zero-One   195

APPENDIX A—Author's Publications

APPENDIX B—A Brief History of the University of Saskatchewan

BIBLIOGRAPHY

INDEX

Foreword

Nearly fifty years ago, Thorbergur Thorvaldson introduced me to a pink-cheeked young chemist who had just joined the staff of the chemistry department at the University of Saskatchewan. Over the years I have watched his career as he became successively professor, head of the department, dean of graduate studies, and then university president. And after I moved to the National Research Council at the beginning of World War II, I had some hand in involving him in Canada's operations research effort, and then in the Canadian atomic energy program.

John Spinks and I were also involved, together with Dr. Steacie, in getting Dr. Herzberg back to Canada in 1950 to head up spectroscopic research at the N.R.C. and to provide a strong impetus to pure research in Canada. The story of John Spinks's experiences makes fascinating reading and reminds one that there are all too few books relating to Canadian scientists or, for that matter, to Canadian university presidents.

Particularly interesting is his account of the way in which many of his pure researches have had very practical applications, for example, his pioneering work in the use of isotopes as tracers, which has led to a better understanding of fertilizer practice, and in turn, to increased crop yield. On the humanities side, his knowledge of operations research was applied to good effect in studies of health services and in developing programs for helping the disadvantaged.

John Spinks was fortunate to be partnered for the last forty years with his wife Mary, who took a more than ordinary interest in the non-academic aspects of university development. I can testify to her warmth and charm as a gracious hostess, and to the depth of her grasp of university affairs.

C. J. MACKENZIE
former President, National Research Council of Canada

Preface

Why does one write an autobiography? In my case it's quite simple. I've had what seems to me to have been a fairly busy and interesting life, spanning a fascinating period in the world's history, bridging the old and new worlds, and at the same time trying to bridge the gap between their two cultures. Just by the luck of the draw, and I think that it was more by luck than by judgment, I have had a series of worth-while experiences which have given me some insight into what makes things tick in this wicked yet fascinating world. The insight is that of a scientist in an academic setting, but this scholarly point of view has its advantages since for the last while, to paraphrase Ortega, the university has been the magic vessel into which we could look to get a glimmering of the future, however fleeting and dim that glimmering might be.

Those who expect to find here a detailed history of the University of Saskatchewan while I was there will not find it. There are many references to the university, but those who wish for academic detail should consult my *Decade of Change*, published in 1972 by the University of Saskatchewan. Equally, those who expect to find here a detailed listing of all the people I have met will be disappointed. Some people, even those whom I met many times and to whom I owe a great deal, have not been mentioned—not deliberately, but rather because they did not fit into the flow of what I was writing.

While events are related more or less chronologically, the book is not simply a chronological list of events; every now and again I try to summarize my thinking about how things really happen, how a modern university operates, how a researcher gets his ideas, or how these ideas affect social change. Even my travel was travel with a purpose—usually to some meeting or another, or as a member of a commission or board of enquiry. And each time I learned a bit—as they say, "If you haven't seen it, you haven't seen it."

Sections IV and V were introduced at the suggestion of the publisher, who thought that my views on the development of science and the relationship of science to the humanities would be of interest to the reader. The resulting essays can be read separately. The essay approach has inevitably resulted in a certain amount of repetition, but not enough, I hope, to be objectionable.

Thanks are owed to a number of sources for illustrations. I am indebted to the publishers of *Culture, Prairie Forum,* the *Journal of Chemical Education,* and *Chemistry in Canada* for permission to reproduce portions of articles written by me and appearing originally in these journals.

I am grateful to the late Miss Muriel Stein who not only typed the manuscript but was earlier a very competent secretary to the president for a number of years.

And, he gave it for his Opinion; that whoever could make two Ears of Corn, or two Blades of Grass to grow upon a Spot of Ground where only one grew before; would deserve better of Mankind, and do more essential Service to his Country, than the whole Race of Politicians put together.

Jonathan Swift, *Gulliver's Travels*

PART I
EARLY LIFE

Chapter 1

A Norfolk Dumpling

I suppose everything has to have a beginning, and I might as well begin with the cold and blustery morning when I first saw the light of day, on January 1, 1908—I was a New Year's baby. I could never quite decide whether that was a good thing or a bad thing—when I was a youngster, Christmas presents and birthday gifts were apt to be lumped together, but later on, when I was attending New Year's parties, someone was bound to know that John had a birthday, and almost immediately after "Auld Lang Syne" I would hear "Happy Birthday to you," and be smothered in kisses.

At the time that I was born, my family lived in a small village called Methwold, on the edge of the fens in Norfolk, England. That part of Norfolk was thick with Spinkses, who had been there since the time of the Doomsday Book. My mother was a Tranter from Setch, near Kings Lynn— one of a family of eleven daughters and one son, so I had no lack of aunts and uncles and cousins, and later on I had scads of nieces and nephews. I was fourth in a family of six in which there were two boys and four girls: Percy, Helen, Jessie, John, Florence, and Winnie.

My father died in a tragic accident when I was quite small, so I cannot honestly say that I remember much about him, except that he was a big man and that I thought him handsome. Actually, I was with him when the accident occurred. We were driving in a horse and trap along a country road when the horse shied at a pile of stones and bolted so that the trap was overturned. I landed in a bed of nettles and suffered no harm, but my father fell heavily and died a few days later from internal injuries.

"In my father's house are many mansions: if it were not so I would have told you. I go to prepare a place for you."

I sat at my father's bedside while my mother read these words. I can still hear her reading, and I still find those words immensely beautiful and moving.

My father bought and sold horses and cattle and was, I think, reasonably well off; at least we were able to afford a maid and to have a tutor in math and French for my brother Percy (later called Bill), who had ambitions of becoming an engineer. His engineering proclivities were shown at an early age by his urge to construct numerous toboggans and little wagons—the latter with wheels of great variety. I remember one wagon pulled by our collie dog in which I was usually the passenger. One day the dog was pulling me at a good pace along a country road when he saw a rabbit. He chased the rabbit until it bolted into a hedge at the side of the road, with disastrous results for me and the wagon.

Other remembrances of those early days are of school. We started at the age of four, and I remember how jealous we were of a boy who could tell the time, although it wasn't long before we all could do so too. And we played word games, did arithmetic of a sort, and made pretty patterns out of pieces of coloured paper cut into triangles and squares. I remember sitting on the seat at the organ in St. George's Church while my mother played the hymns and psalms. And I remember sitting on the rug by the fire on a cold Sunday afternoon, while mother read to us from a weekly magazine; these were simple pleasures, but they were greatly enjoyed.

One of the few early memories which I can date is the Christmas spent with my grandparents at Kings Lynn. For Christmas dinner we all sat around a big table, and I was small enough to be put in a high chair, so I couldn't have been more than two or three years old. We started dinner with Yorkshire pudding, which was traditional with my grandparents, but I had my eye on the turkey and plum pudding, and when my grandmother asked me if I wished for any more Yorkshire pudding I replied "No" quite emphatically, and then added for good measure, "I am quite full. I couldn't eat another crumb." The turkey was served then, but I was left without even a plate. Mother noticed that I was gradually clenching my little fist as it seemed that I was being overlooked, so she came to my rescue and suggested that perhaps I might be served next.

"Indeed not," replied grandmother sharply. "John said he was completely full, and I would not cause him to tell a lie."

So I sat and watched everyone eat a fine dinner while I went hungry. I like to think that the lesson was not wasted on me. Certainly I have always had a good respect for the truth. The incident didn't stop me from being very fond of my grandparents; grandmother even taught me to play billiards as soon as I was old enough to peer over the edge of the billiard table.

When I was six we moved to a nearby town, Thetford, on the border of Norfolk and Suffolk. Thetford was full of churches, ruins of churches and cathedrals—and pubs. The main attraction in Thetford was Burrells' Works, where steam engines and other machines were made, and where my brother was apprenticed to become an engineer. This apprenticeship didn't last long because war was declared in August of 1914. Burrells' was quickly transformed to make munitions, and my brother was put in charge of a group of women workers, who were turning out shells and other munitions. One of my pleasures in those days was to take a hot supper to my brother when he was working on the night shift. I was all of seven or eight at the time, and I enjoyed scampering in the dark across the town—a distance of about a mile, I suppose.

The town and its life were quickly immersed in World War I. Troops marched off, prisoners were brought in to work on the railway unloading supplies, and army camps and an air base were constructed in the neighborhood. These were all exciting changes for a young boy. Almost every weekend there would be a parade of one kind or another, with a military band playing "Land of Hope and Glory," flags waving, and a group of youngsters running beside the troops.

Food became scarce, and one of my chores was to line up to get our weekly rations of meat at the butcher's and of butter at the grocer's. Bread had to be bought from the bakery and milk from the end of the road where the milkman stopped his cart for a few minutes to allow customers to pick up some rather thin milk. Our supply of food received a welcome addition when a jolly Welsh sergeant major was billeted with us. He received relatively generous army rations, which he insisted on adding to the general stock of provisions in the pantry, on the share-and-share-alike principle. We got to be very fond of him and later of his wife, who occasionally came to spend a holiday with him. She enjoyed walking, and I often had the pleasure of accompanying her on long walks in the country.

There were many huge estates in the neighborhood of Thetford with large areas of heathland—the so-called breckland country, which was not much good for farming but did provide a sanctuary for countless birds and small animals. Strictly speaking, this was all private property, but so long as they didn't do willful damage, the numerous gamekeepers would turn a blind eye to casual strollers. On an afternoon's walk we would see rabbits by the score, with hares, pheasants, partridges, and smaller birds too numerous to mention. And occasionally, at the entrance to a rabbit hole, on the pile of freshly turned-up earth, we might find a flint flake which had been chipped to form a scraper, or even a piece of Roman pottery as a reminder of far-off days.

Only on one occasion did we break the law. I had found a nest of pheasant eggs, and I showed them to the sergeant's wife.

"Are they good to eat?"

I had to admit that they probably were, so my friend suggested that we should take half of them—five out of ten. I hesitated and said that if we were caught with the eggs there would be a stiff fine.

"Let me worry about that," said my companion, and with that she put the eggs in the front of her blouse.

Sure enough, a short while afterwards we met a gamekeeper, who asked if I had any eggs. I replied truthfully, "No," but he had some doubts and he patted the front of my peaked cap, which was the usual place for hiding eggs. Luckily I hadn't any there, or there would have been a gooey mess. He didn't suspect my Welsh friend who was very proud of her accomplishment, particularly when we reached home and had the eggs for high tea. They were delicious!

Thetford was almost an ideal place for a young boy to grow up in. It was situated at the junction of two small rivers, the Thet and the Little Ouse. They were slow-moving streams, running through meadows with low banks and frequent groups of trees. A walk along one of the paths bordering the river made a good afternoon's outing, particularly if one had taken a picnic lunch along. And there were several places where one could swim or fish.

The favorite spot for an outing was Two Mile Bottom, some two or three miles downstream from Thetford, where there was a stretch of common land adjoining the river and a spring of water which was cool and safe to drink. I remember going camping for the weekend at Two Mile Bottom with a small friend of mine, Leslie Bailey by name, when we were all of eight years old. We went on our bikes, loaded down with blankets, a canvas sheet, a kettle and frying pan, and a good supply of food. With the canvas sheet and a piece of rope tied between two trees we constructed a pup tent, just big enough to hold us. I still remember the excitement of building a fire and cooking supper in a frying pan over the fire. And I remember the raucous squawks of the pheasants as they flew into the trees at dusk to roost for the night. On Sunday evening we returned home, as black as sweeps but quite unharmed, and all the better for having stayed out on our own for a couple of nights. In those days one didn't have to worry about being molested by young or old—at least not in the Thetford district.

What else can I fit into this 1914–18 period? I remember my brother's leaving his engineering work to join the Royal Flying Corps in 1917. He was seventeen at the time, and I remember the great excitement any time he came home for a few days' leave. Of course I remember my sisters well; Helen and Jessie were older than I was, while Florence and Winnie were younger. We played endless games and got along well together. We had the usual pets, a dog and a cat, and my brother kept rabbits which I had to help feed.

We knew all our neighbors for quite a distance around. Next door on one side was Kenneth Dodds, a bit older than I was, and already at the grammar school. On the other side were the Osbornes, an older couple who occasionally had visits from two of their nieces. Beyond them were the Bonds; Mrs. Bond was quite old but very nice indeed, and she knew just how to handle little boys. The Bonds had a grandson, Teddy, who was just about my age and with whom I used to play. Teddy and I belonged to the Cubs and later to the Scouts, and we sang in the choir at St. Cuthbert's Church. By the time I had run a few errands for my mother and some of the neighbors and had been to choir practice, there wasn't much time to spare. And there was still less when I moved from the elementary school to grammar school at the age of ten.

In spite of the war, the first six years in Thetford went by relatively pleasantly. I had many young friends of my own age, and together we explored the countryside within five or six miles of the town, sometimes on foot, sometimes on bicycles. We knew where to go fishing in the many streams and meres (small lakes), where to find sweet crab apples in the hedgerows, and where to find hazelnuts and chestnuts in the autumn. We climbed trees, chased rabbits on the open brecklands, hid in the bracken, and explored the ditches and dikes that criss-crossed the water-meadows— all the activities that are part of healthy growing up. Occasionally we fell into one of the ditches or tore our trousers scrambling through a hedge in too much of a hurry. For this we were duly spanked and sent to bed without any supper. Life was simple and very pleasant.

Chapter 2

"Loyaute Me Oblige"

When I was nine some of my older friends moved from the elementary school over to the local grammar school, and soon my head was filled with romantic notions of playing football and cricket with the school eleven, of learning algebra and chemistry and Shakespeare and French, and of wearing a black and gold football shirt and a school cap and blazer with the school coat of arms on the blazer pocket. But it all seemed very far away, impossibly so, since it was a private grammar school with stiff fees, and my mother had let me know that she could not afford to send me to grammar school.

I found out much later that when my father died he had left my mother reasonably well off, but that her capital had not been too well invested, and we had lived in too rich a style for the income which resulted from it, considering that my mother had been left with a large young family to bring up. Fortunately one day the teacher in charge of the class in the elementary school that I attended told me that two scholarships were available for admission to the grammar school and asked if I would like to sit for the exam. My mother agreed that I should try, so I filled out the application forms and waited for the day. The only extra studying to be done was the memorizing of about twenty poems. I still remember that one of them was Tennyson's "New Year's Eve."

In due time I wrote the examinations and was successful. The scholarship included an allowance for books and clothes, so I was able to go to grammar school at no great expense to the family. The school was a boys' school with some day-boys and some boarders. Most of the boarders were sons of members of the Civil Service whose fathers had also attended the school. There were only a hundred and fifty students—just enough to have a good-sized group for each form.

In retrospect I realize that I was very lucky. The form masters were all able men and good teachers. The math master, for example, had a double first from Cambridge. We called him Lickers from his habit of sucking on licorice most of the time, but by the time I left school, I not only knew the usual elementary algebra, trig., and geometry, but I also had a fair idea of differential and integral calculus. The other teachers had corresponding qualifications from other universities. French was taught by a French-woman, a widow, whose son attended the school. Although I wasn't a linguist by any means, I did acquire enough French to be able to read French for pleasure, thus acquiring a habit which I still have.

I started in the third form. The classroom was part of the chancel of a former monastery, and the form master sat in the bishop's throne with the hard cold marble somewhat softened by a cushion. This part of the school had been built in the ruins of a monastery that had been given by Henry VIII to Sir Richard Fulmerstone, who in turn had given it to the school. The Fulmerstone coat of arms was used as the school badge and proudly displayed on cap and blazer. Term began and ended with the school song, sung by a hundred and fifty or so lusty voices:

> The roll of pious founders comes first in the book of fame,
> And high in the glorious list appears
> Our founder's honoured name.

I still get a little wet-eyed when I think of it.

Thetford Grammar School was founded in 762, and it had a partial list of masters from that date and a complete list of scholars from about 1500 onwards. Numbered among the illustrious scholars was Tom Paine, who is probably better known in America than in England. The school was for boys only, so we missed the benefits or disadvantages of coeducation. Actually, a full program at school kept us busy, with not much time or energy for other distractions. Every afternoon from about half past three we participated in some form of sport. We had football (soccer) in autumn and winter, and then we had cricket, swimming, and tennis in the summer, together with track and field sports. And the whole of Wednesday afternoon and Saturday afternoon were devoted to games. While I wasn't particularly good at them, I did enjoy sports, and I eventually played in the third eleven at soccer.

The headmaster, Mr. Cole, taught Shakespeare throughout the school, and he used the class to instill into us a love of good English, a love for our country, the idea of honour and loyalty, and a respect for the truth. Lying was one of the unforgivable sins.

When I was about fifteen I wrote the usual Cambridge matriculation examinations and was successful, but I was obviously too young to go to university. The headmaster persuaded my mother that I should study at school for another two years and sit for the Higher School Certificate examination, with the idea that I might eventually go to university. So I spent two years doing mostly chemistry and physics, pretty well on my own, with a free run of the labs., but under the general supervision of the science master, Mr. Whitely, who was affectionately called Wee Willie Whitely, although he was well over six feet tall.

The Senior Prefect, Stewart Cole, and I shared a study for some time. He was studying mostly history and Latin, with his eye on Cambridge and the Overseas Civil Service. He was good company and we got along well together. These two years of working on my own probably taught me a certain amount of self-reliance, although I did not think of that at the time. Each year was marked by a prize-giving day, attended by students, parents, and dignitaries from far and near. At first I would get one of the form prizes, but as I progressed through 5a, 5b, and the sixth form, I won a number of the special prizes in science, math, English, and even in religious studies. The Duleep Singh Medal was awarded to me for an historical essay which I wrote on the old abbey at Bury St. Edmunds. Duleep Singh, maharajah, Norfolk squire, and friend of Queen Victoria, had been a benefactor to the school.

While school took up the greater part of my time from the ages of ten and a half to seventeen and a half, I was still very much taken up with life at home—running errands for my mother, digging the garden, cooking the porridge, peeling the potatoes, washing up, passing the tea cups when ladies came to tea, going for walks into the country, and going on picnics when the weather was sunny. There were many prime spots for picnicking within a mile or two of where we lived.

Scouting took up one evening each week, choir practice another, and Sunday was a succession of services in morning and evening, with just an hour or so free in the afternoon for a walk, if it happened to be fine. Saturday afternoon was always a particular pleasure. Often I would go fishing with a friend of mine, or at the appropriate time of the year we would gather wild blackberries, crab apples, or chestnuts.

After a time I got to know the Reverend Mr. Green, who was keen on local history and archaeology. He had permission from the neighboring landowners to wander over their property, and we spent many Saturday afternoons roaming across heathland and breckland, looking for the remains of ancient man. We would often find scrapers, knives, and borers of flint, and fragments of pottery from old Iron Age and Roman settlements. I learnt a great deal of early history on those walks. Mr. Green had a small parish at Santon Downham, a village about five miles from Thetford which was easily reached by bicycle. Often, after an afternoon trudging over hill and dale, we would finish up at the rectory, where his housekeeper would refresh us with thinly-cut bread and butter, plum cake, and tea out of huge cups. Many years later I told my wife about these outings, and in due time she not only met Mr. Green but also sampled the bread and butter, the plum cake, and the tea, just exactly as I had described them to her.

One of the highlights of my archaeological education was when I was allowed to assist in the clearing of some galleries in the flint mines known as Grimes Graves. These flint mines, dug by neolithic man some thousands of years earlier, had eventually been filled in with rubbish and forgotten, so that only a series of surface depressions remained to mark where the pits had originally been. Eventually some of the pits were investigated, and a whole series of flint mines was found lying about forty feet below the surface and connected by a series of galleries which had been dug in the chalk. In clearing out the rubble from the galleries we would occasionally find the implements which had been used by ancient man, including deer-antler picks. Crawling around the galleries on the tummy and squeezing through small connecting holes was not good for claustrophobia, but at that age such phobias did not worry me. The land surface itself in the neighborhood of Grimes Graves was an archaeologist's paradise, since a good deal of the flint from the mines had been chipped into flakes and implements right on the spot, and as a consequence the surface was littered with chips and flakes and partly worked implements, as well as with occasional fine specimens. A good many of these last found their way into the Thetford museum.

These Saturday afternoon archaeological exercises awakened in me an interest in local history of all kinds which gradually deepened into a broad interest in prehistory. One memory of those days was of meeting a number of archaeologists and historians from Cambridge University on an excursion to Grimes Graves. Among their number was Miss Nineveh Layard, whose father had played an important role in the excavations at Nineveh.

I remember that we always put on an old pair of pajamas over our clothes in order to keep off some of the chalk and dirt when we were crawling around in the galleries. Light was provided by a candle, grasped firmly in one hand with particular care not to let it fall between the blocks of chalk that made up the floor of the tunnels. This mishap actually did happen on one occasion when a young man was showing his girl friend around the galleries. The candle was lost, so they used up their matches trying to find it, and then sat in pitch blackness waiting for someone to come and rescue them. Luckily they had left their motor bike on the surface, near the pit into which they had descended, so when they failed to turn up at home a search party found the bike and eventually them, but not before they had spent a rather terrifying twenty hours, at a depth of forty feet below ground.

My archeological education was greatly assisted by attendance all one winter at a series of lectures on local history, given by a professor from Cambridge. The lectures and slides were supplemented by a big box of books deposited at the local library—I think I read everything in the collection!

That local library provided me with varied fare: lots of weekly and monthly magazines and a large number of books, mostly of Victorian vintage. So I absorbed Dickens, Scott, Thackeray, Bronte and Borrow, and numerous novels of the Jeffery Farnol, de Vere Stacpoole variety. My regular Sunday reading was the Sunday *Observer* and the *Sunday Express*. I was a voracious but not a discriminating reader. At one stage or another I read reams of poetry: Tennyson, Longfellow, Byron, Matthew Arnold, Masefield, and so on—from one end of the book to the other. And I heard a good deal of music on the piano from my mother who played very well and had a lovely voice.

Grammar school occupied the 1918–1925 period during which food and other supplies gradually got back to normal, so that we were adequately fed and properly dressed. But there was no money to spare for luxuries. Pocket money was sixpence a week (approximately ten cents), with tuppence allotted to Scouts, tuppence to church, and tuppence to spend on myself. Actually, the amount didn't matter much since all the boys at school were on a limited amount of pocket money, and the one boy who seemed to have an enormous amount of it was not encouraged to flash it around.

The school underwent a major change after World War II as a result of the 1944 Education Act which brought about a complete reorganization in English secondary education. It became a voluntary state-controlled school, and it ceased to have boarders. Then it expanded enormously, became coeducational, and lost most of its independence. Now, in 1980, a strong attempt is being made by the governors to bring about a reversion to independence, even though this change of status would involve a return to the earlier fee-paying system.

The 1918–25 period was very much school-oriented. There were only two of us children at home most of the time—my sister Florence and I. My elder brother had stayed with the Air Force and was being sent all over the world from one air base to another, seldom spending more than two years at any one place, and my three other sisters, with the financial help of various relatives, were at boarding school on the outskirts of London.

Eventually my eldest sister, Helen, became nursery governess to the children in Lord Fisher's family. The Fishers had a magnificent estate at Kilverstone, a couple of miles outside Thetford. It was my duty to escort my sister back to Kilverstone after a visit home, and we usually rode our bikes. I associate those return trips with the smell of an oil-burning bicycle lamp. The lamp was quite useless as a means of illumination in the dark, but as the road was deserted and I knew every inch of it, the absence of a light was no great disadvantage.

Mention of Kilverstone and the Fishers reminds me that when I was quite young I sang in the choir at Lord Fisher's funeral. Afterwards we went over to the Hall, where the men had port and the boys had hot chocolate and plum cake. We each received a golden guinea, which was a small fortune for a boy in those days. The country around Thetford was largely made up of great estates which sometimes included a score or more of villages and were owned by people such as Lord Fisher, the Earl of Iveagh, and the Duke of Grafton. Smaller estates and large farms were owned by wealthy gentlemen farmers who saw to it that there were plenty of partridges and pheasants and hares for the shooting season.

When I was small, these large land owners ruled the roost and on the whole did not a bad job of it, but by the time I had grown up, World War I had eliminated all the younger sons, and the huge taxes of the postwar period had wiped out most of the family fortunes. Some of the estates survived by being converted into limited liability companies, and some of the huge houses became historical treasures in the keeping of the National Trust, but many of them were destroyed just because nobody could afford to keep them up. While many of the landowning families disappeared, others grew up. The little bicycle shop at the corner expanded into a garage and sales outlet for cars, and the once-weekly movie house became a gaudy picture theatre. Soon the owners of these burgeoning businesses had taken over the imposing houses with the beautifully kept grounds. In a quarter of a century a social revolution took place, in many ways just as brutal and just as effective as some of the earlier, bloodier revolutions. World War II completed the change.

Most of my life in those days was centered on a small area, two or three miles across, with occasional excursions five or ten miles further. Family ties connected us sporadically with the rest of the country and the rest of the world. Numerous remains of cathedrals, monasteries, earthworks, and other reminders of one's ancestors anchored that small area strongly to its past. In some ways this was not a broad base on which to build, but it was a pretty solid one, none the less. By the age of eighteen I was, I suppose, a fairly typical "Norfolk Dumpling."

Chapter 3

Undergraduate: King's College

At the age of seventeen I was in the sixth form, and I didn't know quite what to do next, although it had been impressed upon me by various aunts and uncles that since I had been at grammar school I should certainly try to get into some kind of profession. Eventually things took care of themselves. The headmaster at the school suggested that I write the Higher School Certificate examinations and at the same time apply for a Norfolk scholarship. I was successful in both the examinations and the application for a scholarship, which gave me a living allowance and paid my fees at King's College in the University of London. People have often wondered why I didn't go to Cambridge, just thirty miles away from my home, rather than to London. It was probably because the science master at school was from King's College, and because the scholarship would support me completely at King's but would not have been enough to take care of all the extra incidentals at Cambridge.

My mother and my brother had agreed that I might go to university, provided I could do it on my own. My attending university did mean that I was not doing anything to support the family for that period. This responsibility was seen to by my brother, and I have always felt most grateful to him for undertaking it. Nothing much was said about this aspect of going to university, but it was understood that when I had graduated I would do my share in supporting my mother. My mother was, I think, extremely proud of her family, and she watched the careers of the various children with great interest. Although she would no doubt have liked to have had more of her family at home, I think my mother realized that a small town in East Anglia did not offer many prospects in the period after

World War I, and she was pleased enough to bask in the reflected glory as my brother advanced successively through flight lieutenant to squadron leader, and wing commander to group captain, with postings all over England and most of the world.

So in the autumn of 1925 I packed my bag and my trunk and went up to London to start a new period of my life at King's College in the Strand. At first I found it all very strange and confusing. To start with, I had been living in a small rural town with a population of thirty-five hundred, where everything was within walking distance, and where in a walk through the town I knew nearly everybody I met. It was quite otherwise in London—a great hustle and bustle of people going about their separate ways and a great deal of noisy traffic. Luckily the college formed a sort of oasis between the Strand and the Embankment, where all was quiet. The college grounds served as a jumping-off spot for pleasant strolls through secluded squares and gardens or, if I wanted to go a bit further, to the delights of St. James's Park, Hyde Park, and of the numerous museums, art galleries, theatres, bookshops, and restaurants.

The first day I felt quite lonely. Registering as a student took a matter of only a few minutes, since most of the details had been settled by correspondence some weeks earlier. So I stood in the huge entrance hall watching the other students sweep by, all of them seeming to know exactly what they wanted to do. Luckily, when I was about to leave for the day, I noticed another young man of about my own age who looked just as lost as I felt. I slowly walked over to him and tried a cautious "Hello." He responded with a friendly grin and an outstretched hand. Yes, he was a freshman, his home was in Yorkshire, and he was feeling lonely too. How about finding the refectory and having a cup of tea? So we found the refectory, sat at a long table with twenty or so other students, gravely received a cup of tea poured by a Senior from a huge brown betty, helped ourselves to a thick slice of delicious cherry cake, and were immediately engulfed in a flood of conversation that made us feel completely at home. Meals and snacks in the refectory were to be part of my life from then on, sometimes with a group of friends and sometimes with a group of comparative strangers who did not remain strangers for long.

In the first year at college I took two subjects, chemistry and physics, which both had a good deal of lab. work. At the end of the first year I transferred to an honours chemistry course, and my work started in earnest: inorganic chemistry, organic chemistry, physical chemistry, and a little bit of physics, with again a great deal of lab. work. We were left very much on our own. No one checked whether we attended lectures or not, although in fact we wouldn't have dreamed of missing a lecture. No one inquired whether we had understood what we heard. As a matter of fact, we usually understood only about a quarter of what we heard, and had we understood much more than that we would have doubted whether the lectures were worth attending. The professors were all first class: Allmand in physical chemistry, Samuel Smiles in organic, Cremer in inorganic, Salmon in phase rule, and so on. We took it that we should have to learn to work on our own, and we did.

The lab. was much the same. At the beginning of the term we were given keys to the appropriate labs. Inside the lab. was posted a list of experiments to be done. An assistant checked the results. If they were correct he marked them with a tick and we went on with the next experiment. If we were wrong, a cross covered the page and we started all over again. I remember trying a sulfate analysis which I did carefully, and getting duplicate results which checked very well. Unfortunately, the answer was incorrect. When I asked the assistant where I might have gone wrong, he fixed me with an icy stare:

"You know where the library is? You know how to read? Then why not try to find out for yourself!"

I did as I was told, and after several tries I started to get things right. From then on I seemed to be able to do the work correctly every time. Success certainly gave me a good deal of self-confidence. Of course, some people didn't like this way of doing things, and they just dropped out. Nobody tried to persuade them:

" 'Sink!' she said, or 'Swim!' she said, and the eggshell went to sea."

By this time I had a circle of close friends with whom I regularly had lunch and tea, and with whom I would go to the theatre or to row on the Serpentine if the afternoon happened to be too fine for work. The students had a great variety of tastes. They read all kinds of books, from Voltaire to Aldous Huxley, and went to all kinds of plays, from Shakespeare to Shaw's *Saint Joan* and *The Apple Cart*, with a lacing of Noel Coward's plays and revues. Some of these experiences gave me instant pleasure, and some gave me quite a shock but helped me to grow up. I remember reading *Penguin Island* by Anatole France for the first time and my shock as I gradually realized that the author was poking fun at religion. I remember also my introduction to Havelock Ellis and the realization that many more queer things went on in the world than I had dreamed of in dreamy Thetford.

One of my chemist friends was a good pianist, and with him I went to the Guildhall School of Music to hear chamber music and to become acquainted with some of the more modern composers. We went to various concert places such as the Wigmore Hall and heard such performers as Myra Hess. My absorptive capacity seemed endless. There was so much to see and hear and so little time. I remember with particular pleasure the choir in Westminister Abbey at evensong and the Sunday morning Palestrina at Westminister Cathedral. It was worth sitting through a sermon to hear that.

Each term the college drama group would put on a play. It was usually very well done. Greer Garson of *Mrs. Miniver* fame was one of the actresses. There were women students in college, and occasionally one of the numerous clubs would stage a tea dance down in the refectory. To start with I couldn't dance, but my fellow students soon taught me. College dances were rare, about one a term, and they were held in the Great Hall. I remember them as being very pleasant.

Going to the theatre was usually dutch treat. There would be three or four men students and three or four women students, and we usually sat up in the gallery, the highest part of the seating, which was always known as "the gods."

Most of the men did not have enough money to be able to entertain lavishly, and in those days the emphasis on having just one girl friend, which seems so prevalent nowadays, was almost absent. Of course, being reasonably normal, most of us would at one time or another develop fearful crushes on girls. I remember one gorgeous creature, M.C. by name, who was reading honours French. So I frequented the French Library, where she did most of her work, at all hours of the day, hoping to catch a glimpse of her. Under her guidance I acquired quite a taste for French poetry— Ronsard, Villon, Verlaine, and others—and I have forgotten how many versions of the story of Heloise and Abelard I read when she had that as a subject for an essay. This infatuation had one good side effect—I got to know other books by George Moore after reading *Heloise and Abelard*. Occasionally M.C. would agree to have tea with me in the refectory and once we even went to a tea dance at the Criterion, just off Piccadilly. But she was too good-looking and too popular for me to be able to see her often, and I quickly got over my temporary infatuation. In those days few of the students were married, and hardly any of them got married while they were students; for one thing, marriage wasn't the fashion, and for another, we couldn't afford it.

Sports continued to take up quite a bit of time, usually Wednesday afternoons and Saturday afternoons. I started playing with the soccer third eleven, and later I switched to cross-country running with the college team. We would run six miles or so uphill and downdale and often finish covered in mud, but by the time we had removed the dirt and soaked in a hot bath for a few minutes, we were ready for tea and cherry cake and were firmly convinced that there was no sport in the world to beat running. Still later, when I was doing research, I switched to boxing in the evenings, at 120 pounds. The gymnasium was not too far from my lab., so it was quite convenient to get an experiment going and then to go to the gym for an hour or so to work out.

At weekends I would go sailing with a small group of students who had bought an eighteen-foot boat with a centreboard and had moored it at the clubhouse of the Royal Erith Yacht Club at the Thames mouth. The clubhouse was an old barge, moored by the river bank, and we could always get food there if we felt like it, and there was usually the possibility of going on a weekend cruise as crew for a larger boat. Sailing in a small boat in the Thames mouth was quite exciting. There were strong tides, and often traffic was hindered by a string of barges which had been moored for the weekend some distance offshore. And there was the perpetual hazard of losing one's wind in the lea of a relatively fast-moving liner. Sailing introduced me to a different group of the college's students—medicals, engineers, and so on, who were quite different from the rather too-dedicated chemists. Anyhow, I enjoyed sailing very much.

Most of the time that I was at King's I attended a series of Monday morning lectures given by some distinguished theologian—usually on a reasonably philosophic topic. One year it was Bishop Gore, who was by then quite elderly and venerable but had a matchless power of expression. We wouldn't have missed him for worlds. One day a special debate was arranged between him and Bertrand Russell—to discuss, I believe, the nature of God. No doubt Russell's logic was unquestionable, but there was also no doubt that Bishop Gore had acquired a much more serene outlook on life.

There were literally dozens of lectures by distinguished visiting scholars at King's and nearby colleges, and we tried to go to a number of these. They were usually not on science but on a great variety of other topics. I remember one such series by Maritain—the punch line was "Almost thou persuadest me to be a Thomist."

At one of these lecture series I sat next to a young math lecturer who invited me to his uncle's home for coffee after the lecture one evening. His uncle was a clergyman in Aldersgate. We had a pleasant conversation which I enjoyed very much, but before I left for home I had agreed to spend one evening each week helping to run a Scout troop for the boys in the Aldersgate district, which was a fairly tough spot in those days. The procedure was to go to the rectory and change into Scouting clothes, have a quick supper, spend two or three hours with the Scouts, and then go back to the rectory to change and have coffee and a chat before going home to my lodgings. It was good for me to be exposed to this aspect of London life, which was entirely different from the sheltered life of Thetford, and I soon became very attached to the various members of the Scout troop.

Sundays were kept free from college and study. On Sunday mornings I often went to church and then to tea with my Aunt and Uncle Kindell who lived in Walthamstow and had two sons, one about my age and one a bit older. Sometimes we would go for a walk in Epping Forest or for a drive into the country. Every now and again I would visit the school where my sister Winnie was a pupil. By this time she was a senior student and had common room privileges, so we would sit by the fire in the common room for a while and then attend evensong in the school chapel. The girls had beautiful voices and had been well trained.

In the summer I went back to Thetford, always with a huge pile of books for summer reading. I earned a little pocket money by coaching students for Cambridge matric., but by and large I spent the time studying and just being lazy. I helped with the garden and the household chores, went fishing, played some golf and tennis, and walked downtown with mother and my sisters. Occasionally we would visit friends for tea or go on a picnic. All in all, the time went pleasantly, and eventually I wrote the exams—about a month of them—and then went home to await the results.

At that time, in 1928, I hadn't quite decided what to do next, but I thought that I might go to work as a chemist with I.C.I. (Imperial Chemical Industries). After being at home about a month I received a card from Paris, sent by one of my instructors, Professor A. J. Allmand, a well-known figure in the world of photochemistry, which is the study of the action of light on chemical systems. It was brief and to the point:

> My dear Spinks,
> In a few days you will hear that you have been awarded your degree. Congratulations! As far as I know you have not yet made up your mind what you are going to do. How about working with me? If the answer is yes, you will find that there is a small lab. set aside for you not far from the college machine shop. See you in the Fall!
> P.S. I think I can scrape up enough money for you to live on.

The matter was discussed with my mother, who said that I could do what I liked, provided I saw after myself financially. So a few days later I packed my bags and went back to King's College with the general idea of spending a year or two learning what it was to do research. At that time I had no idea what kind of career it might lead to. I suppose that if I thought about it at all, I assumed that my professor would not have suggested it if it hadn't been a good idea in the first place.

Chapter 4

Research Student: King's College

My lab., which was to be my home for the next two years, was in the basement of the college and was shared with another research student, Lewis, who was a good many years my senior. I saw him infrequently since he seemed to work mostly at night and seldom turned up before three or four in the afternoon—just in time for tea, in fact. I first met him when he was, I think, rather bored with the problem he was working on—which was the precise measurement of gas pressure and volume for very pure gases. He paid meticulous attention to details, and he was constantly checking me for my attitude, which was "good enough". If I had a new idea for an experiment I would set it up as quickly as possible and try it out—if something interesting happened I would improve things and do the experiments with much greater attention to detail, until finally the results would satisfy the severest critic. But I didn't see any point in spending an enormous effort on detail before there was at least some prospect that the experiment would work.

Lewis and I had great arguments about my approach to experiments and about his generally pessimistic attitude towards life and society. He was most scornful about my literary and artistic taste—or lack of it—and about my somewhat naive approach to the scientific method and to the whole question of reliability of results. All this was, however, very good for me because I had to do a good deal of reading and thinking in order not to be absolutely crushed by him. He introduced me to some of the smaller art galleries and to some of the things one can get to see if one knows how to go about it. Under his tutelage I came to know the fine collection of Turner water-color sketches at the Tate and some of the highly specialized collections of paintings by early Chinese and Japanese artists at the British Museum.

I remember one particular sepia work of three field mice precariously perched on ears of corn. It didn't matter much which way you turned the picture to look at it because the composition was still perfectly balanced, and I would sit literally an hour at a time, absorbed in this painting. It induced in me a most pleasurable state which I later came to associate with other sense reactions—the feel of a piece of polished stone, and the shape and feel of a small piece of Eskimo carving when held loosely in the hand, or the smell of certain flowers on plants. I remember one flower at Kew Gardens that had a heavenly perfume—*Hymenocolis speciosa*—I think it was a tropical plant. Lewis was also something of an expert on Palestinian archaeology, and I believe that later he turned his vast chemical knowledge to good use in chemical studies related to archaeology.

Round the corner from my lab. was another prospective chemical researcher named Bateman who came from the West Country. He was a fine pianist, well-read, and a good physical chemist. He got me reading some of the more modern writers and poets. I remember, for example, reading all the books by Aldous Huxley that I could lay my hands on.

Our lab. in the basement of the college had one disadvantage: it was subject to minute vibrations from the London traffic, particularly from the tube trains. The tubes shut down between about one and five o'clock on a Sunday morning, so if we had any experiment to do with very sensitive apparatus, it had to be done during that particular time. One such piece of equipment was a Paschen galvanometer, used in measuring light-absorption coefficients of various materials. Almost every weekend Bateman and I would get ourselves locked into the college by the night watchman, set up our equipment, and then have supper and talk while waiting for the vibrations to settle down. Bateman could always produce something exotic such as a special Turkish coffee, Russian cigarettes, or a specialty food from one of the many little foreign shops in Soho. This passed the time pleasantly until it was time to work. Work kept on until traffic vibrations caused suspension of this particular experiment until another weekend. Then Bateman would go to his lodgings, not too far away, while I would stretch out on a camp cot and sleep for a few hours, lulled to slumber by the soft whirr of motor stirrers and the click of switches in the thermostatically controlled waterbaths, and oblivious of the Strand and the Embankment and of the river Thames flowing softly by, a few hundreds of feet away through walls and foundations and thick London clay.

The problem that I was to work on was indicated on a card lying on a table in my lab. Professor Allmand had evidently felt quite sure that I would fall for the idea of working with him. Anyhow, there was the card:

"Look up a paper by Weigert in *Annalen der Physik*, 1907, p. 243, and try to reproduce the experiments. It might be worth reinvestigating."

The paper described a photochemical experiment in which ozone was mixed with chlorine gas and illuminated with blue light. This procedure resulted in the decomposition of the ozone, the chlorine remaining apparently unchanged. I set to making equipment in which the experiment could be carried out at various temperatures and gas concentrations and with various wavelengths (or colours) of light. I learned to use a lathe and to do simple machine-shop work, to blow glass, and to standardize light intensities. Eventually, after four or five months, I started to obtain some crude results.

During all this time, there was not a sign of my prof., except that he had arranged for me to receive a grant from D.S.I.R. (Department of Scientific and Industrial Research) for about a hundred and fifty pounds a year. Again at his suggestion I sat examinations for two special scholarships, one a London open scholarship worth a hundred pounds, and the other a London exhibition worth eighty pounds a year for two years. I was fortunate enough to win both, so I jumped from rags to riches almost overnight. At least I was able to buy some half-decent clothes, to have something better than a fourpenny meat pie for lunch, to buy the odd book, and to go to see the occasional play. I scarely ever drank anything (alcoholic, that is), but I did like to indulge in half a pound of chocolate caramels over the weekend—a reasonably harmless and inexpensive indulgence by modern standards.

Standard garb for the research students was grey flannel trousers with sports shirt, college tie, and a college blazer to put on when going out of the college—in the lab. we wore a tattered lab. coat—the more tattered the better. Going to church or Sunday visiting required striped trousers, stiff collar, spats, bowler, kid gloves, and a cane—in fact the whole bit. Mother also insisted that as soon as I could afford it, I should get a dress suit. Such costume was snobbish, I suppose, but it did give me the idea that there was such a thing as dressing and such a thing as style for men and for women. I started to take notice.

The scholarship exams. were typically British. The written paper was accompanied by a practical exam. I went to a lab. in South Kensington on the appointed day, and at the entrance to the lab. I drew a number from a top hat—number 3, shall we say. This led me to desk number 3, where I found my instructions:

"On the desk you will see a flask containing some violet-coloured liquid. In the lab. you will find both oxidizing and reducing agents; try their effect on the liquid. Write a report. Lunch will be served at noon. Tell the boy whether you would prefer beer or coffee. Good luck!"

I tried the effect of reducing agents such as metallic zinc on small portions of the liquid, when it was warmed in a test tube. To my delight the liquid changed color to pale blue, green, and yellow. This color change could be reversed by various oxidizing agents such as permanganate. It then occurred to me to do the experiments quantitatively, and I found that the color changes were brought about by amounts of chemical that were in whole-number ratios: 5, 3, 2, 1, as I remember. I deduced that these represented valence or combining states of 5, 3, 2, and 1, and I wrote all this up.

Another physics exam. which I wrote at about that period was in much the same style, asking how you would tackle a problem that you hadn't come across before. In a way the questions were quite brutal because you could get stuck for an idea and get nothing done at all. The particular problem I had was to use a small coil of wire and a ballistic galvanometer to measure the pole strength of a pencil-shaped magnet. This is not a difficult feat if you have books to consult, but when you are faced with a jumble of assorted equipment and have only a pencil and paper and a set of log tables by way of reference, it can be quite a challenge.

As I mentioned earlier, after four or five months I began to get some results, and Professor Allmand started to drop in once a day and look over my shoulder at the graphs I was drawing, based on the results I was getting. The first time he withdrew his pipe slightly, emitted a "Huh," and walked away quickly. However, after another month or so, when the results started to become reproducible and one could begin to place some confidence in them, he would sit down to chat. For my particular conditions of experiment, calculation showed that two molecules of ozone were decomposed for every quantum of light absorbed (light is emitted or absorbed by matter in discrete energy units or bundles called *quanta*— which are like bullets from a machine gun rather than like the continuous stream of water from a tap). This whole number ratio of 2 seemed unlikely to be just chance, so Professor Allmand suggested that I try to develop a theory which might explain it. At that time the subject of spectroscopy was being intensively studied by the physicists, who suggested that when a chlorine molecule, Cl_2, absorbed blue light, it split up into two atoms:

$$Cl_2 + q \text{ (a quantum)} \rightarrow 2Cl$$

I suggested then that the chlorine atom could combine with ozone, O_3, to give ClO_3, and that two ClO_3 molecules would then react to give chlorine plus oxygen:

Thus
$$2ClO_3 \rightarrow Cl_2 + 3O_2$$
$$Cl_2 + q \rightarrow 2Cl$$
$$2(Cl + O_3 \rightarrow ClO_3)$$
$$2ClO_3 \rightarrow Cl_2 + 3O_2$$

This hypothesis explains how the light absorbed by the gas mixture would result in the decomposition of the ozone, two molecules per one quantum absorbed. It seemed too good to be true. The only trouble was that ClO_3 was then an unknown compound.

Then I had a couple of bits of luck, and luck is an essential ingredient in any piece of work. The equipment used consisted essentially of a glass cylinder, having plane ends, which could be filled with a chlorine-ozone mixture, through which a beam of light could be passed. The equipment was enclosed in a box to keep out extraneous light. One day I happened to put my head in the box to line up the beam of light with a light-measuring instrument called a thermopile. To my surprise I could see the path of the beam of light, just like the beam from the head lights of a car on a foggy day. I thought that it would be of interest to analyse the fog, so after letting the fog settle out on the walls of the vessel, I removed the chlorine and ozone from the vessel and washed the inside walls with two or three drops of water, which I then microanalysed. It gave tests for perchloric and chloric acids which were just what one would expect if ClO_3 or Cl_2O_6 were present:

$$2ClO_3 \rightarrow Cl_2O_6$$
$$Cl_2O_6 + H_2O \rightarrow H\dot{C}lO_3 \text{ (chloric acid)} + HClO_4 \text{ (perchloric acid)}$$

It was clear that a minute amount of moisture had remained on the inside walls of the vessel when the equipment was being assembled, and that this moisture had then acted as a trap to react with the unknown ClO_3. The next bit of luck happened when I decided to try using high concentrations of ozone. This trial caused the reaction to speed up markedly, indicating a chain reaction of some sort. I immediately speculated on how this might happen and came up with the following sequence:

$$ClO_3 + O_3 \rightarrow ClO_2 + 2O_2$$
$$ClO_2 + O_3 \rightarrow 2Cl\dot{O}_3 + O_2$$

This sequence constituted a so-called chain reaction, in which the intermediate compound ClO_3 was continuously destroyed and regenerated. Thus one quantum of light absorbed could result in the decomposition of many molecules of ozone. The ClO_2 appearing in the equations is chlorine dioxide, a well-known compound. Thus one could easily check whether the reaction depicted in the second equation could actually take place. It took no time at all to rig up a piece of apparatus in which chlorine dioxide and ozone were mixed. The results exceeded all expectations. Drops of red liquid formed which turned out on analysis to be Cl_2O_6, dichlorine hexoxide.

A few weeks later, Professor Allmand and I published a short note on this discovery in *Nature*, 124 (1929), p. 651. This was my first scientific publication. Eventually two rather substantial papers appeared on the mechanism of this particular photochemical reaction. I have described it in some detail since it does illustrate the way in which experiments and theory go hand in hand in solving a scientific problem. In this problem there was an interaction between two subjects, physics and chemistry. A study of the light-absorption spectrum of chlorine (physics) indicated that light absorption by chlorine brought about the dissociation of a molecule of chlorine into two atoms. This discovery played a vital role in the further elaboration and understanding of a chemical problem. This study was one of the first in which conclusive evidence was given for the transient existence of a highly reactive intermediate compound, nowadays called a free radical. Since then other methods have been developed for detecting and measuring free radicals which have confirmed the earlier speculations. After World War II, I became involved in these new studies, using electron-spin resonance techniques. The chlorine-ozone reaction had by 1975 acquired renewed interest because of its possible occurrence in the upper atmosphere as a factor in the destruction of the ozone blanket that protects life on earth from excessive ultra-violet radiation.

My two years of research with Professor A. J. Allmand were most rewarding. He was one of the leading photochemists at that time, so he attracted good people to work with him, and a number of visiting firemen were constantly coming to the labs. We students thus had the benefit of discussing at first hand the latest work that was going on in various labs. with the actual people who were either doing or directing the work. We did not attend any formal classes, but there were so many research people around that we were constantly stimulated to dig quite deeply into other areas of knowledge. As an example of this sort of experience I should describe a chance encounter with a physics student named Johnson, who was doing spectroscopic research in a lab. not far from mine. He invited me to see his equipment and told me quite a bit about the whole subject of spectroscopy. Soon I was reading papers on spectroscopy in the physics research journals and beginning to know quite a bit about it, acquiring knowledge which was later to stand me in good stead. Another time I attended some lectures given by Professor Rideal on catalysis, and this introduction led me to read rather widely about the subject. Attending a college in London meant that sooner or later one could sit at the feet of all the great and the mighty in whatever field one cared to think about.

Afternoon tea in the refectory, at the table reserved for the research chemists, was a regular ritual and not to be missed. Seldom a day passed without our getting into an interesting discussion. Quite often a visitor from another college would hold the floor. One such was Norman Grace, who was doing graduate work in London but who was originally from Saskatoon. He tells me that I showed quite an interest in the University of Saskatchewan, although at that time I certainly had no idea of the university's future importance for me.

During this time I kept reasonably fit by boxing and cross-country running. Often I would arrive at the lab. early, spend the morning getting an experiment under way, have lunch at the college, and then go for a walk to browse around one of the art galleries or one of the many bookshops. Then I would go back to the lab. to see how the experiment was going. Sometimes Professor Allmand would comment on the rather large gap that occurred in the graph of experimental points, but he never inquired into the matter too closely.

Occasionally Bateman and I would take a leisurely supper in Soho. He was fond of the Italian restaurants and I liked one particular Chinese restaurant, just off Picadilly, where one could have a delicious shrimp omelet and occasionally run into one of the Chinese film actresses who haunted such places and who seemed to have time to talk to the usual crowd of poor but enthusiastic students. Those were the days!

My general education was helped when I was at university by my staying for a time with a pleasant family in Walthamstow. Among the other boarders was a smart salesman who not only made a good living selling to the wholesalers but had a pleasant time going to all the shows, reading the latest books, and spending his weekends on the south coast. He was a mine of information about royalty and the so-called "smart set," whose doings he followed with great interest.

In complete contrast was another boarder from Lancashire, who acted as political agent for the local Labour candidate. At first he thought that as a college student I must be completely in the capitalist camp. However, we eventually became good friends, and he would take me to political meetings and to special meetings at the House of Commons. In the absence of his wife I even accompanied him to social gatherings at places such as the Friends Meeting House in Euston Square, where we would meet Labor celebrities such as Ramsay MacDonald, the Sydney Webbs, and even the Oswald Mosleys, then the darlings of the party. Later I saw the ugly part of the general strike in 1926 and slept for several evenings in my lab. because all the usual communications with the suburbs were out of action.

At another time a practising chemist, Harold Goodwin, was a fellow boarder for a short while. When he established himself and his family in the neighborhood I became a frequent visitor at their house and developed a home away from home. We would talk for hours on matters of science, politics, books, and everything under the sun, and in between times I would play on the rug with their two young daughters, who were about five or six years old. And when the visit was over, Mrs. Goodwin would see me to the door and let me out with a cheery, "Goodbye, and do come again soon." They are a part of me, and I of them.

Once in a long while I would take a weekend off and go to visit my Aunt Jessie and Uncle Charles, who lived at Letchworth, the Garden City, which is about forty miles or so from London and easily reached by train. Aunt Jessie was the oldest in my mother's family and she had been a teacher before marrying Uncle Charles, who was a businessman. They had a lovely house and garden, all sorts of good conversation at the table, and a great pile of magazines and books to be read. Uncle Charles had recently retired from business, and he liked to spend a good deal of time attending to the roses and flowers. Afternoon tea in the garden was a delight, with luscious strawberries and thick cream, paper-thin bread and butter, and lots of cake.

Occasionally in the evenings we would walk across the fields to a nearby village and drop into a pub for a glass of beer since Letchworth was at that time something of an oddity—a completely teetotal town. It was also the home of theosophists, of some people called "morrisites", and of other off-beat but charming and interesting people who wore long robes and long hair and were vegetarians. They anticipated the present vogue by half a century. Quite often my mother would be staying with my aunt when I visited Letchworth, and we would have the pleasure of many long walks downtown and across the fields.

Chapter 5

London to Saskatoon

All good things come to an end. I had realized that one day I should have to tear myself away from King's and get a job. I thought vaguely of becoming a research chemist at the big new I.C.I. labs at Billingham or possibly of getting a junior teaching position at some university. But to tell the truth I was enjoying my research at the college and I didn't think too seriously about the future. Then luck or chance, or whatever you like to call it, came along. My professor came to the lab. one day in the summer of 1930 and told me that a friend of his, Dr. Thorvaldson, was coming over to Europe from Canada and that he was looking for a junior person to work in his chemistry department in Saskatoon—at the University of Saskatchewan. Would I like to meet him? Yes, I would, and a meeting was arranged for the next Tuesday, as I thought.

On the Monday I took a goddaughter of mine to the zoo. She was four years old, and the polar bear had thoughtfully extended an invitation to her to visit the zoo with Uncle John. We had a lovely day, but when I turned up at the lab. next day, expecting to see Dr. Thorvaldson, I found that he had already visited the lab. on Monday. To make matters worse, my fellow students had arranged my lab. to give him the worst possible impression of me, and the story of his visit to the lab. lost nothing in the telling.

I got in touch with Dr. Thorvaldson and made my apologies. Luckily he had taken the pranks of my friends in good part and was still interested in visiting the lab. So another date was made and kept, and after a pleasant visit we had lunch with Mrs. Thorvaldson and her sister, May Paulson, at the Strand Palace Hotel, not far from my college. A day or so later Dr. Thorvaldson told me that Dr. Walter Murray, the president of the

University of Saskatchewan, had authorized him to offer me a position at the university. It sounded interesting, and I had complete faith in Dr. Thorvaldson, so I said yes—having little or no idea what Canada and Saskatoon and the University were like.

I was told that I should plan to reach Saskatoon by mid-September, and having this deadline meant doing everything in a rush. First I went home to consult with my mother. She came to the point right away.

"Are you asking me or are you telling me?"

I said that really I had made up my mind and was telling her, but that I hoped she would agree, and she did. And while I like to think that she missed me, not once did she call into question my decision to leave England and go to Canada, which was a long, long way away in those days.

My professor then came into the picture. Since I was going to Canada, I had better make myself legitimate and get my Ph.D. Had I been staying in England, a doctorate would not have been necessary. Professor Allmand told me that he had taken the precaution of registering me for a Ph.D. degree some time before. If I would write up a report and get him five or six copies, he would arrange with the authorities for an oral examination. Luckily by this time I had written a number of reports about my work, and I had no trouble in putting together a suitable thesis—adequate but not elegant would probably best describe it.

On the appointed day I turned up at Professor Allmand's office and met the examining committee—Professor Cyril Hinshelwood from Oxford, Dr. Norrish from Cambridge, and Professor Heilbron from Liverpool, who were all seated round a small table with my professor. It was a pretty formidable examining committee: both Hinshelwood and Norrish were eventual Nobel Prize winners in chemistry. My professor started by suggesting that Professor Hinshelwood might like to ask me a few questions about my thesis.

"Nothing doing." said Hinshelwood, "It's quite clear that Spinks knows far more about this subject than any of us here, including you. Why should we make ourselves look silly? But don't worry—I do have a few questions to ask." Hinshelwood went on to ask questions in considerable depth about matters related to the topic. I remember his asking quite innocently what the physicists meant by P, Q, and R branches in a spectrum. Luckily I had discussed this sort of thing with my spectroscopic friend Johnson, and I could give quite a good answer. He was duly impressed because in 1930 this had not yet got into the textbooks. Eventually he asked a question on which I had to admit ignorance:

"I'm afraid I don't know!"

"Well, neither do I, so we are even, and you are honest.—That's all I want to ask!"

Norrish and Heilbron went through the same routine, each taking me to the point where I had to admit that I didn't know. Eventually, about two hours after the start of the meeting, my examiners exchanged glances and in turn tapped the table, whereupon my professor leaned forward, picked up a small silver bell, and rang it. His secretary poked her head around the corner of the door:

"Yes, Professor?"

"Tea please, Alice," and that is how I got my Ph.D.

Actually, it was a foregone conclusion, as I have discovered since that Professor Allmand didn't recommend anyone for the oral until he felt absolutely sure that they would pass with flying colors.

A few days later I was on the *Empress of Australia*, on the way to Canada and the University of Saskatchewan. I was twenty-two years old.

Looking back on this period of my life, it seems that a good deal of time was spent in getting a good basic education and in learning to work on my own. Building on this foundation, I had learned the stock in trade of a scientist with specialization in chemistry. After this I had learned how to do scientific research by working on a small but up-to-date problem with a top-notch scientist who had kept an eye on me but had left me pretty much on my own.

By this time I had become aware that there was a whole infrastructure supporting not only my little problem in chemistry but the whole discipline and profession of chemistry. I knew that there were many chemistry departments in other universities all over the world, that there were chemical laboratories in government and industry, and that there was a system of grants and scholarships supplied by the Department of Scientific and Industrial Research and by the universities themselves. I was aware that there were scientific societies such as the Royal Institute of Chemistry (which I was encouraged to join as a student member and to which I still belong, fifty years later), and I knew that these societies held meetings and published journals. I realized that the acquisition of knowledge in chemistry was a continuing process and that chemical knowledge had a worldwide basis, so that Mendeleeff's Period Law held equally well for the chemical elements in Britain and in Russia. My first step into the world of chemistry as a prospective teacher and academic researcher was about to be taken.

Chapter 6

Dirty Thirties

I arrived in Saskatoon on September 12, 1930—a rainy fall day as I remember it, and I was met by one of the graduate students, Alan Nixon. He took me up to the men's residence on campus, Qu'Appelle Hall, where arrangements had been made for me to stay for a day or so while I looked around for a more permanent place.

The university as a whole was beautiful, most of the buildings being in the collegiate gothic style and achieving an architectural harmony by the generous use of a local fieldstone.

Saskatoon at that time had a population of about thirty thousand, and although it was called a city, by old-country standards it was just a small town. It had been established as a temperance colony at the turn of the century, and it had acquired a university in 1907, so the university was just about as old as I was. I must say I fell in love with Saskatoon immediately. Although it was thousands of miles from the ocean and was situated in the middle of the prairies, the immediate surroundings were lovely, especially the South Saskatchewan River, as wide as the Thames in London and crossed by a number of handsome bridges. The east bank of the river was between one and two hundred feet above the water level and was well wooded, while the west bank was much lower. At that time the main business buildings and the two cathedrals were in a cluster on the west bank, producing a sparkle of lights that could be seen from the upper bank in the winter time, a sight that always reminded me of Prague.

I lived with the Hartneys in a house on the river bank for several years after my arrival. Mr. Russell Hartney was a lawyer, and he and his family made me feel very much at home. I was "Spinksy" to all and sundry, and the Hartneys made me part of the family. I lived in a cozy little room on the second floor, surrounded by hundreds and hundreds of law books. From my window I could see gorgeous sunsets, day after day, to the west of the city. And in the early winter I would see large cakes or pans of ice floating slowly down the river until a really sharp frost would come, and practically the whole surface would be frozen over. It would stay that way, the ice getting thicker and thicker, until spring would come once more and the ice would break up and go out with a spectacular rush. It was then part of the life of the city to stand on the university bridge and watch the huge pans of ice, four or five feet thick and perhaps thirty feet across, come crashing into the piers supporting the bridge. Eventually, a dam was put in across the river, and the spectacular break-ups were no more. Forty years later the city's population has grown to a hundred and thirty thousand. Saskatoon has several fine buildings, including an art gallery, a large auditorium, many hotels and high-rise blocks, and still more fine bridges over the river.

Term was due to start about a week after I arrived. After being installed in an office-lab. in the lower level of the Chemistry Building, I got busy with preparing my first lecture. The building was newly opened in 1926 and was very handsome. Dr. Thorvaldson had asked me to help with an elementary chemistry class, one in advanced inorganic, and a half-class (one term only) in my specialty, photo-chemistry. There was plenty to keep me out of mischief. I well remember the first lecture in advanced inorganic. There were twenty or so senior students in the class, most of them not much younger than myself, and in preparation I had got together material for five or six lectures. I started out boldly with all the students taking notes in a businesslike fashion. For a few minutes I thought "There's nothing to it," but then to my horror the students one by one put down their pens and sat looking blankly at me. I thought that they must already know what I was telling them, so I went faster and faster, and by the end of the forty-minute period I had covered five of my precious six lectures. I dashed down to the office of Professor Jack Fraser, whom I had come to know, and told him that I might as well resign right away since I couldn't possibly keep up that pace. Jack just smiled and went out into the corridor where the students were buzzing like hornets. He soon came back with the message that after the first five minutes nobody had understood a thing. So next lecture I started in again, and my six lectures lasted me just about till Christmas. The faculty members were all very good to me, and they helped me to learn how to teach.

The younger students thought I was fair game for teasing. One day in the lab. the women students appeared in dressing gowns, with their hair done up in curlers. One of the girls came and asked me some trifling question and then asked if she could borrow a handkerchief. Luckily I had a clean one, which she used to blow her nose loudly. Then she retreated with much laughter to the back of the lab. It was all a put-up job, of course, and in due time I received the handkerchief back, neatly laundered.

Most of the unmarried faculty members had lunch with the students in the dining hall in Saskatchewan Hall, and this arrangement gave me an opportunity to become acquainted with professors such as Margaret Cameron, Alex Corry, Al Ewen, Grant MacEwan, Edith Brown, Sam Laycock, and Fred Shepherd. Later in the winter some of us would snatch a bowl of soup and a sandwich in the basement of Sask. Hall, and go skating at the Rutherford Rink for half an hour before afternoon labs. started. I met practically all the faculty and their families in the first few months of my arrival in Saskatoon, and I found them all most pleasant and hospitable. They were extremely kind to me, not just once but on many, many occasions. We were, in fact, one big family.

1930 was the start of the Great Depression on the prairies, which were hit with particular severity because a depressed economy coincided with years of drought and no crops. Those with a few dollars in their pockets felt like millionaires—and felt under an obligation to help those who had less. Our entertainment had to be of the inexpensive variety—mostly in private homes, with each person contributing something, perhaps bringing the coffee or the cream, or possibly some buns or cake.

An enjoyable event in Saskatoon in the thirties was attending a musical soirée at the home of Lyell Gustin, a distinguished teacher of the piano who had a number of first-class pupils. The studio would be crowded with people. All the chairs would be taken and some of the audience would be sitting on the floor. Someone would give a paper on a composer, perhaps Chopin, Beethoven, Fauré, or Ravel, and then the pupils would play. Afterwards there would be tea and lots of excellent talk. The studio was well stocked with books so that the students learned much much more than five-finger exercises. I wonder whether many Saskatonians realized how much people like Gustin contributed to the intellectual and artistic life of the city, even in the "dirty thirties." He had a wealth of knowledge, not only about music and composers but also about ballet and books generally. Similarly, he was knowledgeable about artists and painting, and he gave of his knowledge most generously.

It would be invidious to mention names, but I recall with particular affection the members of the chemistry department whom I first met in 1930. Then there were all the good friends of the C.O.T.C. (Canadian Officers' Training Corps). Some friendships came about purely by chance, through an invitation to a dinner or a picnic. Looking at a university calendar for those days evokes dozens of memories. They were grand people, those members of faculty in the early thirties.

In the summertime there were numerous outings into the country for picnics, so the time went pleasantly enough. I did a bit of fishing, mainly using a fly, about two miles below the city, where I caught goldeyes. I went camping too, usually up to Emma Lake but sometimes further afield. The great difficulty was always transportation—once one got there, it was cheap enough to live.

In my first year in Saskatoon I had become acquainted with Ernest Lindner, at that time a struggling young artist who had recently arrived from Vienna and was finding it difficult to make a living by painting. All summer he lived in a small but delightful cabin on Fairy Isle at Emma Lake. There he lived the simple life and did lots of painting. I spent many idyllic weeks there in his company, reading, swimming, canoeing, fishing, doing camp chores, engaging in endless talk, lying in the shade during the afternoon or by the campfire in the evening, and listening to the sounds of bird and animal life. Finally, as darkness fell, the silence would be broken only by the haunting call of the loon or by the splash of a fish jumping a few yards offshore.

In the winter Lindner had a suite in the London Block in downtown Saskatoon, where he paid for the suite by doing any necessary calcimining or painting in suites as they became vacant. There was a regular ritual of Saturday evenings at Ernie's where artists and others would gather to drink coffee and talk endlessly into the small hours of the morning. Ernie was fond of both skating and riding, so we would sometimes go skating on Saturday afternoons at the arena with the kiddies for a nickel apiece. For riding we rented a couple of horses for half a day from Mrs. Cowley, over on the west side of the city. I remember she charged each of us a quarter. The usual place for riding was in the sandhills by the sanatorium. It was great fun.

In my first year or so in Saskatoon I renewed my interest in archaeology, and I would go looking for Indian artifacts in the fields around Saskatoon, usually in company with Dr. Vigfuson, the university analyst. A group of us started up the Archaeological Society, of which Grant MacEwan became the first president while I became the first secretary. All in all, there was plenty to keep me amused.

By Christmas of 1930 I had my teaching duties more or less in hand, although I had still a great deal to learn, and I started to think about getting some research going. Dr. Thorvaldson kindly supplied me with a small amount of money with which I bought the basic necessities to start research in photochemistry. As a matter of fact he had arranged for me to bring a few things from England, and this forethought saved a great deal of time. My main lack was a powerful light source, but even this was soon remedied when Dr. E. L. Harrington, head of physics and a fabulous glass blower, heard of my plight and made a mercury arc lamp for me. He was kindness itself and helped me on many occasions with loans of equipment and with practical advice. Dr. Thorvaldson steered one or two graduates in my direction, and I soon had a modest program going, enough at least to let me know that I could develop a program of my own, independent of the guiding hand of my former professor to whom I owed so much.

In my first problem I merely rang the changes, replacing the chlorine by bromine, and studying the photosensitized decomposition of ozone by bromine. This study yielded some interesting results, and it is amusing to note that the worries about the possible decrease in the upper-atmosphere ozone layer have led to a renewed interest in this reaction after a lapse of over forty years. I then transferred my attention to the photodecomposition of oxides of chlorine, such as chlorine monoxide and chlorine dioxide, and later to the decomposition of dichlorine hexoxide. Studies on dichlorine hexoxide led to the accidental discovery of the highly reactive nitroxyl perchlorate. The students working with me in this period were both able and pleasant. This period covered about ten years and included some interest in spectroscopy and applied chemistry. The spectroscopic studies resulted from the exigencies of the moment, but they did greatly improve my knowledge of the basic phenomena in photochemistry, while giving me a sound basis in quantum theory—a must for modern science.

My introduction to spectroscopy came about in this way. The Great Depression had a major impact on Saskatchewan and my first three years in Saskatoon went by to the accompaniment of a deepening sense of gloom as the air was filled with clouds of dust, crop failures became the order of the day, and salaries grew smaller and smaller. It is to the lasting credit of the first president, Dr. Murray, and to his senior colleagues that salaries did not disappear altogether. As far as I know, no one lost his or her job for financial reasons, even though the university safe was filled with I.O.U.'s. Eventually, in the spring of 1933, a number of the younger bachelors were called to the president's office and given two alternatives: either to resign gracefully or to take a year off on five hundred dollars and have a reasonably good probability of returning to some sort of job a year later. Naturally we all opted for the second alternative. I thought that I would hedge my bets by going to Germany to work with a physicist on spectroscopy. At least I could learn German and something about the German people. With any luck I would learn some spectroscopy too, and perhaps even get out a paper. As it turned out I was lucky on all counts, and I had as an added bonus the circumstance that Germany had just been through a period of inflation. The economy had been stabilized with so-called "register-marks," worth twenty-five cents. The maximum allowance was two hundred r.m. per month, which cost me fifty dollars, so my five hundred dollars lasted for practically a year.

My first step was to go to the Physics Library and look at some recent German physics journals. Almost immediately I came across a paper on experimental spectroscopy, written in English by a physicist named Herzberg, in conjunction with an American. This coincidence sounded too good to be true! I looked up one or two other papers by Herzberg and thought they were just the thing I wanted, so I wrote to him and asked whether he could find room for me in his lab. Herzberg sent a very kind reply, inviting me to work with him in Darmstadt, at the Technische Hochschule, so in the fall of 1933 I packed my bags and went to Germany, sailing by way of New York.

Chapter 7

Darmstadt, Germany

My arrival in Darmstadt had its amusing aspects. I arrived by train at about midnight. Luckily the railway porter knew some English and directed me across the square to the Station Hotel, which was in complete and utter darkness. I pulled the bell repeatedly, and eventually the landlord came down, complete with candlestick and nightcap. In sign language I indicated that I wished to sleep, so he beckoned me in and took me upstairs to a large pitch-black room. He pointed to a huge bed, gave me a candle, said "Gute Nacht!" and went out, closing the door behind him. It was as quiet as the grave and rather spooky. However, I was too tired to go anywhere else and I had nowhere to go, so I undressed and crawled into a soft and comfortable bed, surmounted by a huge but light feather quilt. I was asleep immediately, and I didn't wake until the maid brought me hot water in the morning and threw open the heavy shutters to the window, letting in the autumn sun. After breakfast I got in touch with Dr. Herzberg, who sent someone from the lab. to pick me up and take me to his office.

Darmstadt was a delightful city with a very old inner core of market place and cobbled streets. Surrounding the inner core were rather more modern residential suburbs with a castle, a museum and art gallery, two large theatres, *Grosseres Haus* and *Kleines Haus,* and a good many shops. The city was surrounded by woods and was some twenty or thirty miles from Frankfurt and Heidelberg, more or less halfway between the two.

Darmstadt had been the "Residenzstadt" for the Hesse Landschaft, and the city had strong connections with Britain. I was reminded vividly of it a short time ago when a friend returned some letters to me which I had written from Darmstadt in the 1933-34 period. One letter was dated December 19, 1933:

First of all there is the forest, which is huge and was really beautiful when I came in the fall. The country is quite hilly so that now and again one gets the most gorgeous views. I am able to go to the *Hessiches Landes Theater*, which does some very good stuff—mostly opera—and is ridiculously cheap. As for skating, there are two good sheets of ice within two minutes of where I live. I get endless pleasure from seeing the children going to school with their bags on their backs. Some of the streets are very old-fashioned and quaint—half-timbered houses and cobbled streets. The milk wagon makes such a rattle.

Somewhere to live was easily found. The Herzbergs had a suite in a large house at the edge of town. A number of other paying guests lived there, and I was able to get a room on the ground floor with a large may bush outside my window. It was a delightful place to be—very comfortable, with good food and interesting company. In addition to the Herzbergs there were our landlady and her brother, who was confined to a wheel chair but was full of life and very knowledgeable. Then there were a retired lawyer, a banker's widow, and one or two others.

Dinner together in the evening was never dull. There was always a buzz of conversation, and if things got too dull one could always tease the banker's widow, a dear old lady who had a warm heart but who was a bit gullible. On one occasion when I had a tickle in my throat and coughed slightly she exclaimed, "Oh Dr. Spinks, you have a bad cold," and off she went to her room and came back with a bottle of brandy, from which she poured me a good drink. Next evening the performance was repeated, and then it was repeated again on the third evening, at which point our landlady suggested that perhaps Dr. Spinks was coughing for brandy. The old lady was distressed to think that I should play such a trick on her, but she quickly forgave me.

Sunday morning breakfast was a particular pleasure. The table was laden with a variety of breads, buns, and cheeses, jams and preserves, and with boiled eggs, tea and coffee. Still more important, there was a big stack of newspapers: the *Frankfurter Zeitung*, *Figaro*, the London *Observer*, and many others. Each person filled his plate and then hid behind his favorite newspaper, coming up from time to time to let all and sundry know the latest bit of news from London, Paris, or Berlin. Breakfast usually lasted till about lunch time. If Sunday afternoon was fine, Dr. and Mrs. Herzberg, (Gerhard and Louise) took a walk in the forest, and I often accompanied them. One of my letters describes a walk in spring:

April 8

Today is marvelously sunny and warm—blue sky and just a few lazy white clouds—so Doktor and Frau Doktor Herzberg and I took a walk in the forest before lunch. The forest is within five minutes of the house and is beginning to get green once more. Under the trees are hundreds and hundreds of anemones, and in the damp spots one sees little yellow flowers, rather like buttercups. When we sat down it was quite quiet—just some birds singing in the distance and a soft swishing in the tops of the firs. It was great! Then, as a somewhat rude reminder of earthly things, a big troop of SA men filed past—two by two along the narrow woodland path.

Later in the day

I'm afraid I have been an utter heathen today. Dr. Herzberg lives in the same house, and so all the afternoon and until 7:15 this evening we have been calculating some work I did shortly before Easter—infra red spectrum and isotopic effect. Just before Easter I had a marvelous trip, and at the risk of making you green with envy I'll tell you something about it. First of all I went to Göttingen and visited the university people, saw their apparatus, had a great jaw, tea, etc. That was very interesting, but the town itself was not so thrilling. Dr. Herzberg met his wife first in Göttingen, and he thinks it is quite the most beautiful spot in Germany! So you see that opinions can differ even among scientific folk!

Most weekends I went to the theatre for performances of Wagner, Mozart, Strauss, and other composers. There was a lively musical tradition in Darmstadt, and the Herzbergs were fond of music, so we often went together. For the first two months I had a terrible time with the language. There was a notice up on the notice board in the institute to the effect that German students were not to talk to foreigners in the foreigners' language, so perforce I had to learn German. Suddenly, after about two months, I found that I knew what people were saying on the bus, and curiously enough at about the same time they would say "Guten Tag" to me as I got on the bus. My German was probably very bad, but I was fluent and I understood pretty well anything that was said to me. Herzberg proved to be an ideal person to work with. He showed me exactly how to use the equipment, how to make the measurements, and how to do the calculations. After that he left me on my own. I had nothing to do but work, so we got a lot done, helped by Herzberg's enormous drive and flood of ideas and, as usual, by a little bit of luck.

Dr. Herzberg was a good benchman in his experimental work, and he took pains in working out things to the last decimal. But I remember one time when we nearly had a disaster. We had a glass tube about two metres long in which we confined various gases to examine their absorption spectra. The lab. assistant had been asked to clean out this tube by flushing it with nitrogen gas. We then attempted to seal the tube onto another piece of equipment, but when Dr. Herzberg brought the flame near, in order to carry out the sealing operation, there was a terrific explosion which temporarily deafened us. It did no other harm, luckily, since the explosion blew out the ends of the tube rather than shattering the tube as a whole. The lab. assistant had used hydrogen to flush out the tube instead of nitrogen, thus producing a highly explosive mixture. That time we were lucky!

Dr. Herzberg obtained some spectroscopic plates, sensitive in the infra red, which gave us access to 2000 angstroms of the spectrum not previously reached. It was like having a new window in a house and getting a completely new view. We did the spectra of hydrochloric acid, hydrogen cyanide, and acetylene in this region, and we obtained the first photographic rotation-vibration spectra ever recorded. We then did the spectrum of acetylene in which one hydrogen atom had been replaced by an atom of deuterium (heavy hydrogen). When coming through New York on the way to Germany I had called in on Dr. Urey's lab. where heavy water had just been discovered. I had mentioned my visit to Dr. Herzberg and after some discussion I had agreed to try to make some heavy water.

The attempt was fraught with many unexpected difficulties, but after six months I had about a teaspoonful. It was not much, but it was worth its weight in diamonds, and we used some of it to make some semi-heavy acetylene (acetylene, $H-C \equiv C-H$; semi-heavy acetylene, $D-C \equiv C-H$). Using the spectra of ordinary acetylene and semi-heavy acetylene, we were able to calculate the molecular structure of acetylene—a first for this kind of experiment.

Quite often we would take the calculating machine home for the weekend and spend the time calculating results. Fortunately Mrs. Herzberg was a physicist, so she did not object to the rather noisy calculating machine. Every few weeks we finished a project, did the calculations, wrote up the paper, and sent it off to the editor. Then I would take a few days off, visiting a lab. in another university town: Göttingen, Giessen, Leipzig, Dresden, or Berlin. I even took a week or so to visit Vienna, Prague, and Salzberg.

By the time I reached Salzberg I thought my German was adequate, so I ordered "eine Tasse Kaffee" at an open-air restaurant, and I was mortified when the waiter brought the coffee plus the London *Times*! In Berlin I heard Furtwängler conducting the Berlin Philharmonic and went home for coffee with a friend of Dr. Herzberg's. When we arrived at his flat his wife came to the door and seemed a bit upset to see a stranger with her husband. Husband and wife went into the bedroom for a hurried conference and then came out and told me that they were harboring a young scientist who was being hunted by the Nazis. If I wished to leave immediately they would understand. I said that it didn't worry me particularly—something they knew already, since by that time I had been exposed to some of the Nazi excesses in Darmstadt and I knew that many academics were having a bad time of it. Herzberg himself was just beginning to have troubles because his wife was Jewish, and I am sure that these friends of theirs knew this too. I had arrived in Darmstadt in September of 1933, and the elections were held in November of that year. Hitler obtained over ninety per cent of the votes, and those who voted against him often suffered for doing so.

One old woman who sold fruit and vegetables in the market place in Darmstadt let it be known that she had voted against Hitler, so she was paraded up and down the square, placarded back and front with "Ich bin ein Neinsager—ich habe meinen Fuhrer beleidigt" ("I said 'No!'—I have insulted my leader"). After that no one dared buy vegetables from her. Of course other people were treated still worse.

All the students and professors below a certain age were expected to join the Storm Troops. One new professor neglected to do so, and he was asked to enlist immediately. When he applied to enlist he was given a questionnaire to fill out, and one question asked if he had any Jewish friends. He truthfully admitted that he had, and then he was asked whether he would promise to give them up. He said "No," and a couple of weeks later he was not only discharged from his university position but was given a second-class identity card, which meant that he could not occupy any university position or any position with the Civil Service. As a foreigner I was not molested. In fact, by the fall of 1933, the government was beginning to make some effort to improve its image. There had previously been several hundreds of foreign students in Darmstadt, but by November of 1933 there were just two, myself and a Norwegian, the others having been scared away. So we were treated especially well!

I remember going one day to Frankfurt to see and hear Hitler. He spoke to a crowd of a hundred thousand or so, and he had them completely mesmerized. He started out, "Deutsche Manner und deutsche Frauen" ("German men and German women"). The crowd went mad with "Sieg Heil! Sieg Heil! Sieg Heil!" Whatever he said roused them to the highest pitch of excitement. I was glad to get away from the crowd without getting hurt. Things got worse while I was there, and of course they became still worse later on. In spite of this situation, however, I had a most stimulating year with Herzberg in Darmstadt and I profited greatly from it. We had six publications arising from the work in 1934 and two later, all published in the best journals and, if I may say so, they were not all of them bad!

My mother visited me for a while in Darmstadt. I enjoyed seeing the trees in bloom—masses of them. And when the may tree was in blossom it was occupied almost nightly by a nightingale which sang its heart out and filled me with typical German "Sehnsucht und Heimweh." I read a good deal of German while in Darmstadt, and I acquired a particular liking for Thomas Mann—*Tonio Kroeger* and *The Magic Mountain* especially. I also acquired a taste for Rhine wine—Niersteiner, for example, and I liked the south-German atmosphere at Faschingszeit—the time of Mardi Gras when people seemed to be able to let go and have a fine time, all in a very pleasant way. So a year went quickly by, and once more I packed my bags and then headed back to Saskatoon.

Looking back on the year in Darmstadt and of course on Dr. Herzberg's still longer time in Darmstadt, I see that it had within it all the elements of Greek tragedy: people going about their daily work in a somewhat stoical fashion, knowing that political activities were leading Germany along a collision course which would inevitably and inexorably lead to wholesale destruction and tragedy for millions. On the one hand there was a highly civilized and cultivated existence with books, music, and theatre, and on the other there were Storm Troopers marching with a heavy tread through the cobbled streets. There were also the regular items in the weekend paper, "Auf der Flucht erschossen"—telling how a political prisoner who was being conveyed to an interrogation centre would try to escape and, sad to relate, be shot in flight.

On the lighter side, I associate that period in Germany with some nonsense rhymes by Christian Morgenstern:

Das Knie

Ein Knie geht einsam durch die Welt.
Es ist ein Knie, sonst nichts!
Es ist kein Baum! Es ist kein Zelt!
Es ist ein Knie, sonst nichts.

Im Kriege ward einmal ein Mann
erschossen um und um.
Das Knie allein blieb unverletzt—
als wär's ein Heiligtum.

Seitdem geht's einsam durch die Welt.
Es ist ein Knie, sonst nichts.
Es ist kein Baum, es ist kein Zelt.
Es ist ein Knie sonst nichts.

In spite of everything, Darmstadt was a delightful place to work in, partly because of the natural surroundings, partly because of the charm of Darmstadt itself, and partly because of Gerhard Herzberg, who knew how to help a young chemist with no knowledge of German or Germany and next to no knowledge of spectroscopy to have a very profitable year in his lab.

Chapter 8

Prewar University and Marriage

Saskatoon in 1934 was still in the depths of the depression, but at least I had made good use of what had been potentially a bad year. Almost as soon as I returned, Dr. Walter Murray, the president, asked me if I would like to be warden of Qu'Appelle Hall, the men's residence. When I suggested modestly that I was rather young for the job, Dr. Murray told me that he had done all the necessary thinking about whether I could do it or not. All I had to answer was yes or no. So I said yes, and made it a point thereafter not to question other people's judgment where my abilities were concerned. If they had made a mistake, too bad! All that was required of me was to do my best. That attitude sounds a bit like the protestant work ethic, but I have found it reasonably satisfactory, and it certainly saves a lot of worrying.

I enjoyed the next five or so years in residence. There were about a hundred and fifty young men, of various colleges and various ages. Discipline and the general social life of the residence were attended to by a students' residence committee. I was there just to see that things kept on an even keel. I had a sitting room with a fireplace, and almost every evening half a dozen people would drop in for coffee. I remember coming in late one evening and nearly stumbling over a couple in the doorway. A polite "good evening!" brought no reply, so I invited them to my room, not expecting them to accept the invitation. To my horror they meekly followed me in and sat themselves in silence on the sofa. Luckily coffee and chocolate cake broke the ice, and we not only had a pleasant visit that evening but became fast friends.

Those were the days before student unrest, and students enjoyed the simple pleasures of dining together in Sask. Hall, dancing in the girls' common room, and even going on sleigh rides. There were the usual student pranks but not one really sour note in five years. Of course, students occasionally came back squiffy from a visit downtown and had to be told it was quite possible to have a drink without getting drunk. I came to know literally hundreds of students on an intimate basis, and I valued their friendship highly.

Living on campus in the residence was handy for my research since the Chemistry Building was only a few minutes away from the residence, and I could easily go back and forth to keep an eye on an experiment. I was fortunate enough to have one or two very competent research students, and between us we could make good use of the equipment. I was still doing mainly photochemistry, but I had started to develop an interest in problems with a possible practical value to the province such as determining the chemical constituents in crude oil and developing methods for converting some of the chemical constituents of the oil into more valuable products. I was also giving some of the lectures in chemical engineering, and this experience gave me more of an applied outlook. It also gave some light interludes!

One day when I was giving a lecture to a class of twenty or so students, I saw a little mouse cautiously creeping between two rows of students. One of the students was watching me quite closely while I was talking, so I made a slight motion of the head which caused him to look down and see the mouse. Quick as a flash he leaned down, picked it up, and put it in the pocket of the student sitting next to him—a handsome fellow who was much in love with a woman student who often met him outside the classroom at the conclusion of the lecture. So after this particular lecture the unsuspecting student strolled out into the corridor, met his girl friend, and put his hand in his pocket in a nonchalant fashion. He immediately withdrew his hand. The mouse had bitten him! A crowd of students standing by took noisy pleasure in his discomfiture.

Throughout this time the political situation in Germany had deteriorated badly, and shortly after my return to Saskatoon Dr. Herzberg wrote asking whether Dr. Murray, the president of the University of Saskatchewan, would write on his behalf to the University of Toronto. Dr. Murray did so, praising Herzberg in a letter addressed to President Cody, dated January 31, 1935: "Dr. Herzberg is a brilliant physicist, who is recognized as an international authority on spectroscopy." He added, "I believe that this is one of the opportunities of securing a brilliant scientist and that he will make a very respectable member of the university forces in Canada." Dr. Murray mentioned that he was also writing to Dr. Tory of the National Research Council, and he finished the letter: "Should neither of you feel inclined to invite him to come *we would do so with joy*, although we have not sufficient means to provide him with proper equipment for his work, but a man of his power and resource can make much of little."

I particularly like the statement, "we would do so with joy," when Dr.

Murray knew that the bulk of the university assets in 1935 consisted of a bundle of I.O.U.'s in his safe!

Eventually Dr. Cody wrote that unfortunately they were already committed to someone else, and Dr. Tory wrote, "We have no work going on in spectroscopy, nor have we any equipment at the moment for such work."

On receiving the replies Dr. Murray called me over to his office and told me that the outlook was not good. Then he said, "You know, in the letter of reference which you wrote me about Dr. Herzberg you said some very nice things about his abilities. Did you really mean them?"

I replied with some heat that I did not usually write things that I did not believe.

"In that case," said Dr. Murray, "I think we should get him for Saskatoon."

I replied that that would be very nice and started to leave, thinking that Dr. Murray would do what he thought necessary.

"Just a minute!" said Dr. Murray. "I think you should send a cable to Dr. Herzberg."

"Me?" said I, incredulously.

"Yes, you!"

"And how much shall I offer?"

"Just whatever you think."

So out I went to concoct a suitable cable. Actually, I made a very modest offer, thinking that if things were bad enough in Germany it would still seem attractive and that once he got here there would be two possibilities: if Dr. Herzberg fitted in as well as I was sure he would, the university would quickly raise his salary, and if not, he could certainly go elsewhere for more money.

On March 15 a reply was received from Darmstadt indicating that acceptance of an offer was probable. On April 2, Dr. Herzberg wrote to Dr. Murray:

> Thank you very much for your letter of March 15, which I received today. As I have just cabled to Dr. Spinks, I gratefully accept your very kind offer to come to your university as guest professor of physics for two years. It was extremely kind of you to make inquiries about the possibility for me to come to Toronto. I am certain, however, that I shall spend a very profitable time at your university, and I hope I may be of some use to you.

Dr. Herzberg arrived in the fall of 1935. I met him at the station and took him up to Dr. Murray's office, wondering what would happen next, since very junior faculty members do not usually hire senior faculty members, particularly for another department!

Luckily Dr. Murray greeted me warmly and said, "This is where I take over."

I gathered later that he took Dr. Herzberg over to Dr. Harrington, head of physics, and solemnly introduced Dr. Herzberg as a new member of the physics department, as though this were the customary procedure. I gather that Dr. Harrington gulped once or twice and then thanked Dr. Murray for letting him have another member for his department, although inwardly he was wondering what the dickens he could do with this unknown physicist. However, Lady Luck stepped in again. Professor Alty, who had been giving the lectures in quantum theory, left suddenly to take up a position in England. Herzberg had perforce to be asked to take over Dr. Alty's work. He did this superbly, and soon the physics faculty were thanking the good Lord for the manna which had dropped so unexpectedly from heaven. And very shortly, Dr. Harrington was banging on Dr. Murray's desk, demanding an increase in pay for Dr. Herzberg—all of which was duly related to me by Dr. Murray with a little smile and his infectious chuckle.

Three months after his arrival in Saskatoon, Herzberg was appointed research professor in physics. Reading this through nearly forty years later, it all seems quite incredible, since I was at that time a very junior person in chemistry. It could only have happened under a fairly autocratic system with a president like Dr. Murray who trusted his own judgment, was filled with the milk of human kindness, and was prepared to take a bit of a gamble. The gamble paid off handsomely. Dr. and Mrs. Herzberg soon established a warm group of friends in Saskatoon and found it a good place in which to put down roots. The city was congenial enough for the Herzbergs to start a family, and their children, Paul and Agnes, were born in Saskatoon.

It is greatly to the credit of the university and of its first president, Dr. Murray, that they provided not only a home but also an appropriate setting for the work of an eminent scholar who had become caught up in the troubles of Hitler's Germany. It is greatly to the credit of the members of the physics department that they received Herzberg in such a friendly manner and went out of their way to help him get established in his research. As an example of this kindness, Dr. Harrington constructed a diffusion pump for Dr. Herzberg.

Dr. Herzberg stayed ten years at the university. During this period he published many scientific articles and three major books on atomic and molecular spectra. These books have become classics and they are still widely used. I was lucky enough to be asked by Herzberg to translate two of these books into English. The translations meant a great deal of work and they taught me several things: scientific German, a great deal of spectroscopy, and what hard work is all about. And by thinking out how best to translate each sentence so that the exact meaning was quite clear and unambiguous, even to a chemist, I obtained a depth of understanding of this particular subject which most people never do get. As a footnote to his career in Saskatoon, it should be recorded that in 1971 Dr. Herzberg was awarded the Nobel Prize, not for physics as might have been expected, but, to the amusement of scientists around the world, for chemistry.

During the prewar period I got to know the province of Saskatchewan and Canada as a whole fairly well. I took many trips into the country around Saskatoon with members of the Extension Division, attending field days, crop and animal judging days, and agricultural exhibitions and fairs. Usually I would make myself useful by helping to register boys attending the farm boys' camp or by handing out blankets and pillows. It was all very pleasant and it introduced me to part of the life of rural Saskatchewan.

Somewhat more extensive camping trips were taken with Les Saunders, a biology professor with a keen eye for nature and a considerable talent as a photographer and an artist. One trip took us to the Cypress Hills. We had made a sort of pup tent by stretching a piece of canvas between the roof of the car and the ground. Shortly after dark it started to rain, so we put some of our food supplies in the tent and curled up in the car for the night. After a while Les nudged me and whispered that he thought someone was stealing things from the tent. He switched on his flash light, and there was a skunk, helping himself to a half a pound of bacon. We let him take it!

Another delightful camping trip took me to the West Coast in company with Jack Bentley, a professor of English, and Les Glinz, a professor of education. Dr. Bentley used to stay at a hotel each night while Glinz and I slept in a tent. Bentley's stories each morning, telling us the perils of local hotels in the mid-thirties, kept us in fits of laughter.

In the fall of 1935 I went on a camping trip with Dr. Thorvaldson to Kingsmere Lake, which was then quite isolated and off the beaten track. We went by car to Waskesiu and then by canoe to a portage leading to Kingsmere Lake. We made a sort of tent using a waterproof sheet and a rope tied between two trees. The first evening we sat by the fire for a while, listening to the splash of fish jumping for flies and the haunting call of the loon. Then we crawled into our sleeping bags and Dr. Thorvaldson went to sleep immediately. I was kept awake by a succession of sounds—a coyote barking in the distance, a squirrel which kept dropping onto the roof of the tent and sliding down past my head, and the pad, pad of a fairly large animal, probably a bear. The next evening Dr. Thorvaldson gave me a "nightcap" from an emergency bottle of brandy which he had at the bottom of his gunny sack and I had no more trouble going to sleep.

Each day we explored a new part of the lake which measured about six by ten miles, as I remember, in a boat which we had fitted up with a sail made from our tent canvas and a pole cut from the bush. And each day we caught fish for lunch and supper, mostly pickerel. At the northern end of the lake there was a portage over to a smaller lake, Lake Ajawaan. On the far side of the lake we could see a small cabin with a person moving about near it. We waved arms to attract the attention of this person, and a few minutes later the person stepped into a canoe and paddled across to meet us. It turned out to be Anahareo, the Indian wife of Grey Owl. She kindly invited us over to visit them, and by the time we had crossed the lake, Grey Owl was up, drinking a bowl of tea. With his tanned face, aquiline nose, long braided hair, and Indian clothes we did not doubt that he was an

Indian, although later it came out that he was an Englishman from Hastings. At all events he had quite a way with birds and animals. Birds would take food from his mouth, and the beaver would come from the lake to eat from his hand. And when we returned to the other side of the lake later in the day, a couple of young beavers played with us, appearing on one side of the canoe, slapping their tails on the water, diving under the canoe, surfacing, and slapping their tails again repeatedly.

It happened to be the third birthday of their small daughter, Shirley Dawn, a charming little girl who had great fun flicking water onto Dr. Thorvaldson while they sat on a log projecting out into the lake. The birthday was celebrated with a small cake on which three spruce twigs took the place of the usual candles.

During the day I went in the canoe with Anahareo to get a chesterfield which had been brought to the other side of the lake by outfitters from Waskesiu and had then been left under a bush, covered with a piece of canvas. It had been brought in preparation for a visit by the Governor-General, Lord Tweedsmuir. When we arrived at the other side of the lake I was asked to sit at one end of the canoe, balancing it, while Anahareo picked up the chesterfield and placed it across the canoe. She must have been as strong as an ox. Incidentally, she was extremely good-looking and had a great sense of humor. I remember how delightfully she described to us the film about Henry VIII and his six wives, which she had seen in Prince Albert—she hadn't missed a trick!

During the day Grey Owl took me to visit another small lake nearby, talking all the way about birds and animals and about a trip to England he was expecting to make in connection with a book he had written. I asked him how he had acquired such a good vocabulary, and on our return to the cabin he showed me a pile of dictionaries and scribblers. When he heard a new word from one of his visitors he put the word in the scribbler, he said, looked it up in the dictionary, and then tried it out on his next visitor. I must admit that I am still an admirer of the late Grey Owl and of his Indian wife, Anahareo.

In 1938 I met my wife-to-be, Mary Strelioff, the daughter of a Saskatchewan farming family who had come to the city to live. We actually met at a dance arranged by a ballroom-dancing group, where those who liked waltzes and tangos could dance to the music of a small orchestra. The organization was supported by a number of ethnic groups and by a smattering of university people, and the dances were always most enjoyable. Mary was extremely good-looking, she danced well, and she had a truly regal bearing. Her kind and generous nature was immediately apparent, and in no time at all I was terribly in love. I was at the time still quite shy where girls were concerned. We were introduced shortly before the intermission. After we had danced together, Mary said that she was on the refreshments committee and would have to help serve the coffee and cakes, so I went along and helped too, to everyone's great amusement.

We met often during the summer and fall of 1938, and a warm

friendship developed. Eventually we became engaged, and we were married in June of 1939. All this time our friends had been watching and encouraging us, rather like a bunch of clucking hens, with coffee parties, skating, weekends at a cottage by a lake—putting us together in a variety of situations. I particularly remember one Sunday afternoon tea party put on by Dr. Roger Manning, at which Dr. Manning treated Mary like his own daughter—showing her off in an elegant powder blue dress and a navy blue, wide-brimmed hat. At the beginning of June the King and Queen visited the province, and the university and we were caught up in the excitement. A few days later, in pouring rain, we were married at Rugby Chapel, the Anglican chapel on campus. There was a delightful reception at the Gordons.

In the early evening we were taken to the station and put on the train to Calgary, on the way to Banff, where we were to spend our honeymoon. In those days the train included a diner, so we had a delightful wedding supper with steak and strawberries and cream. We stayed for our honeymoon in a small cabin on Grizzly Street, from which we took long walks to all the usual spots within reasonable distance of Banff, swam in the Upper and Lower Hot Springs pools, climbed Sulphur Mountain—the last hundred yards or so through deep snow—and dined at the Banff Springs Hotel. After dinner we would go to the Mount Steven room to listen to a string quartet with Frances James and Murray Adaskin. We were later to get to know the Adaskins well as members of the university family. Shortly before we left Banff, we got word that a telegram awaited us in Calgary. Needless to say we were concerned, fearing some bad news. The telegram, from an old college friend of mine, J. B. Batemen, read, "Congratulations on the Russo-Anglo alliance!" We were regarded with a great deal of curiosity by the telegrapher!

The honeymoon was over all too soon, and we returned to Saskatoon to have a second honeymoon installing ourselves in a small brown bungalow on University Drive, a couple of minutes' walk from the university gates. Here Mary's skill and innate discriminating taste showed itself to great advantage, and we were soon comfortably installed in the "chocolate box," which was to be our home for the next twenty years, apart from a few years' absence during the war. The "chocolate box," as the name implies, was small, but it had a nice fireplace and a pleasant home atmosphere. It proved big enough for us to entertain our many friends at dinner, tea, or coffee parties. We also entertained hundreds of students, some of whom started out quite suspicious of drinking tea on a Sunday afternoon but became quite converted to the practice.

The house proved to be big enough not only for small groups but for me to entertain a men's club to which I belonged—the Unashamed. This club met once a month to read a play or to discuss a new book or some other topic of interest. Its membership was drawn from all over the campus, and I was lucky enough to be invited to join the club shortly after my arrival at the university. I remember getting papers ready on *The Magic Mountain*

by Thomas Mann and on Spengler's *The Decline of the West*, besides reading
various plays by Aristophanes. I also remember a great deal of fascinating
talk. The evenings would finish with cheese and beer or sometimes with
coffee. Once a year the group had a dinner party organized around some
general theme. One such theme was that the university had been converted
to a bowling alley, while another time it was understood that portions of the
German fleet had somehow got from Hudson's Bay to the Saskatchewan
River. Meetings ended with a sing-song—the songs being parodies of
well-known ditties. Dr. Basterfield was particularly good at versifying, as
was Dr. Lindsay. The Unashamed has disappeared long since, but it will be
long remembered by its former members.

Mary and I had scarcely settled down in our little brown house before
war broke out. Naturally, the war had a major effect on our lives, both
during the actual hostilities and afterwards. Apart from what I might or
might not have contributed to the war effort, I came out of the war more or
less in one piece, for which I was duly thankful, and with some firsthand
knowledge of two new and important fields of research—operations
research and atomic energy—both of which had immediate important
practical applications in the postwar world. Either field would have
provided ample opportunities for a research career, but instead of switching
into one or the other, I kept my main research effort in chemistry and made
use of my two new areas of expertise to advance my former interests.

Maintaining an active interest in three or four research areas inevitably
made me something of a generalist and therefore made me useful to other
people. So when people were being considered for committees or positions
involving overlapping disciplines I came to be thought of, and gradually I
found myself undertaking administrative responsibilities. At first these
were simple: ordering chemicals, arranging labs., drawing up residence
rules, becoming regional representative in the Chemical Society, secretary
to the Faculty Club and to the Archaeological Society, and so on.

Eventually the administrative positions became more important and I
served as head of the chemistry department, Dean of Graduate Studies, and
so on, although people wondered why a research scientist would bother
with anything outside his science. I suppose the answer is that I found it
difficult to say no and that I actually found everything that I did to be
interesting—"amusing" is the word I would probably have used.

Each new thing that I did led to others: membership on the Defense
Research Board, the National Research Council, the Saskatchewan Research
Council, and so forth; each, if you like, was leading me further down the
administrative and bureaucratic garden path, but each was providing me
with additional opportunities and satisfactions. In retrospect, World War II
was not just an enforced absence from the university. It changed my whole
outlook. Before I go on to describe my wartime experiences, however,
perhaps I should say a little more about my personal background by giving
a brief account of the members of my family who have figured in it.

One big drawback of moving from England to Canada in 1930 was that I was almost completely cut off from my family. The only way to get from Canada to England during the thirties was by ship—an expensive business which was almost impossible in those depression years. In the fall of 1933 I did have a brief stopover in Britain on the way to Germany, and it was possible for my mother to visit me in Darmstadt. While my mother was alive we corresponded regularly and frequently, and we corresponded with other members of the family almost as often.

My sister Winnifred was the only member of my immediate family to visit me in Saskatoon. The first time she came was in the fall of 1939, just after I was married and on the outbreak of war. She was an exchange teacher for a year. Her next visit was not to be until some twenty years later. Winnie continued as a teacher, eventually settling down as headmistress of the village school at Elvedon in Norfolk. There she acquired a deep interest in local history and wrote a most readable book on brass rubbing.

My other three sisters were nurses until they married. My brother stayed in the R.A.F. between the wars, and after getting the usual basic training he specialized in the engineering aspects of aircraft. After participating in the construction of the Schneider trophy seaplanes, he was transferred to flying boats and went out to Singapore to help set up the first overseas flying boat base. His Asian experience was to stand him in good stead during World War II, when he was for a time C.O. of the air base at Ascot Vale near Sydney in Australia. After the war he retired with the rank of Group Captain to live at Mundford in Norfolk, a few miles from his birthplace.

In the postwar period Mary and I visited England many times, usually to go to a meeting of one kind or another. We would see as many of the family as we could, but on two occasions when the visit necessarily had to be brief, we persuaded most of them to come to dinner with us. Once we met in London, and once at the old Bell Inn in Thetford.

Of course, we were able to see more of Mary's family since they lived near Saskatoon. Her father died in the early thirties, and at first her mother continued to live on the farm. Mary's sister and two brothers remained in Saskatchewan, and we watched children and grandchildren growing up. There are pleasant memories of summer picnics and of Christmas parties at which as many as a dozen would sing carols around the Christmas tree and have the usual family fun and games.

PART II

SCIENTIST IN WAR AND PEACE

Chapter 9

World War II

Mary and I had scarcely settled down to married life when World War II broke out. The impact on the university was instantaneous: large numbers of young men enlisted, many professors left to join the armed forces, university research shifted to wartime problems, and various wartime training programs were based on the campus. In addition, all those who were left on campus took part in the greatly expanded operations of the C.O.T.C. I joined as a private, quickly attained the rank of sergeant, and then became lieutenant, and finally obtained my captain's papers. No one who participated in the C.O.T.C. will forget the regular drill periods and the exercises among the sand hills in camp at Dundurn. The academic staff put their professional backgrounds to good use: Dr. Larmour and I took courses in chemical warfare and then acted as instructors, the legal people lectured on military law, and so on.

At the beginning of World War II, scientists working in Canadian universities were told quite firmly that it was their duty to continue working at the universities. They were told that as opportunities arose they would be called upon to assist with the war effort. I quickly became engaged in chemical problems involved in the production of toluene, in problems with the viscosity of smoke-producing liquids, and in chemical warfare instruction with the local C.O.T.C. unit.

Dr. C. J. Mackenzie, dean of engineering, had left the University of Saskatchewan at the beginning of the war to head up the National Research Council. Just before he left he had told me that he would keep me in mind if a suitable project came along. So it was with great anticipation that I answered a long-distance phone call from Dr. Mackenzie one day early in the war, some months after he had left Saskatoon. He asked me whether I would be interested in going to Ottawa for some "war work". Can you tell me anything about it?" I asked.

"Not much."

"Can you at least tell me whether it has anything to do with the armed forces or is it more of a lab. job?"

"It's more of a lab. job," replied Dr. Mackenzie.

"Would you mind if I said no, since I really would prefer something to do with the armed forces?"

"I quite understand," said C. J., and sure enough, about two months later he phoned me again.

I started the conversation by saying, "You know what I asked last time?"

"Yes," he said. "This time it is something to do with the armed forces."

So I said yes, quickly obtained leave from the university, packed my bags, and went to Ottawa, where I was sworn to secrecy, finger-printed, and so forth. I was then told that I was to be part of the establishment of the Operational Research Centre at Air Force headquarters in Ottawa, under the late Professor J. O. Wilhelm.

This centre had been established in August, 1942. The Royal Canadian Navy and the Army set up similar organizations (under Dr. J. A. L. Johnstone and Dr. J. T. Wilson, respectively). Up to this point my military experience had been limited to training with the C.O.T.C. and a gas course taken at Nanaimo, B.C. And I had never taken a flight in an aeroplane. The Air Force quickly remedied this deficiency. After being attached to the R.C.A.F. I was sent to fly in all sorts of aircraft at Rockcliffe, Halifax, and Vancouver, and then sent to various technical establishments such as Research Enterprises. Then I was drilled on radar by a physicist and finally sent to England by air in the Commando—in itself quite an exciting experience—in early 1943. The Commando aircraft was often used by Churchill in World War II.

I had been told that a visit to the United Kingdom was impending, and I was warned to have a bag packed ready for immediate departure. After a day or so I received a phone call telling me to proceed to the Windsor Hotel in Montreal. There I received a further phone call telling me to be at the corner of Peel and St. Catherine's at 8:00 A.M. sharp. A biggish black car would pick me up. Sure enough, the big black car drove up to me, and I got in. I was relieved to see an assorted bag of one army major, a Polish engineer, and an admiral, all looking as puzzled as I was. We were whisked out to Dorval and given a briefing on the use of life jackets, parachutes, and similar items, and then told not to bother too much, since if we came down in the Atlantic no one would pick us up, and it was probably much nicer to die quickly.

We were then bundled up in teddy-bear suits and packed like sardines in a Liberator aircraft which had been stripped of all armaments—hence the security precautions surrounding our movements. We left on an afternoon early in March. After we cleared the coast it became very cold— the heater was "u.s." However, blankets and hot coffee warmed us up, and we had a jolly time laughing and joking.

After a time I felt quite woozy and thought I was going to faint. I asked the man in front of me to tell someone, but he said he felt horrible too. At this point the door between us and the crew was opened, and a red-mustached Air Force type said to us, in a very English accent, "I say, you fellows, we are up at 22,000 feet. Plug in the oxygen!" We put on oxygen masks and plugged them in and were immediately very sick, as a result of anoxia, I presume. However, in a few minutes we were all fit again and none the worse for our scare.

Another scare came when we were approaching Ireland. There was a violent crack like something hitting the outside of the aircraft, but it was just the radio antenna which had broken loose and was flapping against the side of the Liberator. A few moments later we landed in Prestwick to see green grass and daffodils—a very welcome sight.

A few minutes later we were escorted to the bar and inducted as members of the Short Snorter group—composed of those who had flown the Atlantic when the number so doing was still relatively small. Induction consisted in putting one's signature on a dollar bill or other paper note together with that of someone who was already a Short Snorter. Failure to produce the Short Snorter bill on demand by another Short Snorter made the defaulter liable to stand the challenger a free drink.

A week or so later, when visiting Air Force headquarters in London, I ran into Dr. Ken Mann (now at U.B.C.). I was delighted when he told me that he had seen C.J. I was still more pleased when he arranged for me to get in touch with Dr. Mackenzie. Eventually we got together for lunch in a pleasant restaurant just off Picadilly, known to Dr. Mann. Dr. Mackenzie's thoughtfulness and charm on that occason were typical of the warmth of his interest in anyone who worked for him. The conversation was interspersed with some real gems of scientific wisdom and with lots of homely advice, all given in a tactful way. I was, of course, completely sold on Dr. Mackenzie from my early Saskatoon days, and these wartime meetings served only to strengthen my respect and admiration for him.

In the United Kingdom I visited Fighter Command and heard about night fighter operations and aircraft interceptions, about special operations such as "Rhubarb", "Ramrod", "Rodeo", and "Roadsters", and about the relative effectiveness of machine guns and cannon. A visit to Coastal Command followed, where I heard about U-boat habits, radar performance, analysis of U-boat attacks, planned flying, losses caused by weather, convoy coverage, and so forth. Then came a tour of radar stations on the Isle of Wight and at Inverness, with an exciting landing at Jerbey in the Isle of Man.

I was taken to Inverness by a Free French pilot in a small two-engined aircraft, starting out from near London. As we went north the weather

deteriorated, and soon we were bouncing up and down and slightly west of
Liverpool. At this stage the pilot decided to land on a nearby airstrip. The
first attempt was unsuccessful, and we zoomed up and circled for another
try. This time we were lucky, and we were met on the landing strip by
ground personnel who told us we were in Jerbey and suggested that we had
better stay overnight. Actually it was a very pleasant stay, since the Isle of
Man seemed not to be subject to the usual rationing. My pilot turned up
next morning looking very pleased with himself, and I later decided that the
"forced" landing in the Isle of Man had been a put-up job.

After visiting the newly formed American Operations Research team at
8th Bomber Command, I went to Bomber Command headquarters, where I
met such fine people as Dickens, Saundby, Harris, and Tizard. There I
heard about the analysis of bomber operations, about navigational aids,
bomb damage, battle damage, pathfinders, and even about Oboe, at that
time a highly secret bombing device. I remember that on this particular visit
I was accompanied by another Canadian named Smith (Dr. E. C. Smith,
now of Acadia University). We had some difficulties in finding out all we
wished to hear about Oboe, and this secrecy led us, on the way home, to
compose the following limerick:

> Said Smith one day to a hobo,
> "Pray tell me, what is an oboe?"
>   Said he, "Go to the dickens!"
>   He'll give you small pickin's,—
> It's something you're not meant to know, bo!

We had to have our little jokes, even in wartime.

From Bomber Command I was sent to T.R.E. to hear the latest on H_2S
(which was not what it seems, but a code name for a blind-bombing device)
and on various types of radar, and then on to Farnborough, where I heard
about aircraft, instruments, and weapons, including rockets, oxygen masks,
and low-level bomb sights.

While in England I visited Dishforth, where a Canadian squadron was
in the process of converting from Wellingtons to Lancasters. I was present
at a debriefing after a bombing raid over the Ruhr when flack and losses
had been particularly heavy. The coolness with which the twenty-year-olds
told of their experiences filled me with admiration. Wing Commander E.
McNab dropped into the mess that evening from a nearby fighter wing, and
we reminisced about the University of Saskatchewan. Other memories are
of strolling across Trafalgar Square and meeting Dr. Jim Campbell of
Saskatoon, who was attached to one of the military hospitals. He said
"Hello" as casually as if we had met on campus in Saskatoon, and took me
off to a cafe for coffee and a bun. There was not a question about what was I
doing—just lots of good talk about the war generally and the people back
home. Then it was outside and "Cheerio"—not to see each other again till
the war was over.

Another memory is of taking Smith down to Thetford to see my mother on the first weekend I was in England. I had sent a telegram, but it didn't arrive till long after the weekend, so when we arrived at my mother's house and knocked at the door, we were a complete surprise. I hadn't seen my mother for five or six years, but she opened the door wide, as though she quite expected me, and said, "Come in, the kettle is just boiling and you are just in time for tea!" My friend Smith thought this was slightly overdoing the British coolness, but by the time we left next day and my mother gave me a kiss and said "Bye-bye—see you next time," he was quite accustomed to the seeming casualness.

Smith was over six feet tall and always hungry. I remember one day going back from High Wycombe to London by bus, and Smith's eagle eye spotted a cake in a cafe window as the bus sped through a small village. He quickly pulled the cord stopping the bus, and we got off and made our way back to the cafe. Seating ourselves at a small table, we nervously asked whether we might have tea and a piece of cake.

"Why not?" said the waitress. The cake was delicious and the slice quickly disappeared.

"May we have another piece?"

"Why not?" and in a few goes the whole cake disappeared.

We got on the next bus to London, very pleased with ourselves. Big pleasures came in small packages in those days.

Finally I came back to Canada, and was sent first to Western Air Command at Vancouver under Dr. C. W. Leggatt, a very knowledgeable statistician, and then to Eastern Air Command at Halifax. Among the problems tackled which can now be mentioned were statistical analyses leading to an improvement in the flying effort and in the coverage of the West Coast approaches, bombing trials, navigation logs, and searches for missing aircraft.

While I was stationed at Jericho Beach I spent a good deal of time in the operations room. In order to get better acquainted with the flying operations, I drew up a monthly statistical report of the flying effort at the various stations. A casual glance indicated that the squadrons showed a wide variation in the amount of flying per aircraft per day. One obvious reason for differences was the weather—Prince Rupert was often fogged in, while Pat Bay was usually sunny. One could easily allow for the weather by using the meteorological records and so calculate hours per aircraft per flyable day. There was still quite a difference, and the next possible factor seemed to be type of aircraft. Luckily, some stations had two or more types of aircraft, and so one could calculate a factor converting Liberators to Venturas, and so on. One thus obtained hours per flyable day per theoretical aircraft. There was still quite a difference between stations, and the next factor which seemed of importance was the variability of the flying.

Some squadrons would have all twelve aircraft in the air for two or three days running and do a huge amount of flying, but they would then have all the aircraft unserviceable and out of action for a week. Other squadrons would have, say, seven out of twelve aircraft in the air most of the time. They never did as much on any one day, but over the month they averaged much better. Thus variability seemed to be a factor. The mathematical measure for this is called the coefficient of variation, per cent. An analysis of several months' flying effort indicated that there was a definite negative correlation between variability and flying effort—the more variable, the less the actual flying.

Next month the C.O. sent out an order saying that no squadron would fly more than so much per day, or less than so much per day—thus pulling in the variability by about ten per cent. That month flying went up about ten per cent, and by repeating the process of pulling in the variability, the flying effort was improved by a hundred per cent in six months. It should be noted that the planes, weather, and pilots were exactly the same, and the stations were merely optimizing their effort—in this case adjusting the maintenance schedules so as to get optimum performance. Since the analysis was based on actual operations, the predictions made were bound to work.

From the point of view of decision theory, operations research had indicated what decision to make in order to step up the flying effort, using the system "as is". Another way of describing the situation would be to say that the factors influencing the system had been analysed, and that this was an example of systems analysis. Still another description would be to say that the flying effort was controlled by a formula, or that we were practising "formula flying". The British would have said that we were practising "planned maintenance", since fundamentally it was by altering the maintenance schedules that the improved regularity of flying was achieved and the desired goal reached. It should be noted that the formula was used as an instrument to arrive at a definite goal, namely to optimize the flying effort—to get more flying using the same men, machines, and weather.

Two other problems might be mentioned in some detail—bombing trials and searches for missing aircraft. They are described in order to indicate some of the trials of the operations researcher.

The bombing trials were to be held in a large inlet of the sea at Coal Harbor on the west coast of Vancouver Island. I was up in the aircraft with a number of pilots, each of whom had to drop twelve bombs onto a towed target, simulating twelve attacks on a sub. I was sitting up in the co-pilot's seat when the first pilot brought the aircraft in over some hills, and we saw the target way down below us. The pilot put his heavy aircraft into a forty-five degree dive towards the water, which gradually looked harder and harder. At the critical moment he pulled back on the stick and dropped the bombs, and my head went forward and was cracked on the instrument panel. Twelve times this happened, and twelve times I died—each time expecting the wings of the aircraft to fall off.

At the end of all this the pilot suggested that we go down, but I was just beginning to enjoy myself and I insisted that the other four pilots also do their stuff, though not at quite such a steep angle. In the meantime, the pilots who were not bombing were in the back of the aircraft, being shaken about like peas in a pod, so that by the time we settled down on the water again (it was a flying boat), I was the only one able to walk. Sweet triumph! By the time the mess settled down again around me (after the usual round of drinks put up by those who were sick), my reputation as a good fellow was made, and I had a hundred per cent cooperation from then on. This rather silly incident did me more good than all the advanced degrees after my name.

There was an amusing sequel when I came to write up the report on the trials. On each of the flight logs the navigator had written the name of an imaginary pilot, F. O. Zilch, which was a standing joke on the station. I thought I had better include him in the trials, with all bombs on target, in the shape of a letter Z. I took the report in to my C.O. in Vancouver who commented knowledgeably on the various pilots until we came to Zilch. I mentioned that I had left the best till the last, and I put the diagram of Zilch's bombs, in a neat $\vdots \!\cdot\! \vdots$, under his nose.

"My God, they're all on target!" He looked again, "What did you say his name was?"

"Zilch," said I , with a deadpan expression.

"I can't believe it! It's pattern bombing!"

I realized then that I had committed the unpardonable sin of pulling my superior officer's leg without making quite sure that he would realize that there was a joke. So I hastily picked up the papers, excused myself, and went out and destroyed all traces of Zilch's famous bombing trials. It was a near squeak for me, and it taught me a lesson.

The other problem of search procedures for missing aircraft started out with the loss of a Hampden aircraft at sea off Vancouver Island. Maps indicating the areas searched came to my attention, and I tried to make a quantitative estimate of the efficiency of the search procedure.

My estimate came to ten per cent, and it seemed to me that even though I had never been on a search, my estimate could not be that much in error. So I wrote up a little report and sent it in to one of the senior officers.

A day or so later someone phoned me. "Spinks!"

"Yes," I replied.

"Don't you say sir to me?"

"Not unless you say sir to me!"

Wham! The person at the other end had hung up with a bang. A bit later he phoned again and this time I replied, "Yes, sir?"

"Come to see me at once, room 103!"

So I put on my cap and went to room 103, where I saw Air Commodore X, sitting behind his desk and looking very cross.

"Did you write this report?"

"Yes, sir."

"Have you ever been on a search?"

"No, sir."

"God damn your impudence, writing about something you know nothing about!" And he proceeded to give me quite a tongue lashing. When he had slowed down, I asked him whether he had flown on any searches.

"Hundreds of hours!" was the scornful reply.

"Then perhaps you will tell me what is wrong with the report?"

"It's not a bad report."

Then I made mistake number one. I said, "I'm sorry, sir."

"What do you mean, you're sorry?"

"Well, you say the report is all right. It indicated ten per cent efficiency, and in my book ten per cent isn't very good."

He looked even more grim and then went on to say, "I suppose you know who put on this search?"

"No, sir."

"I did!"

Then I made mistake number two. I said, "I'm sorry, sir."

"What the hell do you mean, you're sorry?"

At this point I could only say, "Let's not go into that again."

By now I felt sure he had made up his mind to get rid of me, especially when he said, "I suppose you have told everyone up and down the coast about this?"

Throwing caution to the winds I replied, "No sir, you and I are the only two people who know about this, and if you are as sticky as you seem to be, when I leave the room you will tear up the report and drop it in the wastepaper basket and no one will ever hear of it! Good day, sir!" And with that I saluted smartly and went back to my office, waiting for the axe to fall.

Some time later, the Air Commodore phoned. "Do you ever go to the bar?"

"Occasionally," I replied.

"Meet me there at five to six. Consider this an order."

Sharply at five to six I went to the bar in the mess, and there sat the Air Commodore with ten glasses in front of him, each with the appropriate amount of amber-colored fluid.

"All right. You start there and I'll start here, and we'll see who's better at this."

By dint of forgetting my connection with the U. of S. I got to number six by the time he had reached the fourth. It took a long time for the mess to settle down, but by the time it did we were good friends, and he had given me a chit authorizing me to investigate searches whenever and wherever I wished. In due time I made a general examination of the principles underlying searches for missing aircraft. Probability areas were defined in which the aircraft was most likely to be found, and search procedures were outlined for the various types of terrain which might be encountered, since a search in wooded mountainous country would obviously be quite different from a search over the sea. The search reports sent in by the search aircraft were standardized, and a mathematical method was worked out for indicating the progress of the search and the areas to be searched next. The importance of keeping an exact chronological record and of assessing each search for the guidance of future searches was clearly indicated.

The Air Commodore checked everything from a practical flying point of view and put his initials on the document, which was then used in conducting searches. Some thirty years later these two or three typewritten pages have grown into a fat I.C.A.O. Search and Rescue Manual, but a few of the initial paragraphs are still straight Spinks.

One purely personal aspect of this work was that it brought me into close contact with the fighting men and women of the armed services and gave me a great respect for the way in which twenty-year-olds could go out on highly dangerous bombing missions with all the sang froid in the world.

The moral of this recital of my wartime experiences is that I was another one of those fortunate young men who ran into some very fine people while he was growing up, who overlooked the fact that he was an impudent young pup and who gave him a chance to develop. One of the most outstanding of these fine people was C. J. Mackenzie, and I confess willingly that I am immensely in his debt. Various bits of his philosophy have stood me in good stead time and again:

"Never be afraid to stand up for your principles, but try to avoid being maneuvered into a position of having to die for them—you're a long time dead."

"When you're delegating authority, delegate authority. If anyone to whom I have delegated authority puts a piece of paper in front of me to sign, I'll sign it without question, but by God, he'd better be right. I don't sign twice for people who make mistakes."

"Set your sights on the stars and try to accomplish some of those impossible things Canadians have always been capable of doing."

After listening to Dr. Mackenzie and observing what he has done in various situations over a long period of time, it has gradually dawned on me that Dr. Mackenzie is one of the few scientist-statesmen of our time. You don't become a statesman by sitting in an armchair, no matter how good you are or how well you philosophize. You must have experience in the world of hard knocks, where your judgments on matters involving men by the thousands and money by the millions can be tested. Dr. Mackenzie is a scientist and an engineer who has been fortunate enough to have had these other experiences and to have come through them victoriously. He has long benefited us greatly by his wisdom.

Like everyone else's, our home life was greatly upset by the war. Soon after the outbreak of hostilities Mary enrolled in a training program for volunteer nurses, and she proved to be a born nurse. After receiving her training she helped at a number of hospitals, at first in Saskatoon and later in other cities, such as Vancouver and Montreal, where I happened to be stationed. When I first went with the R.C.A.F. Mary stayed in Saskatoon, but after I had been in Vancouver for a while, living in the mess, we found a small flat close to Jericho Beach, at the corner of Fourth and Trimble, where we lived all one winter. I was often away on "business" up the coast or in Ottawa, but at least we were able to see each other much more frequently in between absences than if Mary had stayed in Saskatoon. Eventually I was transferred to Halifax. After I had been stationed there for a while, one of the university families, the Theakstones, took us into their home. We shall always be grateful to them for their many kindnesses to us.

Chapter 10

Atoms in Wartime

Life with the Operations Research Group at Halifax under Professor Barnes was never dull. Dr. Barnes had a razor-sharp brain, and woe betide anyone who wrote up a report in anything but perfect logic and impeccable English style. We tackled a number of interesting problems related to convoy protection and antisubmarine operations, and we felt that we were more or less pulling our weight. Then one day I had another phone call from Dr. C. J. Mackenzie, suggesting that I was required on a still more urgent project. I agreed to go wherever was necessary, and shortly thereafter I was transferred to Montreal and became a part of the Canadian atomic energy project, working in the new wing of the University of Montreal. This was a joint project between Canada, the United Kingdom, and the Free French. By the time I joined the group Dr. E. W. R. Steacie was in charge of the Canadian aspects of the project, while Dr. John Cockcroft was in overall charge of the laboratory, which was working in a general way on the development of a uranium-heavy water reactor. It seemed a curious coincidence that I was once more involved with heavy water after a ten-year absence.

Dr. Cockcroft was an excellent director for the lab. Not only was he a first-class scientist and at the top of his field, but he did a superb job in welding together some rather incongruous members from several different countries and quite different backgrounds into a good working group. In spite of wartime shortages, Mrs. Cockcroft (now Lady Cockcroft) managed to entertain us at their home, usually on Saturday evening or on Sunday afternoon, when we had the pleasure of meeting their young family. On a return visit to the Spinkses' apartment, their young son Christopher had a grand time trying all the electric switches and noting with grave attention which switches did what. And when we played the record of *Peter and the Wolf*, their daughter Katherine disappeared into the bedroom. After a minute or so I was sent to see what Katherine was up to. Looking through a tiny crack as I barely opened the door, I saw Katherine having a marvelous time, acting out the story of *Peter and the Wolf* all to herself. The Cockcrofts told us later that acting out *Peter and the Wolf* became one of Katherine's favourite pastimes.

The particular lab. that I was assigned to was under the immediate direction of Dr. Bertrand Goldschmidt, who had worked extensively in the Curie laboratories in Paris and who was one of the few people in the lab. at that time to have had much experience of working with radioactive materials. He gave vigorous leadership to a young team and inspired its members to work long hours. Nowadays one would say that he had charisma. He did everything with a great flair. His contacts with other prewar radioactivity workers proved a great asset in cutting through some of the wartime red tape. Such was his skill in piecing together odd scraps of information that top ranking scientists from the U.S.A. would visit with us, just to get a general overall view of what was going on. We were also fortunate in having Professor Paneth of Vienna and Durham in the lab. He had worked for a number of years with radioactive materials, and he had a sound research reputation—a great asset in a lab. full of keen but relatively inexperienced researchers.

The time flew by as I became familiar with radioactive techniques: working with invisibly small amounts of horribly radioactive materials, using geiger counters and lead shields, and wearing rubber gloves to avoid contaminating one's hands and rubber overshoes to avoid carrying contamination from one place to another. My closest colleague was Dr. Leslie Cook, and we cooperated in working out a method for separating small amounts of plutonium from slugs of uranium which had been irradiated in one of the American reactors. The slug of uranium was cylindrical, about one inch in diameter and six inches long, and it was extremely radioactive—very "hot" as we used to say. Actually, everything was top secret, so code names and numbers were used for everything—a uranium solution was a "dog" solution, and a highly active uranium solution was a "hot dog" solution. The lead container in which the geiger counter was housed was called a "castle" and the lab., in general, was engaged in "green cheese" research. The presence of highly radioactive fission products in the irradiated slug complicated problems enormously. At one stage when we had dissolved up the slug and had successfully removed the greater part of the uranium, the plutonium seemed to disappear. It was found adsorbed (or stuck) on a few flakes of white material which had dissolved out of the stainless steel from which the container was made. That was bad enough, but practically all the fission product activity had been adsorbed on the same material, and separating them was a nightmare.

One day my wife said to me, "John, your neck is red—I wish you would get rid of this silly habit of scratching your neck." I replied that I hadn't been scratching my neck—probably I had a scratchy collar. "Then change your shirt!" I did so, and in a few days the redness disappeared. Two or three weeks later the same thing happened again and my wife remarked, "It's odd that it's the same shirt." That evening I took the shirt to the lab. and tested it with a geiger. It was lousy with radioactivity—evidently a spot of highly active material had been splashed on my collar. Quite obviously, splashes might have gone in other places and would have dried off without leaving even a stain.

On testing the floor of the lab. I found it was highly radioactive, and so were the walls and the ceiling, as a result of radioactive dust. Next morning I reported on this. Pontecorvo happened to be present. He immediately made some tests himself and found that my report was correct. His reaction was to phone Dr. Cockcroft and recommend that chemists be barred from entering any other part of the building for fear of carrying contamination with them. At the same time a radiation safety committee was set up on which I sat, together with Dr. Mitchell, a radiologist of great experience from Cambridge. This was one of the first committees to recognize the dangers which might result from chemical operations involving highly radioactive materials. I always credit Mary's acute observations for this very necessary step, and I think she should have got a medal (She didn't know anything about these things until some time after the war.)

At about this time it became necessary to build a pilot plant in which the equipment would be heavily shielded and operated by remote control. It was necessary to get overall approval from Dr. Mackenzie. I was sent with the necessary documents to get his signature.

"Well, John, isn't it nice to see you? Just tell me what has been happening."

After a time I suggested that he must be busy and might like to look through the documents.

"Where do I have to sign?" asked Dr. Mackenzie, and before I could protest, he had put his John Henry in the appropriate spot.

"But don't you wish to read it?" I asked.

"No," he said. "I presume you have, and if you have made a mistake that is your funeral. You won't make two. Do you want me to scratch out my signature?"

I said, "No, I am quite satisfied."

Dr. Mackenzie said that he had found this method to work very well. If you are going to trust the person, trust them until they indicate that they aren't to be trusted. He said that C. D. Howe worked on this principle, and later I used it to good effect in promotions committees at the university.

In the general survey of contamination, Dr. Goldschmidt's shoes were found to be contaminated and were confiscated. Dr. Goldschmidt demanded compensation. His claim didn't fit in with the usual categories for which compensation could be requested, and eventually the request went to Dr. Paneth, to Dr. Cockcroft, to Dr. Steacie, to Dr. Mackenzie, to C. D. Howe, to MacKenzie King, and so on back down the line, by which time the document was worth a fortune—or so the story went. It's almost too good to be true, so I have avoided trying to verify it. I do know, however, that when the chemistry labs. were taken back by the University of Montreal at the end of the war, a thorough decontamination job had to be done.

After this episode I was transferred to physics to do odd jobs of a chemical nature. It was good for me in that I learned a good deal about neutrons and the design of ZEEP, the zero energy experimental pile involving heavy water and uranium, and I met many of the physicists involved in the work. This transfer led to my involvement in making a high intensity neutron source, which was required at that time by the medical scientists attached to the project. It was known that when the alpha particles emitted by polonium were allowed to impinge on metallic beryllium, neutrons were produced. Only small amounts of polonium had been used up to that time, a few tens of millicuries at most, because of its dangerous nature. The Americans had offered to supply about a thousand times as much, ten curies in fact, in the form of a deposit on a thin piece of platinum foil.

I was given the task of making this neutron source, and I had the idea of making a sandwich of the piece of polonium-coated platinum between two slices of beryllium metal. The whole would be placed in a brass cylinder closed by a screw top, which could be soldered in as an extra precaution. The whole operation was to be carried out in a box fitted with a glass top and with rubber gloves projecting in from each side. Such boxes are commonplace nowadays, but they were quite unheard-of in those days. After doing a dummy run many times until I thought I could do it perfectly, I put the real thing into the box, closed the lid, and started to work. At first everything went well, but at the last minute the sandwich refused to slide neatly into the brass cylinder. I was horrified, since such a possibility had not even entered our heads. I started to sweat, and I stepped back for a couple of seconds to think what to do next. I disengaged the parts and tried again. This time everything worked to perfection, and I breathed a sign of relief and finished the operation.

Actually, one thing we didn't know at the time was how dangerous the neutrons were. We found later that they were horribly dangerous, and for a long time after the war I would wake up in the night, thinking that the finger and thumb which had held the neutron source were warmer than the rest of the hand. I have decided since that the problem was psychological, but at the time it was quite a worry.

In the summer of 1945 people were starting to drift back to the university, and I was asked to make up my mind whether I would stay with the atomic energy project and go to Chalk River or go back to the university. My first loyalty was to the university, and so Mary and I packed our bags and went back to Saskatoon, expecting to go back into our little house. When we turned up on the doorstep late one evening, the tenants told us that an act had recently been passed according to which they could stay in their wartime accommodation, so they were going to stay put. Fortunately the Ferns found room for us. A few weeks later provision was made for those who had been away on war service to make an appeal, which we did, and we were soon back at home. It seemed a curious homecoming after we had endured discomforts and a good many dangers while someone else had enjoyed our comfortable little house for a very low rental. However, we soon forgot about it in the hustle and bustle of helping to take care of the postwar flood of veterans.

As a final postscript, some months later, on a windy day at the Saskatoon airport, I stepped forward smartly to have Field Marshall Earl Alexander pin the M.B.E. on my lapel in recognition of my efforts with the R.C.A.F. and with the atomic energy project. Much later, in 1979, the Military College at Royal Roads, Victoria, B.C., awarded me an honorary Doctor of Military Science degree, in recognition of my war work. I was fortunate to come out all in one piece and with firsthand ground-floor experience of two important principles—operations research and atomic energy. I had also seen at first hand how horrible man can be to man, and yet how self-sacrificing men and women can be.

Chapter 11

Atoms in Saskatchewan

Early in August of 1945 the "bomb" was dropped and the war with Japan was over. I was shocked that the atom bomb had been used against a city, and I deeply regretted that it had been used at all. The Canadians had, of course, been working on the development of a heavy-water reactor and not on the bomb, but it was generally known that something of this kind was in the wind, and that at one time it had been felt to be terribly urgent that the Allies get such a bomb before the enemy did so. Now the shadow of the mushroom cloud was to grow bigger and bigger, to influence for all time public feeling toward atomic energy.

A day or so later, a small item in the local paper listed the names of a number of Canadian scientists who had been working with the Canadian atomic energy project, my name among them. I was immediately deluged with questions by my colleagues and with requests to speak to service clubs and church groups. I did my best to oblige, keeping in mind that all the wartime work on atomic energy was still top-secret. Fortunately the Americans soon released a good deal of information, so that it became possible to say quite a bit about atomic energy without revealing any secrets. One professor came hightailing down to my lab. to assure me that when he had quizzed me about atomic energy shortly after my return to campus but before my connection with atomic energy had been announced, he was asking the questions quite innocently. I assured him that I understood.

It is curious that many people, including very highly educated ones, really don't know what the word *security* means and don't appreciate the trouble to which other powers will go to find out how things operate, particularly on the defense level, in another country. Some of my colleagues were quite annoyed when I bluntly refused to tell them whether I had visited such and such a lab. during the war. They didn't want to know what was done there—just had I met "so and so." I tried to explain that had I passed on this seemingly innocent piece of information, they might have passed it on in all innocence to someone with ears attuned to picking up useful bits of information which would later be made part of the jigsaw puzzle that someone not so innocent was assembling.

With the partial lifting of the secrecy veil I started to make preparations to use radioactive isotopes in non-secret work. The National Research Council was most cooperative in loaning me the basic equipment for measuring radioactive isotopes that I had used in Montreal—a scaler, one or two geiger counters, and even some lead bricks. Dr. Steacie took special pains to loan us a 250 mg. radium-beryllium neutron source which could be used to make small amounts of radioactive isotopes. As an example, radioactive phosphorus could be produced in small amounts by irradiating carbon disulfide with the neutrons from the source.

Shortly after I had assembled the equipment, Dr. John Mitchell, head of the soil science department, dropped over to my lab. for a chat, and I proudly showed him my new toys and asked whether he would be interested in doing some cooperative work using isotopes. When he asked me how, I had to confess that I didn't have much of an idea, and I asked him to give me a rough idea of what sorts of research he was doing. After outlining the soils mapping for which his group was famous, he said, "Of course, we also do some work on phosphate fertilizers, finding out how the application of fertilizer improves the yield." I immediately had an idea, and I asked whether there would be any interest in knowing how much of the fertilizer was being used by the plant. He said that there certainly would, since at that time there was no way of telling where the phosphorus in the plant had come from, whether from the soil or the fertilizer. I suggested that we could make radioactive fertilizer and measure its intake by the plant, using radioactive methods. If we then measured the total phosphorus uptake chemically, the difference between this and the fertilizer phosphorus uptake would be the amount of phosphorus coming from the soil. This procedure is the basis of the so-called tracer method, in which the material is labelled with radioactivity and can then be traced wherever it goes.

Dr. Mitchell lent me a student, Stan Barber, who did some greenhouse experiments during the winter with three or four wheat plants growing in a pot to which small amounts of radioactive phosphorus, P-32, in the form of phosphate (made by using the neutron source) had been added. When we tried to publish an account of the experiments, the reviewer said that the experiments were quite accurate but that they didn't mean anything to anyone except Dr. Spinks. I developed an explanation using red and green balls mixed in a bag labelled "fertilizer" and I sent it with a rather sarcastic letter to the editor, who had the article reviewed by other reviewers.

Fortunately they agreed with me, and the article was published—the first in the world along these lines.

We then wished to do some field experiments, but for this purpose we needed much larger amounts of P-32, which were not then available in Canada. I wrote to various people in the United States, but they all replied that their particular atomic machine was under the McMahon Act, and radioactive materials made in it could not be exported. Eventually Professor Urey suggested I write Lawrence in California, who suggested that I try Evans at the Institute for Terrestial Magnetism in Washington, D.C. For some strange reason his cyclotron had been overlooked in the McMahon Act, so for the next year he regularly sent me one mc. of P-32 each month in a small wooden box labelled "chalk sticks". It was quite harmless from the point of view of radiation, but it would have been somewhat difficult to explain to the customs authorities, had they ever asked to examine the sticks of "chalk". With this P-32 we did the first field experiments in the world at Floral, just outside Saskatoon. I have always felt deeply indebted to Dr. Evans, who did not know me personally but who went out of his way to help a fellow scientist.

In subsequent experiments we tried the effects of different types of soil, weather, crop, method of application, and so forth, and developed improved technical methods of measurement. These all seem terribly simple nowadays, but in those days no one had thought about them, and each one represented quite a breakthrough. Once again I was lucky enough to be in on a new series of experiments, and I got a great stimulus from taking part in it.

In no time at all we were using isotopes to measure phosphorus and calcium in eggs; the movement of wireworms; the dispersion of grasshoppers, mosquitoes, and blackflies; the effect of dicoumarin as an anticoagulant; the effects of vitamins K_1 and K_3; and so forth. Each time I worked with an expert in the field, who contributed his particular knowhow while I contributed some radioactive knowhow. This approach seemed to work well. Quite apart from doing a particular piece of research, I gradually acquired a better-than-average knowledge of the scientific work in progress on the campus and of the corresponding scientists.

A good deal of the work we did had practical applications, and doing this type of research was good for me. As an example, the fertilizer experiments led to literally thousands of pieces of work by research workers all over the world, and they led in turn to a better understanding of how fertilizers work, of the availability of soil nutrients, and of how to make improvements in fertilizer practice. Instead of effects being guessed at, they could now be measured accurately and the proper advice could be given to farmers on fertilizer practice for their particular types of soil. The value of such advice can only be measured in millions of dollars, and it will become particularly valuable as food supply becomes the determining parameter in relation to population limits.

After working on a good many different applications of isotopes, I became convinced of the long-term value of this work, and I urged that a laboratory be set up to exploit this new tool. Unfortunately, a number of people in powerful positions felt that isotopes were just like a new piece of equipment, and they failed to realize that radioactive isotopes produce many different effects, and that in fact they open up a whole new world. These people probably thought that I was out to do some empire building, which actually was not my intention. Anyhow, I had to console myself with writing a general paper on green cheese research, explaining the general green cheese philosophy, and let it go at that.

I did get minor consolation from unexpected references to the Saskatoon work. One was in Geneva, in 1955, when Mary and I attended a public lecture on radioactive tracers given by Nobel Prize winner Hevesy. After introducing the subject, he said that he would now point up the practical application of isotopes by referring to some work done in far-off Saskatchewan by a young man named Spinks. He then showed two slides taken from my first P-32 paper on fertilizer uptake. It was quite one of the most thrilling moments in my life, and afterwards Mary and I introduced ourselves to Professor Hevesy. I had had no idea that he knew of my work.

On another occasion, nearly twenty years later, I visited an agricultural research station just outside New Delhi in company with a number of university vice-chancellors. In the entrance to the building were several large panels illustrating various types of isotope work. The first panel was illustrated by the same graph that Hevesy had shown, and I innocently asked our guide who had done the work.

"A chap named Spinks, lives way off in Canada."

After a few minutes the guide came up to me and said, "Say, your name is Spinks too, isn't it?"

I agreed that it was, and he remarked, "Curious—must be a relative, eh?"

I agreed that just might possibly be right. A few minutes later we came to a panel on a neutron moisture meter for use in irrigation work—again from one of my papers. Again I enquired about the author, and the guide said, "It's odd that you should ask—it's also by a chap named Spinks—might possibly be the same fellow."

Then he suddenly blushed and said, "Good Lord, it's you!" And he made amends by announcing to all and sundry, "Gentlemen, here is a vice-chancellor who really is a vice-chancellor." People being what they are, I must admit that I enjoyed the episode.

The development of the neutron moisture meter came about in an interesting fashion. Professor Torchinsky was at that time interested in soil mechanics, and he needed to be able to measure the per-cent moisture in the soil. So he came to my office and asked if one could use isotopes for this purpose. I said that one could probably use tritium, but that it would be very awkward—much more bother than the usual method of weighing and drying. However, Professor Torchinsky had no sooner left my office than I remembered that the famous Italian physicist Fermi had written a paper in 1934 in which he had found that the ability of neutrons to induce radioactivity in metals was much enhanced if the whole system was surrounded by hydrogenous material. Quite obviously, since water contained hydrogen, the method should work for soil containing water. A few experiments using wet sand in a beaker and a silver quarter, with the neutron source as measuring instrument, showed that the idea was sound. Later the quarter was replaced by a slow-neutron counter filled with boron trifluoride. Actually, what was happening was that fast neutrons, emitted by the neutron source, were being slowed down by collision with the hydrogen in the water; the more hydrogen there was, the more slow neutrons were produced. We did think of patenting the idea, but we were eventually persuaded to publish the data instead, since ideas as such are not patentable, but only devices making use of the idea. It was thought that large corporations could probably have broken the patent anyhow. In any case, it was suggested that not many of these devices would be produced. Actually the device is now widely used in irrigation work. A one-inch diameter pipe is pushed into the soil, the instrument is lowered into the hole, and the percentage moisture read on a dial—a very simple device which does not require removal of the soil. Our main satisfaction was again to get the first publication in the world on this particular topic. Which brings me back to green cheese research!

As I mentioned earlier, we had used green cheese as a code name for the uranium research done at the University of Montreal. One day one of the scientists, while riding on a Montreal tram, overheard two dear old ladies discussing the work being done in the top-secret laboratory.

"You won't believe it, but they are working on green cheese."

"You don't say!"

"And would you believe it, they are starting a green cheese factory at Chalk River?"

This incident led the scientist to work out an imaginary conversation about his activities: "Dr. X, what kind of research are you doing with green cheese?"

To this he gave the historic reply: "My dear madam, the possible uses of green cheese in research are naturally conditioned by the properties of the green cheese."

Having once uttered this statement, the scientist repeated it, and was taken not only with its euphonious nature but also with its enormous philosophic importance. It was a true "Open Sesame!"

What are some of the properties? One is to give off green cheese radiation, which can be detected by using green-cheese-radiation detectors. So if you put a dab of green cheese on an object and bring a green-cheese-radiation detector nearby, you can detect the object and you can even find it or trace it in a dark room. This is the underlying principle of tracer experiments in which a radioactive isotope is used as a tracer or tag. The object being tagged may be an object, an animal, an insect, or even a molecule. Even exploring these possibilities would take ten scientists ten years and would produce at least one hundred papers. One can extend the idea by saying that the radiations are characteristic of the type of green cheese and can thus be used for analytical purposes—again, ten scientists, ten years, and one hundred papers, as perhaps Appendix A testifies. The radiations carry energy, which can be used to produce chemical or biological effects. Finally, in emitting these radiations, the radioactive material decays at a certain rate, and the radiations can thus be used to measure time. The green cheese analogy can be carried still further. One can publish in green cheese journals, attend international green cheese meetings, and so forth.

Actually, one of these meetings came to pass in 1978, when the eleventh International Congress for Soil Science met in Edmonton with fifteen hundred people from all over the world in attendance. I was asked to give the lead-off paper in a seminar on isotopes in agriculture. I gave an historical overview of the early beginnings of the research in Saskatchewan under the title, "First Steps in Green Cheese Research." The paper attracted a good deal of favorable attention. At the conclusion of the symposium I was given an honorary membership certificate in the Canadian Society of Soil Scientists, much to my surprise and pleasure.

Eventually one gets tired of green cheese, and so I gradually switched my research from tracer research to radiation research—the action of radiation on chemical systems. It turned out to be an exciting and rewarding field of research. Shortly after World War II, the Chalk River reactor started to produce isotopes in large quantities, and these became available for use in scientific research. In particular, the radioactive cobalt, Co-60, provided an ideal source for gamma rays, which could be used for therapeutic purposes and in radiation chemistry. As is well known, Dr. Harold Johns of the University of Saskatchewan developed a cobalt radiation therapy unit for use in cancer therapy. At the same time he acquired other sources of high-energy radiation, including a betatron. This seemed to offer an ideal opportunity for me to extend my photochemistry, which involved the action of light on chemical systems, to somewhat higher-energy radiation. So I gradually switched my research interest to radiation chemistry, and again I hit pay dirt. Practically everything one thought of led to a new type of experiment and to new results. And the students found this new area of research interesting because one could almost guarantee that results would be forthcoming.

We had an enormous advantage, of course, in that we could talk to members of the physics department, and get a good understanding of the physical effect of radiation on the system being studied. Very few chemists were in this fortunate position. So we studied the effect of different types of radiation on gaseous, liquid, and solid systems, studied reactions at both low and high temperatures, and eventually started to study the fundamental particles produced when ionizing radiations interact with matter. It is thought that free radicals are produced; for example, when water, H_2O, is irradiated, H and OH radicals are produced. These radicals can be studied using electron-spin equipment. Concurrently with the research on radiation chemistry, I gave lectures in the field and eventually wrote a book, *Introduction to Radiation Chemistry*, in collaboration with a colleague, Dr. R. J. Woods. Our rather wide-ranging research had put us in an ideal position to write such a book. At the time there were highly specialized books on the action of radiation on gases, on water, or on solids, but no one had thought of taking a general approach, so we were quite lucky again.

In recent years there has been an increasing interest in studying the properties of free radicals in greater and greater detail; for example, the lifetime of a free radical is a matter of considerable interest. Studies of the lifetime can be made by using intermittent or pulsed radiation, in which the material under study is irradiated with short bursts of radiation, rather than continuously. The observed rate of reaction then depends on the relation between the rate of pulsing of the radiation and the mean lifetime of the free radical in question. We had access to a powerful beam of gamma rays in the University Hospital, and we were able to pulse this beam by interposing a slotted lead cylinder, about one foot thick, between the source of radiation and the material being irradiated, and then rotating the cylinder. We were able to rotate the cylinder about one thousand times a second and to measure radical lifetimes of one thousandth of a second— some of the first measurements of this kind.

Later we were able to extend the measurements to one-millionth of a second, using the linear accelerator on campus which produced a pulsed beam of electrons, pulsed at one million times a second. Still more recently, the method has been extended to a few nanoseconds. Free radicals have now been studied in great detail by a variety of techniques, so that chemists have a considerable degree of confidence that free radicals really do exist. Without getting into the problem of what one means by exist, let us say that the free radicals now have the same degree of reality for the chemist as, say, the chair in which he sits.

Possible industrial uses of radiation are now being actively explored in a number of countries. In 1950 Dr. Armstrong worked with me on the synthesis of ethyl bromide by irradiating a mixture of ethylene and hydrogen bromide with gamma rays from Co–60. The reaction takes place rapidly at room temperature, producing ethyl bromide which is 99.8% pure.

$$C_2H_4 \quad + \quad H\,Br \qquad = \qquad C_2H_5Br$$

ethylene   hydrogen bromide   ethyl bromide

The process has now been used by Dow Chemicals to produce ethyl bromide, a common organic chemical, at the rate of five thousand tons a year—not a vast output, but an indication that the process can be done commercially.

The mining and refining of uranium in Canada received a big boost at the time of the 1973 oil crisis. Just before that, the price of uranium had been at the level of eight dollars a pound, at which price only the richest mines could operate profitably. However, the oil crisis accelerated the atomic energy programs of oil-poor countries such as Germany and Japan, and thus led to an increased demand for uranium. This demand in turn led to an increased price for uranium, which in a short time reached about fifty dollars a pound. This attractive price for uranium resulted in a renewed interest in known ore properties and in an increased exploration for uranium ores.

In the course of this increasing activity, new uranium ore bodies were found in northern Saskatchewan, some of them with relatively high percentages of uranium. The Amok company, for example, found high grade ore at Cluff Lake. Other ore bodies with mine potential were found at Wollaston Lake and Key Lake. It should be noted that the Saskatchewan Government had a financial interest in some of the companies.

A worldwide anti-nuclear feeling, which had been growing for some time, but which had seemed rather remote from Saskatchewan, suddenly surfaced as a strong feeling when the public realized that nuclear developments were on the verge of a major escalation in Saskatchewan. A proposal to link the mining developments with the building of a uranium refinery at Warman, just outside Saskatoon, added fuel to the fire. Two enquiries were set up by the provincial government—the Bayda Commission, to report on the Amok mine, and a commisson to report on the Warman refinery proposal. I avoided direct involvement in these two public enquiries, but I did speak to numerous groups such as the Board of Trade, Rotary, and others, on the energy question in general and on the uranium environmental problem in particular. I tried to give a simple factual account of the processes involved in producing relatively pure uranium oxide ($U O_2$) from ore containing, say, 0.3% uranium.

In a typical operation about 5,000 tons of ore is processed per day. The ore is finely ground, and the uranium is removed in a chemical process which produces about 15 tons of "yellow cake" (uranium oxide, 85% purity) and a slurry containing about 4,985 tons solids and 85% of the original activity. The slurry goes to a settling pond, where it receives further treatment designed to reduce environmental hazards to an acceptable value. The yellow cake goes to a chemical refinery, where the oxide is brought up to 99.99% purity in a relatively simple chemical process. It is proposed that any radioactive wastes be returned to the mill for disposal with the mill wastes. The refinery has the hazards associated with any chemical process involving acids, but it does not pose any large radiation hazards. It would probably be less hazardous than, say, an oil refinery. As for the question of the mill waste, most of the activity settles out in a settling pond, with only one or two per cent of the activity remaining in the liquid phase. The overflow from the settlings pond is treated in a smaller precipitation basin with barium chloride solution, producing a precipitate of barium sulfate which carries down the radium with it. The overflow from this basin will meet federal and provincial requirements. The tailings pond eventually fills up and can be grassed over. It is then comparatively safe, provided any seepages are monitored and corrective action is taken if required. In a general way, present practices can take care of tailings for the lifetime of the mill, twenty-five to fifty years, and for as long after this period as the surveillance is maintained.

There is a long-term problem when we think of times such as a thousand years. In this time period, one has to think of possible hazards caused by flash floods, changes in water table, and geological disruptions. Alternative methods of long-term disposal include deep burial and disposal in deep lakes, where the layer of tailings would first be covered with a layer of clay and then with a further layer of sludge by natural accretion. A more positive solution would be to make a chemical separation of the activity at the mill site, and then to encapsulate the resulting small amount of high-activity material in glass or ceramic bricks. These bricks could be used as a source of radiation in a radiation chemical industry. The possible consequent savings of energy would be equivalent to many millions of barrels of oil per annum.

The key to all the foregoing is the paramount importance of an educated public which can make a rational assessment of the hazards associated with radiation developments in relation to the often far greater hazards accepted by the public in everyday life—hazards caused by cars, electricity, and so forth. We have to bear in mind the very real energy crisis which will be upon us before the end of the century. The educational approach would cover not only radioactivity but all the other energy possibilities—solar, tides, winds, and so on. Other educational considerations should include the provision of adequate skilled manpower to meet the demands of the public, whatever they may be, and the provision of the necessary knowhow, which requires top-level scientists, engineers, and experts of all kinds.

Chapter 12

Atoms for Peace

My interest in peaceful uses of the atom has covered a span of over thirty years and has paralleled world interest in this subject. This world interest has been brought to a focus on a number of occasions at international conferences. Four of the biggest and most general conferences were held in Geneva, under the auspices of the United Nations. Such conferences form an essential part of the infrastructure of science, and attending these conferences gave me firsthand experience of one of the social aspects of science.

The first conference on the peaceful uses of atomic energy was held in Geneva in 1955. I was fortunate to be asked to give a paper on "Studies of special problems in agriculture and silviculture by the use of radioisotopes," and to be named as a member of the Canadian group of delegates and observers. Mary accompanied me to the meetings, which were held in the Palais des Nations. Most of the Canadians stayed at the Hotel de la Paix—a delightfully comfortable hotel.

The first Geneva conference on atoms for peace was regarded by many as the celebration of an unparalleled achievement of the scientific world—namely, the harnessing of the energy of the atomic nucleus. This achievement resulted from the scientific work of scientists of genius from many lands. It was therefore fitting that representatives from many nations should gather together to discuss how this new source of power could help the future development of their own countries and of the whole human race.

The conference received the biggest press and air coverage of any scientific meeting ever held—and rightly so. Everyone knew that a very noisy infant was to be shown to the public for the first time—an infant whose christening had, for one reason or another, been delayed for thirteen years. It differed from most christenings in that several fathers wished to claim paternity. This dispute naturally gave an added flavor to what was bound to be in any event a fascinating meeting. And fascinating it was for two whole weeks.

It was first and foremost an all-star scientific meeting with many Nobel prize winners present such as Cockcroft, Hevesy, Seaborg, and Bohr. Although its creation wasn't intended, there was the same kind of excitement in the air that one would expect at the Olympic Games. Comparisons between countries aren't meant to be made at scientific meetings, but they were made at this one. Everyone was curious about the Russians—what they were like and what they knew. No one had seen their atomic scientists since before the war, and no doubt the Russians were curious about the others, too. The Russian scientists turned out to be just like anyone else. They had a good sense of humor, they were extremely well-informed about their own work, and they were much better informed about ours than some of us were about theirs. They were ready to be friendly, and they were extremely polished—just as ready to talk about Shaw, Beethoven, or the ballet as about isotopes.

All those who attended agreed that it was a friendly and a human conference. Scientists from seventy-three nations of the world enjoyed the easy opportunity to meet and to tell of their work and discuss the work of other scientists. As a result, individuals who formerly knew each other only by reputation developed mutual respect and friendship.

The sessions took place in the United Nations Building in Geneva, and they were attended by about fourteen hundred delegates plus fourteen hundred observers. Canada had five official delegates, headed by Mr. W. J. Bennett, president of Atomic Energy of Canada. There were also thirty-two advisers, including representatives from government laboratories, universities, and industry. Canada submitted thirteen papers, covering such topics as the role of nuclear power in Canada, experience with the reactors at Chalk River, use of radioisotopes in medicine and in agriculture, studies of waste disposal, and so on.

The great interest at the sessions was in power from atomic energy. The U.S.S.R. produced one of the surprises in this field by describing a nuclear power station located just outside Moscow. It had been feeding five thousand kilowatts of electrical energy into the grid for nearly two years. There was a good deal of behind-the-scenes discussion of useful thermonuclear energy, the sort of energy that is released in the hydrogen bomb. This topic was first mentioned by Bhabha, the president of the conference, in the opening session. The general opinion seemed to be that it was still at least twenty years away.

The physics session revealed what have actually been the only real atomic secrets, namely the fission cross sections of the fissile elements, such as U–233 and plutonium. These figures allow one to calculate the probability of fission and hence the size of a nuclear reactor, or, for that matter, of a bomb. There was a good agreement between the values submitted by the United States, the United Kingdom, the U.S.S.R. and Canada.

These sessions produced another surprise when the U.S.S.R. was the only one to produce data for americium, named after America. Corridor gossips suggested that it should be renamed siberium as soon as possible. There was general pleasure when the names for elements 99, 100, and 101 were announced at a meeting: einsteinium after Einstein, fermium after Fermi, and finally, mendelevium after Mendeleeff, the Russian who proposed the first system of the elements.

A Russian named Vinogradov acted as chairman for a highly technical session on fission products. After the session he went along to a press interview with two hundred members of the press. Vinogradov, who spoke only Russian, asked through the interpreter if they really wished to hear about such a highly technical session. When one of the reporters said that he did, he gave them a five-minute summary, which was very good but quite incomprehensible to the reporters. After this, one or two of them set about quite deliberately to try to needle him.

"Did you learn anything new?"

"Yes, I always learn something at a scientific meeting."

"Will you please be specific?"

"Well," said Vinogradov with a delightful smile, "I heard all about a square-wave polarograph. Would you like me to tell you about that?"

By this time most of the reporters were chuckling and enjoying the sparring match. Vinogradov was then asked if they might use his name when reporting this session.

"Why not?" he said.

An obstreperous reporter immediately asked, "Isn't it true that you might get into trouble if this is reported in Moscow?"

"Not if you report me correctly," said Vinogradov.

"Will you please give us an example of incorrect reporting?" asked the next reporter.

Vinogradov took a newspaper clipping from his pocket and replied, "Here I have an excellent photo of myself and your charming Admiral Strauss. Underneath the photo it says 'Admiral Strauss discusses important diplomatic matters with the French Ambassador,' Gentlemen, I am not the French Ambassador, but I really shall get into trouble if anyone in Moscow thinks that I am."

This reply was greeted with loud applause by all the reporters present.

At other sessions the many fruitful applications of radioisotopes in biology, medicine, agriculture, and industry were dealt with in considerable detail. The agricultural sessions were of great interest to western Canada.

At any conference, one of the most valuable features is the opportunity provided to meet other delegates—in corridors, and at luncheons, dinners, and special receptions. The United Nations started off the first evening with a general reception. This was followed by receptions by all the major countries, each with its own distinctive style and each extremely friendly. There were vodka and caviar at the Russian party, but there were also orange juice and ginger ale for those who preferred them.

Apart from the formal luncheons, there were informal gatherings. One of the Canadian delegates had lunch one day with a Russian from Moscow and an Englishman from Oxford. The Russian indicated that he had never been outside Russia before and that he was enjoying Geneva very much. He mentioned particularly the mosaics in the Russian Orthodox Church in old Geneva. He was a bit worried by the absence of smoking factory chimneys in such an obviously wealthy city, but he said that there were similar resorts in the Crimea. His English was quite good, and it made the Canadian feel somewhat ashamed of his two words of Russian.

Another point of interest was the exhibits. Canada had a good spot for its exhibit—in a long gallery just outside the Assembly Hall, with huge windows overlooking the ornamental gardens. The exhibit featured models of our famous nuclear reactors at Chalk River and of the cobalt therapy unit. The latter attracted a great deal of attention, and it was always surrounded by photographers and cameramen.

All in all, the conference turned out to be much more successful than even the most optimistic had dared to hope. It demonstrated that there are really no secrets in scientific work, and that scientists in the atomic field can meet on common ground and discuss their problems in an atmosphere of mutual respect and understanding.

In 1958 a second conference on the peaceful uses of the atom was arranged by the U.N., and it too was held in Geneva. This time there were six thousand delegates from seventy-three countries, as compared to three thousand before, and about twenty-five hundred papers were submitted as compared to twelve hundred before. Naturally, all these papers were not given orally, but about eight hundred were, during the course of two weeks, from September 1-13.

Naturally, one can't get six thousand people to one meeting, and no person can listen to eight hundred papers, so after the first day or so there were always five or six parallel sessions, for example, on plans for the construction of nuclear power plants, controlled fusion devices, power reactors, basic chemistry in nuclear energy, and biological aspects of radiation and ore treatment. The U.N. buildings in Geneva are almost ideal for such a meeting since they have a large number of assembly halls and lecture rooms which are equipped with devices for multiple translation, for projecting slides, for printing, for feeding people, and so on.

Perrin of France was the president. The chairmen and vice-chairmen for the various sessions were chosen from the various nationalities. I had the honor of being chairman of session D 22 on use of isotopes and agriculture, and my vice-chairman was Thabet from the United Arab Republic. At each session, the chairman was responsible for keeping things going according to schedule and for allotting questions to the discussion period—a matter requiring some diplomacy since there were always far more questions than there was time for. Incidentally, the atmosphere at the session was excellent. Following the session, the chairman and vice-chairman and some of the speakers had to go to a press conference in the main council chamber. At this conference, the main interest was in power reactors and controlled fusion, with a much smaller attention to the uses of atomic energy in industry, agriculture, biology, and medicine.

At the first conference, just three years earlier, information had been revealed for the first time about the various reactor programs. This conference revealed a great deal of progress by numerous countries, so that there could be no doubt at all as to the practicability of using nuclear power on a large scale. Fusion reactors were thought to be at least twenty years away. Special evening lectures were given by Nobel Prize winners Cockroft and Seaborg, and there were the usual huge receptions and parties given by the larger nations, and endless smaller ones by the smaller nations. A roster was drawn up for the Canadian delegates, indicating which parties had to be attended and which could be left to individual taste and endurance.

One particularly pleasant feature of the conference was the opportunity it afforded to meet a number of the friends made at the first conference. We were particularly pleased to see that one of our Russian friends, Klechkowski, was listed in the program, and so we went to the Metropole, where all the Russians were staying, to meet him. At first the secretary manning the Russian information desk denied all knowledge of our friend, but eventually, after quite a battle, we were able to see him and to have coffee together. I explained to him that I had been sorry that I hadn't been able to accept a kind invitation to attend a special meeting in Moscow in 1956, but that I had been grateful for the invitation (I didn't tell him that I had been fairly bluntly told by the Canadian authorities that it would be "undesirable" for me to accept). To this he replied that by some strange chance he had not been able to accept an invitation to attend a meeting in Canada, either!

One amusing experience on the way back stays in my mind. Our plane landed at Manchester to pick up one or two passengers. After a time we were asked to disembark and go to have coffee in the restaurant. Eventually we reboarded the plane and slowly traversed the runway which to our surprise was lined with cars with the lights on. Eventually we took off, and the captain explained that the delay had been caused by the difficulty of locating a cow, which was lost on the airfield. As the plane gained height, one of the Canadian delegates was overheard to say, "So we've split the atom!" and everyone exploded with laughter.   ·

The third Atoms for Peace conference was again a huge international meeting held under the auspices of the U.N., at the Palais des Nations in Geneva between August 31 and September 9, 1964. Some one hundred nations were represented by a total of four thousand delegates. At such a meeting, each country is allowed five so-called "country representatives," plus a more or less unlimited number of specialists and observers, varying from zero to five or six hundred; the larger number was for countries such as the United Kingdom, France, the U.S.A., the U.S.S.R., and, curiously enough, Germany, which had made a great comeback in the nuclear field.

Canada's group consisted of five government representatives: Dr. W. B. Lewis, head of the delegation; Dr. G. C. Laurence, president of the Atomic Energy Control Board; I. F. Macrae, president of the Canadian Nuclear Association; C. A. Grinyer, the director of A.E.C.L.; J. W. T. Spinks; plus H. E. Mr. S. F. Rae, the Canadian ambassador in Geneva, and fifty other experts and advisers of one kind and another.

The president of the conference was Professor V. S. Emelyanov, Deputy Chairman of the U.S.S.R. State Committee on the Uses of Atomic Energy.

The topic for the third conference was nuclear power plants, with emphasis on new industrial applications for atomic energy and related technical topics. There were formal opening and closing sessions, eight general sessions, and thirty-six technical sessions. The technical sessions were organized in four series dealing with reactor applications, fuel and material problems, reactor physics and control, direct conversion of heat to electricity, and miscellaneous applications of atomic energy. The general sessions dealt with the role of nuclear power in meeting future energy needs and with the applications of isotopes and radiation sources in the physical and life sciences. Twenty-six Canadian papers were accepted by the conference, and they dealt mostly with Canada's program of uranium-heavy water reactors.

An important adjunct to the conference was a governmental scientific exhibition held at the Palais des Expositions on the other side of the city. Eighteen countries had exhibits, including large exhibits from the U.K., U.S.A., U.S.S.R., France, Germany and Canada. The Canadian exhibit included models of the 20,000 kw NPD Reactor, the 20,000 kw Douglas Point Station, and the reactor that was being constructed for Whiteshell. It also included the cancer therapy machine, which was first developed in Saskatoon.

The general atmosphere of the conference was once again excellent, as is customary at international scientific meetings. There were friendly relations between all the groups, and many helpful comments were made when papers were under discussion. The Russians and the Americans got along extremely well; as an example, the president of the conference, Emelyanov, a Russian, was nominated by an American.

When the third conference is compared with the first and second, it is of course evident that the air of the first conference, at which the so-called atomic secrets were revealed for the first time, will never be repeated. That was without doubt the most exciting scientific conference the world has ever seen. I almost said, is ever likely to see, but of course one can't tell about that. It certainly was remarkable—a drawing aside of the curtain to see the whole new world of atomic energy. The second conference, some three years later, was by contrast something of a let-down. Atomic energy had not developed as fast as had been expected, although actually, not much progress could have been expected in three years. At that second conference the main emphasis was on fission. The third meeting, on the other hand, which was six years later, was again buoyant and optimistic. Atomic energy is here to stay, and it has already many solid achievements under its belt all over the world. There is no longer any doubt of the industrial use of atomic fuels on an increasingly large scale.

From a Canadian point of view, the third Atoms for Peace conference was a landmark. Canada had something to sell that the world wanted and that she didn't mind talking about. This was the heavy water reactor. Canada had had more experience in this field than anyone else in the world —good large-size experience—and everyone was prepared to listen. The Canadian team had a pleasantly aggressive approach, from Dr. Lewis down. Instead of sitting in the corner and waiting until they were spoken to, as is customary for Canadians at big international meetings, the Canadians were in there pitching. The same approach was taken with the cobalt therapy unit, another example of Canada's having produced a slight better mousetrap which she is able to sell in competition with anyone.

Altogether I got a great deal out of the first three meetings, and they indicated to me in a vivid way that Canada and the rest of the world are on a two-way street. We can learn a great deal from the rest of the world—about planning at an O.E.C.D. meeting, about the role of science and technology at a U.N. meeting, and about the general importance of an awareness of the potentialities of atomic energy, as at the Geneva meeting. We can also contribute to the world in ways that are most appropriate to us —in aid to the developing nations, for example, particularly in areas that are peculiarly Canadian, and in atomic energy too, again in areas that are peculiarly Canadian.

In 1971 the university was represented at the fourth Atoms for Peace conference by myself, as one of the delegates, and by Dr. Rennie, as an adviser and co-author of one of the papers delivered at the conference. About ninety nations and five thousand representatives attended the meeting, held in the Palais des Nations in Geneva. The general aim of the conference was to bring to the attention of the public the growth in the practical applications of atomic energy, with emphasis on nuclear power and special applications; nuclear fuels, fuel cycles and materials, health and safety, applications of isotopes and radiation, international and administrative aspects, and aspects of nuclear technology of particular interest to developing countries.

Mitchell Sharp gave the opening address, "Nuclear Energy and World Peace." After the opening plenary session, the conference divided into four parallel technical sessions dealing with the main conference items. Some thousand papers were presented and discussed. Each day there were receptions given by the major participating countries, which provided an additional opportunity for the delegates to meet and exchange views. The Canadian group, numbering about fifty, met each morning to review conference activities. There was an exhibition which included a display from the University of Saskatchewan on the Matador project, which was concerned with the use of isotopes and radiation in investigations into soil—plant nutrition and plant physiology.

At the technical sessions it became clear that the industrial nations already have major commitments in atomic energy developments involving very large units of about one million kilowatts, and that the smaller nations are most anxious to secure quite large units. There is at present a gap between desirable developments and public acceptance in a number of countries. Analyses of opposition tactics sound very much like the corresponding analyses for campus unrest. Related to this gap is an apparent technology—university communications gap which should receive some attention from the universities.

One paper at the conference discussed a systems analysis approach to environmental problems associated with atomic energy. This leads to the thought that a systems analysis study of any reasonably large operation might yield worthwhile results as with A.E.C.L. itself and, of course, with provincial higher education. Another paper indicated that fusion power seemed unlikely for the next fifteen to twenty years.

The papers on isotope and radiation applications indicated that the University of Saskatchewan is relatively advanced in this field and has played a significant role in the opening up of this important type of research. The lack of any significant number of papers on the use of radiation in the chemical industry indicates that this potentially important use of radiation is either still open to development or is being developed in complete secrecy by countries such as the U.S.A., Great Britain, and France.

I enjoyed attending this meeting, the fourth in the series, and I feel that once more I gained a great deal from it. One gradually realizes that any system involving some tens of billions of dollars annually has to have a public exposure every five to ten years, quite apart from the desirability of exchanging information on an international level. I have to add that thirty years' acquaintance with matters atomic have convinced me that any industrialized nation must be well up in nuclear technology and that it is helpful, to say the least, if a university president has a somewhat better-than-nodding acquaintance with the atom.

I must add too that at this meeting Mary made her usual helpful input. This time she inquired tactfully whether A.E.C.L. and A.E.C.B. had ever thought of having women members. I raised the point equally tactfully at the next meeting of the Canadian delegates and planted the seed. Some months later women were appointed to these boards, and I like to think that my Mary can take a bit of the credit.

The social side of these meetings was again pleasant and rewarding. Particularly pleasant was a one-day outing to Chateau d'Oeux, near

Montreux, where we had once stayed for a week or so in an eighteenth-century chalet—Chalet Bon Acceuil, part way up the side of a mountain on the edge of the village. We were able to go to the chalet for lunch and to experience again the great pleasure we had felt when staying there some years earlier. Visits to places like Chateau d'Oeux (and Settignano, outside Florence) gradually take on an almost religious significance, so strong does the emotional attachment to them become. Without any effort at all I can shut my eyes and walk from the station at Chateau d'Oeux through the village, across the railway tracks, and up to the chalet, feasting my eyes all the while on the beautiful mountain scenery.

PART III
POSTWAR
UNIVERSITY

Chapter 13

Graduate Studies

I have already described my early life in England and how I came to move to the University of Saskatchewan in 1930. And I have described my first nine years in Saskatchewan which were really a continuation of my life up to that point. The six-year period of World War II made a dramatic change in my life: I was married, I was away from the university for several years, I was taking part in the war effort, and I was doing research in two absolutely new fields. For the first time I knew for sure that I could have original ideas of my own that were of some consequence. I suppose I could say that in this period I grew up. C. J. Mackenzie once told me that I was a late bloomer and added kindly, "but none the worse for that!"

While the war period had been dramatic for me, people who had stayed at home had not sat still either, and my first need on returning to the university was to try to catch up with what had happened while I was away. I had to prepare new courses, mostly in physical chemistry and chemical engineering, but also to satisfy the needs of students who wished to know some science without becoming specialists. Dr. W. P. Thompson, the dean of arts, was keen on this last type of course. I helped in one called "Physical Sciences A," in which I gave lectures on chemistry from an historical point of view. Time was always left to pursue difficult points, and in these discussions I found that I had a good deal to learn in linguistics, semantics, philosophy, and symbolic logic. I gradually developed a somewhat more analytical approach to anything that I read, and I began to take pleasure in spotting ambiguous paragraphs or downright errors in the textbooks.

In the immediate postwar period there was a huge influx of students who had to be accommodated in hopelessly inadequate space and with faculty who were much overworked. But the veterans were strongly motivated, and that made teaching them a pleasure.

In the immediate postwar period, Dr. Thorvaldson, who was then head of the chemistry department, had many extra duties with the Committee on Graduate Studies (which had gradually become the equivalent of a college), and he was consulted on many university and provincial matters as one of the wise men of the university community. So I and other senior faculty members would be given jobs of an administrative type to do—arranging lab. programs, arranging timetables for lecture rooms and classes, ordering chemicals, and so forth. These administrative duties were in addition to a fairly heavy teaching load, usually three or four full classes—elementary chemistry, physical chemistry, a class in chemical engineering (usually unit operations), and then one or two graduate half classes (a half class covered just one term) in one of my specialties—chemical kinetics or radio-chemistry.

Altogether, the period 1945–59 was a busy one for Mary and me. We gradually made ourselves comfortable in our little house, and we had a host of friends with whom we visited back and forth in the wintertime and went on picnics and longer trips in the summer. We entertained many students in our home and we took part in various university functions: banquets, dances, chemistry parties, football games, and so on. Mary took a particular interest in students and in the students' wives, who were appearing in greater and greater numbers, and who needed someone to look after their interests. We took every opportunity to attend concerts and plays, whether on campus or downtown.

I did a certain amount of travelling to meetings, such as those of the Chemical Institute and the Royal Society of Canada. At one time or another there were meetings of the National Research Council, the Canada Council, the Saskatchewan Oil and Gas Board, the Saskatchewan Research Council, and the Defense Research Board. I had joined the professional association of chemists shortly after my arrival in Saskatoon and had participated in local and national meetings, with the result that I was eventually elected local chairman and, in due time, national president. Holding these offices meant a lot of work, but it taught me quite a bit about the organization of professional groups, and about their value. Membership on the National Research Council, the Canada Council, the Saskatchewan Research Council, and the Defense Research Board also gave me an insight into the role of the humanities and the sciences in the life of Canada, and it brought me into close contact with a large number of able and charming people.

Membership on the Saskatchewan Oil and Gas Board occurred at an interesting stage, when the oil and gas resources were beginning to be developed. It was a three-man board, one of the other members being the deputy minister, Verne Hogg, who was succeeded by James T. Cawley; the other member, Professor Harry Edmunds, was a soft rock geologist with a wide experience in the oil industry. I suppose I represented the "uncommitted" part of the Board. In any event, we soon learned to work well together and to act as a liaison between the minister, Mr. Brockelbank, and the oil industry. I gradually developed a wholesome admiration and respect for both parties, and again I think I learned quite a bit from the experience.

Mary often accompanied me on my travels, and in this way we gradually became close friends with a large number of people, both academics, and members of the scientific and business worlds. I gradually started to think of education and science in a general way, and from time to time these thinkings resulted in studies such as an essay prepared for the Massey Commission on Arts, Letters, and Sciences, and two reports, *A Forecast of the Needs of Basic Research in Canada* and *The Development of Graduate Programs in Ontario Universities.* All this effort was, I hope, good for me. On campus I did the usual share of committee work, and gradually I got to know a bit about university organization and structure.

Eventually, in 1948, I was made head of the chemistry department, succeeding Dr. Thorvaldson, and in 1949 I succeeded Dr. Thorvaldson as dean of graduate studies. Both positions involved me in a good deal of administrative work and in long-range planning. Dr. Thorvaldson had developed work at the honours level in the 1930s, and he had developed a number of good lines of research in the chemistry department. He had seen graduate studies grow from a committee of Council to full college status. When I inherited the deanship in 1949, the university was just ready to start graduate work at the Ph.D. level, and so a good deal of time was spent in working out acceptable procedures for ensuring that Ph.D. work was kept at a proper level and that adequate standards were maintained. Excellence is the key word, and I'm afraid that many of my friends got tired of my constant references to research and excellence in my public utterances.

Over the course of thirty or so years I gradually covered a number of fields of research in a certain depth, and this experience let me see the interlocking nature of various branches of the physical sciences. My own knowledge of research gave me a good deal of confidence in the ability of the sciences to provide a coherent picture of the physical world—I had the feeling that one could indeed think to some purpose with the grey matter which the good Lord had given us. My liking for the humanities and the fine arts led me to think about the limitations of science and about the complementary nature of the arts and the sciences. I speculated a good deal about the nature of thought and the limitations imposed on the thought process by the structure of the brain.

I may say that I was helped a good deal by my wife's interest in the arts. Through her I probably heard more music and saw more ballet than I would otherwise have done. And we were constantly getting books about ballet—biographies and autobiographies especially, which provided a fascinating insight into the times in which these ballet dancers and choreographers lived. Usually on our travels we would try to get to the theatre as much as possible, and so in the course of time we saw a good many ballets, not just the *Sleeping Beauty* and *Romeo and Juliet,* but *Les*

Sylphides, Giselle, Cinderella, and a host more. We also saw a number of the top dancers, including Fonteyn, Nureyev, and Lepeschinskaya, the last as the result of a piece of good luck. On one occasion when I was attending an international meeting on radiation chemistry in Moscow, Mary went to a tea to "meet the Soviet women." At this tea she did indeed meet a number of Soviet women, including the famous Lepeschinskaya who, on finding that Mary was interested in ballet, arranged for her to have the director's box at the Bolshoi Theatre. So the next Sunday the Spinkses and the Thodes (from Hamilton) saw the ballet *Cinderella* in great style.

On one or two occasions, when we had an overnight stopover in London, we would stand in line to pick up tickets an hour or so before a performance at Covent Garden, and we were usually lucky. On one occasion we went backstage after the performance and met Margot Fonteyn, who was incredibly beautiful and charming. On another occasion we got standing room just behind the stalls. There was a continual coming and going of aspiring ballerinas, and at one point Anton Dolin came and stood next to us, watching the performance and being greeted by many theatrical acquaintances, usually with a dainty kiss on the cheek. I was duly jealous.

It seemed that this kind of life could go on forever. I enjoyed my teaching, I enjoyed my research, Mary and I had a host of congenial friends, we travelled frequently, and things seemed to happen without any conscious effort on my part. And then, without warning, a major change occurred. One afternoon, when I was busy supervising a chemistry lab., I was called to the phone. W. B. Francis, a Saskatoon lawyer whom I knew fairly well, wanted to see me. Would he care to come over to the lab? No— could I come to the parking lot—the one near the library? And he gave me his car license number. Somewhat mystified, I went out to the lot and found Mr. Francis in company with C. H. Whiting, a farmer from the Melfort district whom he introduced as the chairman of the university Board of Governors. I was still more mystified when Mr. Francis suggested that we might go to his home for a cup of coffee. I racked my brains for any possible reason why the chairman of the Board might wish to see me. My first thought was that one of my friends was in deep trouble, but I couldn't think of anyone in that situation.

Eventually Mr. Francis brought the conversation around to the qualifications needed in a university president. I spoke quite frankly about this question.

Then Mr. Whiting said, "I guess he doesn't know why we are talking to him."

I said, "I haven't a clue."

"Well, how would you like to be considered as a candidate for the position of president?"

"Are you offering me the job?"

"Well, I guess we are."

"In that case I'll say yes, subject of course to my wife's approval."

"But how can you say yes so quickly?"

"Well, I assume you have decided whether I have the qualities you are looking for, and all I have to do is decide whether to try it. If you have made a mistake, that's too bad, but I can promise that I will do my best." So that was how I came to be president of the University of Saskatchewan. I can say quite honestly that I had no thought of occupying that position before being asked. Of course I knew that President W. P. Thompson would be retiring soon, and I had heard some gossip about likely candidates. But no one had ever suggested me, as far as I knew.

1959 was the fiftieth anniversary of the founding of the university, so Dr. Thompson stayed as president until November 1 of that year, presiding over the many anniversary activities. I walked over to see Dr. Thompson one day, asking for some wise words.

"You'll find out soon enough," said he, pulling at his pipe. "Just do what comes naturally to you, and you'll do all right." And he added as an afterthought: "But don't forget where the money comes from." Wise words indeed!

Chapter 14

Dumpling to President

Settling into the president's office was quite a business. On November 1 I turned up at my new office to find nothing at all on the desk. So I sat down in the swivel chair—and promptly fell over backwards—the tension on the spring was too weak for my weight! I seated myself more cautiously in the chair and braced myself firmly with both elbows on my desk. The phone rang.

"Inspector Shakespeare."

"Inspector who!"

"Shakespeare—you know, R.C.M.P."

"Good heavens!"

"Yes, we have twelve of your engineers, caught in the Nurses Residence yesterday evening."

A phone call quickly established that the whole thing had been arranged specially for my benefit, so I was able to relax. A few minutes later, Colb McEown, assistant to the president, asked whether he could come in to discuss plans for the fund-raising drive which was about to start. Colb McEown, a graduate of the university, had been assistant to President Thompson for a number of years. I was lucky to inherit a man of his ability and background, and I quickly learned to appreciate his good judgment on a great variety of matters.

From then on there was never a dull moment: meetings of the university Council to chair, of Senate at which I had to act as vice-chairman or resource person, convocations to attend, monthly Board meetings, and endless meetings of college faculties, buildings and grounds committees, budget committees, long-range planning committees, residences and discipline committees, and so forth. At a few of the meetings I was just an interested observer, but more often than not I had to be well prepared for any topic that might come up, and often I was responsible for the preparation of the agenda. Naturally there were always other people involved, but I quickly found out that meetings went better if I was fully informed about every item on the agenda and if I was prepared to play something of a leadership role at the right moment.

One of my first acts as president was to initiate a series of changes designed to increase the degree of participation of faculty in decision making. Council was asked to set up an executive rather larger than the usual size, which would participate in budget planning, both operational and capital, in building projects, promotions, tenure, research grants, and so on. These arrangements are now taken for granted, but in 1960 they were somewhat revolutionary in Canada, and a number of faculty were actually quite suspicious of them. In the middle sixties, Professors Duff and Behrdal were asked to make a study of university governance, and it was interesting to see in how many areas we had anticipated their suggestions.

In a somewhat similar way, the University of Saskatchewan has always been community-oriented, so it was not strange that as the province evolved from its agrarian beginnings, the research which had initially been focused on agriculture began to move to a broader base. Saskatchewan's unique role in diversifying its research received favourable comment from Professors Bonneau and Corry in their study, *Quest for the Optimum*.

Research in agriculture has not of course been neglected, and the subject has been surveyed by Carlyle King, in *Extending the Boundaries*. We are proud of the research in agricultural engineering that led to the development of the grain-loss monitor, which tells the combine operator what speed to run at in order to keep the loss of grain to an acceptable level. Other recent developments have been in large-scale animal feeding research, in the provisions of a dairy research barn and of a new crop science development research centre, and in research in several areas related to the rapeseed crop. Here a number of unexpected problems arose. The trade wanted a rapeseed oil with low erucic acid content. The researchers who were investigating the relation of variety to erucic acid content were able to breed a variety having the desired characteristics. Next it was necessary to have a less toxic meal remaining after the oil had been expressed. The animal science group did the necessary research to achieve this end. Although the university did not do all the research, of course, its input was significant and received favorable comment. The university's interest in rapeseed culminated in the establishment of a P.O.S. pilot plant on campus to do mainly applied research related to proteins, oilseeds and starch (POS). The pilot plant is operated as a cooperative venture involving the federal government, provincial governments, universities, and industry, with industry having the major say in policy.

Health is now a matter of general concern, and medicare is in vogue, Saskatchewan being one of the leading and early exponents of the medicare philosophy. It is not just chance, of course, that we have on the Saskatoon campus not only a medical school but also a university hospital, a dental college, a college of nursing, a college of pharmacy, and a college of veterinary medicine. Provision of these professional institutions required planning of a high order extending over many years. It is true that the government had to supply the money to build the buildings and to hire the professors, but the role of the university in developing and implementing these plans over several decades should not be overlooked. Implementation of the plans required the closest liaison between university and government—several governments, in fact. One or two little stories will illustrate the point.

The question of whether the university should have a veterinary college had been debated several times in Senate before 1960 and had been turned down each time. Then in the early sixties it was pointed out that the need was growing, and in a re-examination both Council and Senate agreed that the university would be prepared to establish a college if the government was prepared to give it the necessary support, over and above the existing level of spending. By this time other universities had shown an interest in veterinary science, and the Western premiers agreed to refer the matter to a committee of deans of agriculture of the Western provinces, with an independent chairman. On the appointed day Dr. L. Hutcheon, then dean of agriculture, dropped in to inquire just how badly the province wanted the school in Saskatchewan. I suggested he call Toby Nollet, who was then Minister of Agriculture. I got Mr. Nollet on the phone and then handed the receiver to Dr. Hutcheon, who put it to his ear.

After a minute or so he slowly put the phone down and said, "I guess he really wants it!" Armed with this information, Dr. Hutcheon went to the meeting in Edmonton and came back with a favorable decision. Late that night he drove by our house and saw a light on. I came to the door in my dressing gown and was greeted with a rapturous shout, "We got it! We got it!" I think that this was a high point for Les Hutcheon—it certainly was for me. Incidentally, the federal government had agreed to support the capital funds to the extent of twenty-five per cent, up to a total of 0.625 million dollars. Eventually the cost of building, including the Animal Hospital, went up to 8.25 million. Fortunately the federal government authorities were persuaded to raise their ante to 3.25 million, for which we were most grateful, especially to Dr. K. F. Wells, who was then assistant deputy minister in the health of animals branch.

The two simple words "were persuaded," cover a long story, and the same could be said of almost everything connected with a university or, for that matter, of anything to do with any large and complex operation. A year or so after something is in operation it is taken as a matter of course, and no one thinks any more of the planning and effort which went into the project. As likely as not, the directors will be getting kicks from a variety of people who know very little, if anything, about the matter. This extract from a letter by Dr. Wells gives his appreciation of the importance of personal relationships in establishing the veterinary school at Saskatoon:

> In actual fact, the veterinary school at the University of Saskatchewan came about through your very active interest on the occasion of our very first meeting on the subject in your office.
>
> I recall vividly, and have told the story many times, that after I had put the proposition to you with respect to the possibility of a veterinary school at the Saskatoon campus, your reaction was immediate and favorable when you said that the University of Saskatchewan would be interested, would be willing to participate with the federal authorities, and what were the next steps necessary to move the proposal forward to reality. This was the most positive approach we had to the proposition up to that time, and I have been ever grateful to you for it.
>
> We did have a bit of haggling with outside interests as to whether a veterinary school in the West was or was not necessary, but fortunately because of your continuing interest and influence, the Western College of Veterinary Medicine was established, and in the few short years has become internationally recognized. In addition, in spite of earlier questions with respect to its necessity, it has, in fact, carved out for itself a reputation as an institution of high repute amongst the livestock industry of Western Canada.

Another story which has a moral concerns dentistry. The proposal to have a college of dentistry had been brought up and turned down several times, until the time seemed ripe to reintroduce it once more. This time one of the strongest opponents was chosen as chairman of the committee of enquiry—the idea being that if he were convinced, the case must be good, and everyone would be happy. And so it turned out. Having received the approval of the university's Council, Senate, and Board, the project was referred to the government for final approval. There was no reply for some weeks, so I phoned to Premier Thatcher's office to ask whether additional information was required, adding that I would be willing to appear personally, with other resource people, if I were asked to do so. Shortly thereafter the secretary phoned to say that the Premier would be in Saskatoon in a few days' time, and would be available for lunch.

On the appointed day, part of the morning was spent in showing the Premier some of the strictly business operations of the university. Lunch went pleasantly with the usual chit-chat, and finally the Premier asked me, "What about this dental college?"

I explained that it had been carefully studied, and I added that we were willing to make the necessary arrangements at any time that the government was prepared to provide X millions for a building and Y millions a year as an operating grant.

"Let me have a few statistics," said the Premier, and Dr. Begg, then dean of medicine, supplied the necessary figures.

"You're satisfied?" queried the Premier of his Minister of Health, who accompanied him.

"I'm quite satisfied," replied the minister.

At this the Premier tapped the table in approval and got up with a typical, "Let's go—you'll hear about this in good time."

And sure enough, the secretary phoned the next day to say that the matter had gone through the Cabinet, and a day or so later we received an official letter authorizing funds for the dental school. Of course in some ways this luncheon was just the icing on the cake, but there was more to it than that. I am quite sure that the Premier was sizing up our reactions, making sure that both the dean of medicine and I were a hundred per cent behind the proposal. It must not be forgotten that over the years the university had built up a high degree of confidence with successive governments. Deciding whether to go ahead with veterinary medicine or dentistry was essentially a political decision, arrived at by weighing the costs against other equally important public demands, and the government quite properly made the decision. But having the decision, it was up to the university to meet the requests in the best possible way.

Another major change involving university-government interaction was the decision to transfer teacher training from the Teachers' College to the university. This transfer took many months of negotiating, but eventually the transfer was made smoothly, and it has been eminently successful. This change was accomplished by the university's agreeing to take over the teacher-training function. By an arrangement between the Board and the provincial government, the university agreed to teach anything requested by the government on payment of any additional expenses. The university, however, reserved the right to give academic credit only to those courses which had been approved by its Council and Senate in the usual way. Members of the Council agreed to this arrangement, but had the proposition to take over teacher training been put to them in the same way that they would have considered the establishment of a new college, it is unlikely that it would have gone through.

A somewhat different example of government-university cooperation at several levels is supplied by the Linear Accelerator Laboratory. The story started in 1962 or thereabouts, when Dr. Katz and I formed part of a party going to Cold Lake to inspect some Air Force training facilities. We sat side by side on the plane and talked research. Dr. Katz explained that he and his colleagues had done most of the interesting things that could be done with their betatron and that it was time to be thinking about a new machine.

I immediately asked, "How much?"

"About two million dollars," replied Dr. Katz—"a million for the machine and a million for the buildings."

"And where will the money come from?"

"I thought you would tell me that."

"Good enough!" And each one set about his job—Dr. Katz to get a machine of superior design, and I to try to get the money. By good luck I was a member of the National Research Council, and when I approached Dr. Steacie, then president of the National Research Council, he said he would do something about it. Over the next few months he suggested that it was time the National Research Council started providing substantial capital grants, and eventually the governing body agreed. Dr. E. W. R. Steacie then said he had had an application for about $750,000 from Saskatchewan. He quickly added that he wouldn't do anything about it until everyone had had time to put in a bid, and that he would then put the matter to a committee on which Saskatchewan would not be represented, so everyone was happy.

In the event we got the first big grant, which reacted still better for those who received still bigger grants later. And by the time the proposal was taken to our university's Board, they were quite happy with it, since they knew that the N.R.C. would not support the proposal without getting good outside advice on the matter. Mr. Tommy Douglas, then Premier, was equally quickly convinced, and the Linear Accelerator Laboratory was built. Drs. Cockcroft, Wilkinson, Panofsky, and Vladimirski, world-renowned physicists who had acted as consultants, eventually came to the opening of the building and received honorary degrees.

Apart from the value of the work done in it, the lab. had a good psychological effect on the university. It indicated that we understood the meaning of the word *excellence,* and that if we wanted the best, we could get it in competition with the best. Incidentally, there was a valuable spin off to the Canadian nuclear industry in the researchers trained in the laboratory. Perhaps I should have pointed out earlier that before the university went ahead with the Accelerator proposal, the matter had been approved by the academic Council. At first there had been some grumbling on the part of the humanities people, who claimed that they could never expect to get such favorable treatment for any suggestion they might put in. The grumbling diminished markedly after a request for research support by Professor Hilda Neatby had been approved by the campus Humanities Research Committee and then by the Board, in double-quick time. The amount was considerably less than that involved with the Accelerator, but on the other hand, the total amount came from university funds.

Two other research projects, the Institute for Northern Studies, and Indian and Metis Studies, fit in here as illustrations of how a university gets interested in a new area of research and study.

An examination of grant applications for research support in the late fifties shows clearly that it was easier to get support for a straight research project in basic research than it was to get support for a more general applied research project, such as an area study in northern Saskatchewan. So to offset this problem in obtaining funds, a request was made to the university's Board of Governors to set up an institute for northern studies which would support general projects related to Northern Saskatchewan and contiguous northern areas.

As dean of graduate studies I wrote a memo., dated July 30, 1959, to Dr. W. P. Thompson, then president of the university. In this memo. I suggested that "serious consideration be given to establishing a center for northern studies," and I described the aims, area of interest, disciplines involved, projects and studies, together with suggestions for administrative structure, staff, finance, and so forth. A number of deans and heads of departments gave the proposal their unqualified support, as did a number of people outside the university, including the Hon. T. C. Douglas, John H. Brockelbank, Woodrow Lloyd, Alvin Hamilton, and Graham Rowley.

Some scribbled notes made at the time show the genesis of the original idea: "A casual enquiry reveals that although there have been people in this area (Northern Saskatchewan and neighboring territories) for centuries, and settlements for many decades, we are still lacking in knowledge about a good many aspects of the North, and it therefore becomes the logical focal point for an intensive research effort. From a university point of view, such an area of research is particularly attractive since it involves an interdisciplinary approach. . . . In these areas, some of the studies will involve not only scientific and engineering matters but will also embrace subjects traditionally considered to be the province of the humanities and of the social sciences."

The proposal to establish a northern institute was brought to the Board of Governors of the university in September 1959, and it resulted in the following motion: "That an amount of $10,000 be placed in the 1960–61 budget to provide for the establishment of a center for northern studies." The late Dr. J. Mawdsley, who had a great knowledge and love of northern Saskatchewan, was persuaded to chair the university Council's Committee on Northern Studies, which had its first meeting in December of 1959. Dr. Mawdsley was appointed Director of the Institute for Northern Studies in January 1960, and so the institute was born. The baby grew and flourished, and I take some pride in claiming paternity.

In order to get the institute going, Dr. Mawdsley suggested that grants be given to support research projects related to the North, and that there be a number of Musk-Ox scholarships and a *Musk-Ox* journal. Each of the ideas was developed, and there is now a well-established *Musk-Ox* journal with a good and growing reputation. Space was found on campus for offices, and for a small library and research space. At one stage I heard that Dr. Bob Williamson, who had had long experience in the North, particularly at Rankin Inlet, was interested in getting a university post. A temporary appointment was made in the institute, and in due time Dr. Williamson received a regular appointment in anthropology and archaeology as associate professor. The Donner Foundation supplied a generous grant to erect a "laboratory" at Rankin Inlet, where classes in the Eskimo language and in arctic studies are given in the summertime and a variety of courses in the winter. The lab. also serves as a home base for numerous researchers from various parts of the world in the summertime. The institute operates under the general guidance of an advisory committee composed of a number of knowledgeable people, and it now undertakes contract research as well as the usual basic and applied research.

There has been a succession of directors, Drs. Kupsch, Williamson, and Bone, each of whom has made his own particular contribution. The institute is now to share space in the Diefenbaker Center, which is newly established on campus. The institute has played a significant role in the development of coordinated plans for the dozen or so Canadian universities interested in northern research, and this planning function again has added to the local expertise on the role of the university in promoting social change. All in all, the institute has come a far step from its early beginning.

Indian and Metis studies bear some resemblance to the I.N.S. in their mode of development. The seed was sown at a reception at which Mary and I met a number of young Indians and Metis who had just completed courses in cooking, sewing, woodwork, welding, and so on. I was much impressed by these alert and lively young people, and I told one of the supervisors that if ever the university could be of assistance, say, in teaching the teachers, they would only have to let us know. A few months later this supervisor phoned to say that he had heard of a Father André Rénaud who had been teaching Indians for many years and to ask if I could possibly arrange for Father Rénaud to give a Summer School workshop for teachers of Indians and Metis. There was one problem: Father Rénaud was a member of a congregation of Oblate Fathers and was answerable only to his religious superiors. Next time I was in Ottawa I arranged to lunch with the bishop, and the advantages to Church and university were discussed, with the result that Father Rénaud appeared on campus to give the suggested workshop. It was an instant success, and in no time at all Father Rénaud was Professor Rénaud, with a regular faculty position and a lively program. The fame of this group has spread abroad, and Father Rénaud has been asked to act as a consultant in many countries. Naturally it is the abilities of the man which are of chief importance, but I like to think that the opportunities provided on the campus for many interdisciplinary contacts also helped. The College of Law now has a program of legal studies for native peoples, and the Saskatchewan Indian Community College and the Saskatchewan Indian Cultural College were housed on campus for some years.

As I read over this chapter, I see that my life-long preoccupation with research and academic excellence shows through perhaps a little bit too obviously. However, given the way I had been brought up and the experiences I had had, the transfer of this preoccupation to the university was to be expected, and it was not entirely bad—in fact, I think it was all to the good. The University of Saskatchewan was just at the stage of developing into a well-rounded university, with a good research capability, and the leadership of someone willing to take a few initiatives paid off handsomely in research services provided by the university to the community.

Those who are interested in discovering more about the history of the institution will find extensive discussion of university developments in all areas during the 1959–70 period in my book, *A Decade of Change: 1959–1970*, published by the University of Saskatchewan.

Chapter 15

Blue Spruce

The president's house, which was to be our home during my term as president, is worth a mention. It is a handsome building, something after the style of a Scottish manse, built of prairie limestone and standing on the top of the river-bank, with a magnificent view out to the southwest. Almost every day we were treated to a splendid sunset, which would often cover half the sky with a wild splash of color. And in the wintertime we could look out over the city and see columns of steam rising from each building— a reminder of the still air and low temperatures.

The road leading down to the house is lined with blue spruce which were planted in 1941 and are now a good size. The house is on the edge of the campus, and this location had two advantages: I could walk to and from my office—about eight minutes each way—and yet, because it was on the edge of campus, the house was accessible to animals and birds from the tree-covered river bank. There were porcupines, rabbits, squirrels, chipmunks, gophers, skunks, and the odd deer, with all kinds of birds, including partridges and pheasants. It was a great delight to see the tracks of birds and animals in the fresh snow near the house during the wintertime. Mary kept closer tabs on these visitors from the sun porch with the help of a pair of binoculars and a bird book.

The house is well built, and equally suitable for family living or for large-scale entertaining. Although there were just two of us, we immediately felt comfortable in this big house and made, I think, good use of it. At the front of the house is a large drawing room, with a delightful little sun porch opening out from it, and with a view across the river. The room is well suited to entertaining numbers of people. The sun porch was originally an open porch, largely unused, since in the wintertime it was incredibly cold, and in the summertime it was too hot and often windy and dusty. Mary suggested closing in the porch by the simple expedient of putting in two windows and a baseboard heater. Going towards the other end of the house one passed through a medium-sized reception room, a fine library, well stocked with books in English, French, German, and Russian, and a medium-sized dining room, before arriving at a sun porch or conservatory. The conservatory was full of potted plants which Mary saw to with the help of a useful green thumb. It was a pleasant spot in both winter and summer.

Our first entertaining was a buffet-style dinner for about sixty people in honor of the Governor-General and his lady. We were told pretty much what to do, but General and Madame Vanier immediately put everyone at their ease, so entertaining them was no problem. And after that, anything else was relatively simple. Official entertaining did, however, involve a great deal of hard work, particularly for Mary. I doubt whether any of the faculty had much idea of the work involved. At the beginning of term we customarily had a "tea" for the faculty and their husbands and wives, some hundreds of them. As numbers increased we would divide our guests into two or three groups. Eventually numbers became so great that we had to limit ourselves to new members of faculty and their wives or husbands. The ladies usually helped with the arrangements. The teas served to introduce people to those whom they had not already met, and altogether we felt that they were a good thing. We had somewhat similar gatherings for the members of the Board of Governors and the Senate and their spouses. We also had teas for the Students Representative Council, at which we usually tried to mix incoming and outgoing council members. Of course there were many less formal occasions when we would entertain some visiting dignitary, a group of carollers, or just one or two students or friends. The house lent itself well to these smaller gatherings, too.

One very successful tea party followed a visit to Ile à la Crosse and some places further north taken by Mary and myself with Father Rénaud. The guests included students from his classes, together with about forty young women of Indian ancestry from Duck Lake. They were enrolled in a special class for teachers' aides, so that they could assist the teachers of kindergarten classes for Indian children. We were invited to participate in a return visit to Duck Lake, and a few days later we were seeing classes in session at the residential school at Duck Lake and some practical classes on the Beardy and One Arrow reserves. The aides were getting considerable enjoyment out of the whole exercise, which I judged to be a great success. The need for the aides was obvious on the One Arrow reserve, where only one in twenty-five of the preschool children spoke English—the rest spoke nothing but Cree. We were much taken with the enthusiasm generated by these courses.

One of the aides had developed a most artistic "quiet book" out of pieces of cloth, which could be used to teach all sorts of fairly abstract ideas.

She had, for example, a cloth "apple" fixed by a dome fastener to a cloth "tree," from which it could "fall" to the right or left. Developing a book of this kind showed a good deal of imagination.

On one occasion we had an instant tea party. I had been away, and on returning to Saskatoon on a Saturday I had brought some mail back to the house from the university. Mary was looking at this on Sunday morning, and she came across a letter from a student saying that he regretted that he would not be able to come to tea on Sunday. Mary knew that we were not having any students to tea, so she had visions of someone else expecting this student, and of there being a disappointment when he did not turn up. A bit of detective work put her in touch with the student's landlady, who informed Mary that the student had certainly received an attractive invitation card. Mary then had the horrible thought that other students might have received an invitation. A phone call to one or two members of the S.R.C. confirmed her worst suspicions that someone had gone to some lengths to perpetrate a joke on us.

It was too late to let everyone know that it was a hoax, so we decided to put on a tea. We did this with the help of John Bardwell and his wife Millicent (Mickey). By the time 3:00 P.M. rolled around, everything was ready, and about a hundred and fifty people had a pleasant time, so it would have been a shame not to have gone ahead with entertaining them. The pranksters had gone to a great deal of trouble to get special invitations printed. We never found out for sure who was responsible for the hoax, but we had a good idea who it was.

Mary spent many hours arranging the furniture in the house until gradually she got things to her taste, and I think she did a particularly good job of the furnishings. When we first moved in from our little house we had just about one piece of furniture for each room and a number of pictures. Little by little, Mary acquired the right things: rugs, chairs, tables and the rest, and the whole took form. It was a labor of love indeed. Each piece had a story to it—there were several oriental rugs from Winnipeg, an India rug from Montreal, a polar bear skin from Resolute, glass from Murano in Italy, and so on.

Going into the house was fun, too. When the W. P. Thompsons had left the house in November of 1959, it had been decided that some necessary repair work should be done on old electric wiring and similar matters before we moved in. This repair work seemed to drag on a long time, and we were still not in the house when I was installed officially in January. After the installation there was a dinner and reception. We didn't feel like going to bed right away, so we went down to the president's house to see how things were coming along. A number of rooms seemed just about ready for occupancy, so we had the bright idea of bringing over our dog Skipper, with some bedding, several bouquets of flowers, and a few things in our suit cases, and settling down for the night. The workmen were surprised to find us sleeping there in the morning. We said that we intended to stay, so they took the hint and finished up the decorating in double-quick

time. It made a wonderful start to life in the president's house. The W.P.'s
had told us that they had gradually become very attached to the house and
that they hated to leave it. With us, it was love at first sight!

At the east end of the house there were two large gardens—one could
be used for vegetables and flowers, while the other had in it fruit trees such
as crabs, apples, and plums, raspberries, currants, and some asparagus.
Each spring we would have fresh asparagus, and then many, many baskets
of raspberries, and later, apples and plums. The garden was too well known
to the public to be altogether satisfactory—a number of young folk (and
some older ones) thought it was their privilege to help themselves to fruit
and vegetables, and they could not seem to realize that we had rights too.
Most years we had a large crop of vegetables—potatoes, corn, tomatoes,
lettuce, radishes, carrots, peas, beans and so forth. Some we ate, some we
put in the deep freeze, and some we gave away. One specialty was broad
beans. Dr. Harold Moss of the soils department was an authority on broad
beans, so together we constituted the Royal Broad Bean Society. We took
turns at being president and vice-president respectively. Often at Christmas
time I would receive a selection of broad beans from Dr. Moss, ready for
spring planting, accompanied by a solemn little note from the "President of
the Society." Very few of the people who heard about the Royal Broad Bean
Society realized that this was just a private little joke that we had.

During the summer things grew like mad under the influence of many
hours of bright sunshine. Then the raspberries would ripen, and for about a
month or six weeks I would pick raspberries—at first a basket or so, and
then at the peak of the crop as much as twenty baskets in a day. Some of
these we ate, some we put in the deep freeze or converted to jelly, and
many, many baskets we gave away. Mary had a special way of arranging the
berries in a tray with their cups up, dusting them lightly with sugar, and
putting them in the freezer for a few hours until they were like marbles.
Then they were put in plastic bags and returned to the deep freeze. We
would take them out during the winter, and after they had thawed out they
had the full aroma and flavour of fresh raspberries. Some of them found
their way into a delicious fruit punch, made from Mary's special recipe.
Mary did not drink alcoholic drinks herself, but she always kept a supply
on hand for visitors. Serving raspberry punch in silver goblets from a large
silver bowl always added a festive touch to a party.

Sometimes we would have a party of one—a student would stroll down
by the house and ring the bell and be invited in. On other occasions I would
encounter a student on campus while I was walking home. He would
accompany me to the house and be asked to join us. One such encounter
occurred quite late at night, after eleven o'clock. The young man in question
more or less drifted out of a parking lot and got into conversation with me.
He was a bit of the hippie type, with long hair, a beard and whiskers, and a
dressing gown or something similar as an outer garment, but withal he was
a handsome fellow. Eventually we reached the house and I asked if he
would come in.

"May I?"

"Why not?" I replied, and ushered him into the library. He picked up the first book that came to hand on the library table, which was a book of reproductions of paintings by Lauren Harris.

"I didn't expect to find anything like this here,"he said frankly.

"Look around," I said. He seemed still more surprised to come across a booklet describing the Bahai Temple at Haifa. I said that I was not a devotee, but that hadn't stopped me from visiting the Temple and being very much taken by it and by the Bahai philosophy. This topic launched our visitor into an account of his philosophy, or search for a philosophy, which I found fascinating. In the meantime Mary had heard the sound of voices, had looked in unknown to us and had returned to the kitchen to make coffee. In due time she appeared with coffee and cakes and completely overwhelmed our unexpected visitor by her friendliness. We almost had to throw him out at two o'clock in the morning.

People often pitied us for having a life so completely dominated by the university, but that was our life, and anything less than total immersion would have been insufficient. There was a negative side in that a few people were resentful of our spacious accommodation and made unkind remarks, often without troubling to verify the accuracy of the rumors which they spread. One rumor was that we had put the university to great expense to furnish the house. Actually, of course, we had gradually acquired the furniture ourselves, over the years. Another strange tale which was even relayed to the provincial government, was that we had put in air conditioning at a cost of seventy thousand dollars. There was no air conditioning at all, and as a matter of fact none was needed. I suppose the real problem was that the university president's living in a big house gave those interested in attacking the "establishment" another point of attack. And there were plenty of such people in the late sixties. On balance, however, I think that the president's house served a useful purpose. It might probably have been useful, in that day and age, to make an effort to explain to the public in general and to the faculty in particular, the proper role of the president's house in the total university operation.

Chapter 16

Travel within Canada

As university president I was often called upon to travel all over the province, all over Canada, and pretty well all over the world. Some of the travel was related to the alumni and fund raising, some to contacts with the broader university community, some to attending chemical and scientific meetings, and some to membership of one commission or another. Many times a year I would visit a town or city in the province such as Lloydminster, North Battleford, Kamsack, Yorkton, Melville, Esterhazy, Assiniboia, Rosetown, Prince Albert, or Uranium City. Sometimes I would address the alumni, sometimes a group such as the Rotarians or Chamber of Commerce, and sometimes a group of students at the local high school. Usually two or three things would be combined: an appearance on radio or television, a visit to the high school, and a dinner meeting, which often would be followed by coffee at someone's house—it was all fairly strenuous but most rewarding.

Often I would be driven by Mr. Frank Lovell, director of the Development Office, or by Mr. Gordon Saunders, director of the Alumni Office, and we would discuss university matters on the way to and from our appointment. Often Mary would accompany us. One visit I shall never forget was to Patunak, a small settlement in northern Saskatchewan, which we reached by float plane. Most of the people spoke Chipewayan, and I had to describe the university, with the help of an interpreter, as the school beyond the school beyond the school.

My listeners were both attentive and charming, and I regretted that I could not speak to them in their own language. The talk was preceded by a service in a small Anglican church, the faithful being called together at short notice by the tolling of the church bell. On the way back to Buffalo Narrows we flew low over a small lake set in a landscape of muskeg, and we saw two moose standing in water three or four feet deep, lazily twitching their ears and occasionally thrusting their heads under water to come up with a mouthful of vegetation.

Another time I visited a number of schools in the neighborhood of Kindersley, including one in a Hutterite Colony. The school was of the one-room variety, with about twenty youngsters from six to fourteen years old, all looking rosy and healthy. The girls had clean aprons over their dresses and kerchiefs over their hair. I spoke to them generally about the importance of education and amused them with some of my space-age doggerel:

> "Apollo, Apollo, where have you been?"
> "I have been to the moon, to see and be seen."
> "Apollo, Apollo, what saw you there?"
> "No man in the moon, no green cheese, and no air!"

This was at the time when the astronauts were landing on the moon. Later the children sang for me, and then they took me to have coffee and cakes in the communal dining hall, which was somewhat spartan but as clean as a new pin.

I was very much taken by the obvious prosperity of the settlement. There were about one hundred and twenty people all told, and they practiced mixed farming, keeping many cows and pigs, thousands of chickens, and hundreds of ducks. It was at least a million dollar operation and it was obviously well run. The leader of the group took me to visit his home, which was part of a barnlike building housing six or so families. Here again the dwelling was a bit spartan but spotlessly clean. I started to query him about their up-to-date procedures, and I asked how they managed without radio, T.V., a big library, and so on. He replied that they did get newspapers and some farm journals, and then he added, "The salesmen come along and sell us such things as the automatic milkers."

At this point a door leading into the living room partially opened, and the sweetest little face, again framed in a kerchief, peered round the corner and said, "That's not true. We women said we would not milk fifty cows any longer, and you had to purchase the milkers," and the door shut.

"You might as well come in, if you are going to listen at the keyhole," said her husband.

"But it's much more fun listening at the keyhole," replied his wife, quick as a flash.

I inquired how they kept the young people happy in the absence of the usual T.V., shows, and dances. He admitted that lack of popular entertainment was a problem, but he said that so far they had managed to forestall complaints by having the young people visit back and forth in neighboring Hutterite communities. We couldn't help wondering how long this idyllic existence could last.

Sometimes I would talk to a group of farmers and their wives, who were all interested in the university and who regarded it as *their* university, which of course it is. I would usually talk first about agricultural research and extension, things of prime importance to them, and then I would gradually get around to the importance of having a well-developed all-round university that would be regarded as first-class—not just in agriculture but in a number of other areas as well, depending on the interests of the professors. Again the bits of doggerel came in handy in livening up a speech and in getting across the idea that atomic energy and computers, for example, are of importance in our modern world, and hence important to the province and to them. It is important to have a feel for the province and not to get too much out of step with the thinking of the people. These talks within the province averaged out to about sixty every year or about once a week, and though they were quite a chore, they were well worth while.

Out-of-province travel occurred quite often, with visits to alumni groups and to fund-raising contacts from Victoria to Montreal, visits to Ottawa to attend meetings of the National Research Council, Canada Council, or the A.U.C.C. (Association of Universities and Colleges of Canada), visits to university cities to attend meetings of the learned societies, particularly the Royal Society of Canada and the Chemical Institute of Canada. I occasionally went on a speaking tour for a national society. On one such tour for the Canadian Club, I visited a number of towns and cities in British Columbia. All this travel helped me to maintain contact with academic and other scholarly groups right across the country. I made an average of one long trip a month. To be added to my other travel were trips to Regina averaging one per week, year in, year out.

One pleasant friendship which I was fortunate to enjoy as a result of frequent visits to Ottawa was that with Maurice Haycock and his family. I met him at a meeting of the Canadian Royal Society through Dr. Jim Mawdsley, head of our geology department. Haycock was himself a geologist with the federal government in Ottawa, and he had done much geologizing in the North. He was a good painter and he would often paint what he saw in the North. He knew some of the Canadian painters, such as A. Y. Jackson, and he had had the good fortune to accompany Jackson on many of his painting trips in northern and eastern Canada. So in due time I met A. Y. at the Haycocks, and I am indebted to them for letting me share in their friendship with an outstanding Canadian.

One time I was visiting the Haycocks and A. Y. Jackson turned up. We were left chatting on the sofa with a glass of sherry. He seemed thoroughly wound up, and any little thing I mentioned triggered off a burst of reminiscences. I asked what he thought of Emily Carr, and he told me that he admired her paintings, and then he went on to tell me in great detail of meeting her when she was in Paris in the days before World War I. His anecdotes were fascinating, and he was extremely frank in his comments about everyone.

After a few minutes I noticed that everyone else had disappeared, and they did not come back for over an hour. Eventually they all came in, looking rather pleased with themselves. It turned out that the sofa had been bugged with a microphone and that our conversation had been recorded. Apparently they had an agreement with A. Y. Jackson that any time he was with a new person and the conversation seemed to be going well, they would tape it, as a way of getting on tape some of his thoughts. Anyhow, I enjoyed the experience.

The Haycocks had two charming daughters, Karole and Kathy, who were both quite young, eight or ten, I would say, when I first met them. The first meeting was not to be forgotten. Maurice was much interested in the Ottawa Symphony, and one time when I phoned them on a Sunday, he said that he and his wife were going to a concert, and asked if I would like to join them. I met them at the theatre and was introduced to their young daughter, Karole, whose partner I was to be for the evening. At the intermission we visited the candy counter and stocked up with chocolate bars, the better to help us through the second half of the concert. After the concert, Karole's parents attended a large reception for the members of the orchestra, so Karole and I tagged along too. After a bit we spotted a table of refreshments, starting with sandwiches at one end and gradually changing to cakes and cookies, and finally ending up with a pile of cream puffs covered with icing sugar.

"Could we try those puffs?" asked Karole.

"I don't see why not," said I, who already had designs on the cream puffs.

When everyone else was busy with sandwiches we each took a cream puff. I bit into mine and I immediately received two squirts of cream, one on each cheek, and was enveloped in a cloud of icing sugar. Karole was overcome with laughter to see the university president in such a pickle. We were quickly joined by others who liked cream puffs just as much as we did, and who didn't wish to be left out of the fun. With due modesty, I feel that Karole and I stole the show. And if anything else was needed, this sealed my friendship with the Haycock family.

In the early sixties I visited Ottawa on an average once a month, attending meetings of the N.R.C., D.R.B. (Defense Research Board), and Canada Council, and being able to drop in more or less unannounced on the Haycocks greatly increased the pleasure of my visits to the capital city. This travel all over the province and all over the country served to keep me in touch with a broad spectrum of people and with their views of the university and its program.

Every now and again I would be invited to attend a meeting or undertake some kind of mission outside Canada. After consultation with the Board of Governors I would usually accept on the grounds that I would learn enough from the assignment to compensate the university for any time I might be away from campus. And the requesting body invariably paid my travel expenses, so the university was not out of pocket on that account. Mary accompanied me on all these foreign travels. She has always enjoyed travel, enjoyed meeting people, and had a reliable memory for names and faces. Additionally, her knowledge of Russian was most helpful at international meetings. Mary's travel expenses came out of my pocket, but we counted that a good expenditure. These long trips averaged about three every two years, and I found them most helpful in keeping in touch with world trends in university education, in university rationalization and coordination, and in research.

Total travel averaged fifty to sixty thousand miles every year, mostly by plane. Luckily most of it was by jets which ate up the miles and allowed us to get up above the weather and be in relatively smooth flying. Countries visited outside Canada included the United Kingdom, France, Germany, Poland, Russia, Switzerland, Italy, Israel, India, Ceylon, Jamaica, and the U.S.A., with brief stopovers in a number of additional countries.

Chapter 17

"Da" and "Niet"

One of the most fascinating countries we visited was Russia. Our first visit was in 1960, and we made other trips in 1965, 1969, and 1978. The 1960 trip came about by accident. We had been in London attending the three hundredth anniversary celebrations of the Royal Society of London, and we had a week or so to put in before returning to Canada. On inquiring at a travel agency about possible tours, we were advised that a quick trip to Russia would be amusing. We were also advised that since the occurrence of the U2 incident, many people had cancelled their bookings, and it would be relatively easy to get a visa. This information proved to be correct, and the Cook's Travel Agency arranged a semi-independent eight-day trip to Moscow for us without any great trouble. On arrival in Moscow we were taken to the Ukrainian Hotel, which we found to be quite comfortable. If our rooms were bugged we certainly didn't know it, and if we were followed, it wasn't obvious.

On one occasion, while we were walking along one side of the Red Square, a tall blond youth sidled up to me and asked if I wished to sell my nylon raincoat which I was carrying on my arm. I told him that we weren't interested, and he moved off. A few minutes later a young woman speaking French said that she had something urgent to tell us if we could see her in some private place. She seemed to be quite flustered and agitated. I tried to find out what her difficulty was, but she refused to say anything specific, and I told her that we could not do anything for her, so she also left us. Apart from these two incidents, nothing untoward happened during the whole of the time we were in Moscow. I say this because so many visitors to Russia claim to have had their rooms searched, and so on.

While we were in Moscow we went to the Bolshoi Theatre, the Tretyakow Art Gallery, and the Kremlin, and in fact to all the usual places —mostly on our own, and we thoroughly enjoyed the sightseeing. We managed to get in touch with two Russian scientists whom I had met previously at international scientific meetings—Nicolai Nicolaiovitch Semenov and Dr. Klechkowski. Nicolai Nicolaiovitch is an Academician and Nobel Prize winner in chemistry. We had met the Semenovs in Cambridge at the Royal Society Tercentenary celebrations. At one of the garden parties Mary had noticed a couple standing by themselves, so we walked over to them and tried to start up a conversation. We had no success until Mary tried Russian. This initiative triggered a flood of words and led to a warm friendship.

The Semenovs had suggested we phone them if we ever visited Moscow. We did so, and as a result Madame Semenova took us to see a "scientists' rest home" on the outskirts of Moscow. It had once been the home of one of their nobility and had been left almost unchanged, with paintings, a billiard table, beautiful furniture, and spacious grounds. It is now used by senior scientists who wish to enjoy a quiet time to prepare a book or a lecture, or just to rest or recuperate after illness. On the way back we called in at Semenov's institute to meet the professor and to visit his laboratories. This visit turned out to be the first of a number of pleasant meetings with the Semenovs in Moscow.

Dr. Klechkowski worked in the Timiraziev Agricultural Institute on the outskirts of Moscow, and I had met him in Geneva in 1955 and 1958. Klechkowski is a soil scientist who had done a great deal of isotope work. He took us to see his laboratories, which were quite impressive, and then he invited us to dinner on a river steamer. We met him at about half past seven at a station on the river's edge and went on board the *Joseph Stalin,* a boat taking about four hundred passengers, with young people dancing to loudspeakers on the rear deck and supper in the dining salon. The Moscow River is quite wide and is partly a canal, connecting with the Volga. Outside the city the banks are lined with country houses or dachas. We saw people fishing and strolling along the banks, and it looked very rural and peaceful. Four of us went to dinner—Mary, Klechkowski, his assistant Pleshkow, and myself. We started with a bottle of cognac and drank many toasts.

Before drinking the first toast Klechkowski rose and made a little speech in our honor. When I sipped the cognac it seemed very strong, so I put down my glass and drank some water. Klechkowski said, "What do you say? Bottoms up!" At this point Mary kicked me under the table and I took her signal to mean "Drink up!" so I tossed back the rest of the cognac. In the next thirty seconds the top of my head slowly lifted off and then settled back into place, after which I felt no pain and was able to rise and toast Klechkowski in fluent Russian, or so it seemed to me. Mary said later that she had really meant me to go slow with the drinks. We finished with a bottle of Sovietski Champagnski.

Other people in the dining salon seemed to be having a pleasant time too. One group was singing by a piano. In a pause in the conversation our host became aware of the singing and thought it a bit noisy—a word from him to the waiter and it stopped. We left the boat at about half past ten and had some difficulty in getting a taxi. Eventually Pleshkov spoke to a policeman, who brought us a fine police car which took us into town in short order. I reflected that I would not have been able to do the same thing in Saskatoon. However, we had had a most enjoyable evening with a pleasant colleague.

Two other evenings went pleasantly at the ballet, seeing *Lotus Blossom* and *Taras Bulba*, which were both well done. While we did not go out of our way to talk to people, we did have many pleasant conversations with those with whom we came in contact—a young couple from Baku sitting next to us at a puppet show, a farmer from near Lake Baikal, shopping in GUM, the big state-owned department store on the Red Square, and so on. So ended our first trip to Russia. Like others we had been frustrated at times by the Intourist officials, but we had found the average Russian to be most friendly, and certainly the whole trip was fascinating.

Some five years later, Mary and I revisited the Soviet Union, although this time we visited the country under somewhat different circumstances. For three weeks I was the guest of the Soviet Academy of Science, as part of an exchange scheme between Canada and the U.S.S.R.; for one week I attended an international chemical congress, and during the week after the congress we took a tour to Uzbekestan. Under the exchange scheme I visited institutes and universities in Moscow, Leningrad, Kiev, and Tblisi, and I gave lectures (with the help of an interpreter) on the radiation chemistry research that was being done at the University of Saskatchewan. The lecture was usually followed by a discussion of research problems of mutual interest, and I was shown work in progress in the Russian scientists' laboratories. In each city I visited a number of research institutes, which are rather more common in the U.S.S.R. than in Canada, as well as going to the universities. I was taken to see the Nuclear Research Institute at Dubna and the Physics Research Institute at Tashkent.

Everywhere the reception was most cordial, and our hosts went out of their way to be nice to us. We were met at the plane or the train and seen off, each time with a bouquet of flowers for Mary, and often with a little gift. We were entertained in private homes and country houses (dachas) on numerous occasions, and we cannot speak too highly of the hospitality shown us. In travelling around and meeting people we were greatly aided by Mary's Russian; often our hosts could speak English but were shy about doing so until Mary broke the ice by speaking Russian to them, and afterwards they did not mind using their English on me. Mary's knowledge of Russian was equally invaluable in the casual contacts made with people on the plane, or in the street or shops. People were anxious to talk to the two foreigners, and they were most friendly when they discovered that we were "Kanadskis."

I recall a pleasant chat on the plane to Kiev with a football enthusiast who had just been to Moscow to see a game between Russia and Brazil. In the absence of a common language we would have sat together for three hours without a word passing between us, and Mary and I would have missed the interesting fact that a garage mechanic could afford to take a relatively expensive trip costing a hundred dollars, just to see a game of soccer. Incidentally, he was wearing a sports shirt of Canadian make.

Going on the plane from Kiev to Tblisi was fun. We were waiting at the exit gate for an announcement to board the plane when the people started to stream out on the tarmac to a plane parked not far away. We followed and boarded the plane with the rest.

After a few moments a young stewardess appeared at the front of the plane:

"Now aren't you tiresome! You know you mustn't get on the plane without giving up your boarding passes! Just be good children and let me have your boarding passes without any fuss!"

And she collected our boarding passes. Then she announced, "I knew it! Someone is very naughty! There are seventy of you and I have only sixty-nine passes. Who didn't give me their pass?"

At this a young man called out, "Me, Miss—come and search me!"

All the passengers roared with laughter. The young man then passed around a bottle of Armenian wine while someone else shared out delicious pears from a big strong bag. No one bothered to observe the usual signs for take-off, and we had a riotous time all the way to Tblisi. The further we got away from Moscow, the more relaxed the atmosphere became.

The work that I saw in the various laboratories was similar in many ways to that done in Canada, and the Russian scientists were familiar with our work. Perhaps the biggest eye-opener came in Tashkent, the capital of Uzbekestan. Until a few years ago, Uzbekestan would have been considered a primitive and undeveloped part of the country. In fact one can still see there, side by side, both ancient and modern ways of life. However, just outside Tashkent is the Physics Institute, started only a few years ago, which now has a swimming-pool reactor, a cyclotron, and a huge irradiation facility with 160,000 curies of Co-60 and a thousand workers doing what looked, at a quick glance, like pretty good work.

Paralleling this progress in the city are electricity; trolley buses; a new department store, complete with escalators; an opera house; and parks with lakes and fountains. In the department store I helped a dear old granny dressed in highly colored garments, to get on to the escalator, which obviously terrified her, and I took her safely to the top to join her children and grandchildren, who were splitting their sides laughing at the spectacle. Just outside, smartly dressed people were walking by a mother, also in gay Uzbekian dress, who was sitting casually on the edge of the pavement and nursing her baby au naturelle. Now I'm not a Communist and I have no particular wish to try to convert anyone to the Russian way of life, but I can't help being impressed by the considerable achievements of the Russians in certain areas of science, and also by the rate of development achieved in some out-of-the-way areas that were previously backward.

One little incident in Tashkent was quite revealing. Mary and I were taking a walk in a large park, and we heard singing under the trees. On investigating we came upon a small open-air kindergarten, with about forty children, all four or five years old, in charge of two young women. One of them spoke to us in English, having recognized that we were foreigners. She then turned to the youngsters and said something to them, after which they sang "Three blind mice" in English—not bad for five-year-olds, we thought.

While in Uzbekestan we also visited Bokhara and Samarkand. I had dreamed of Samarkand since I was about ten years old, and it lived up to my expectations completely, with mosques and elaborate tombs and a generally medieval air. Actually it was about half medieval and half modern, whereas Tashkent was ten per cent medieval to Bokhara's ninety per cent. Many of the buildings were surmounted by incredibly beautiful domes of blue glazed tile, while others were built of biscuit-colored bricks, some standing out in relief, so that as the sun moved round during the day, the amounts of shadow produced by the projecting bricks varied and changed the apparent color of the building, as it was seen from a distance. The tomb of Tamerlane itself was most impressive. It was a single slab of jade, about sixteen by four feet in size, and about a foot thick. We visited a bazaar—very Eastern and colorful, with old men sitting on gay rugs and drinking tea from bowls, and with huge piles of melons and other fruits as a backdrop.

As well as visiting laboratories and universities, we were entertained in a number of private homes and we visited several museums, historical monuments, and theatres, all of which gave us a more general picture of Russia.

One visit to the home of a young Russian scientist brought unexpected dividends. In the course of conversation Mary said she would like to visit an ordinary school. The wife of the scientist offered to take us to her school, so we went there the following morning. The children were aged about six to thirteen, and the school was fairly old, so that the desks were all carved with names. The children were well dressed and healthy, and very well behaved. We started with the six-year-olds, who were learning English. There were about thirty in the class, and each pupil had a series of crayoned cutouts on the desk in front of him—a red pencil, a black handbag, and so on.

The teacher said, "Nikolai Nikolaiovitch," whereupon a rosy-cheeked young boy stood up, obviously pleased to be asked a question.

The teacher picked up the black handbag and said, with a pronounced accent, "These ees a red pencil."

To this the youngster replied, "Noo, eet ees not a red pencil—eet ees a black hand bag!" and he sat down, very pleased with himself.

There was a delightful atmosphere in the classroom, and we were duly impressed with the knowledge of the six-year-olds. I scarcely knew "Da" and "Niet" ("Yes" and "No").

In another classroom, some children of eight or nine were doing arithmetic. On examining their workbooks I found that they were solving simple quadratic equations. In yet another classroom, a young boy was asked who had recently landed on the moon. He gave the names of the American astronauts and then showed us where they had landed, using a large moon globe for the purpose. At that time I hadn't seen a moon globe, so on my return to Saskatoon I quickly made inquiries and—with some difficulty—obtained one. At least I had brought myself up to the astronomical level of ten-year-old Muscovites. Each classroom gave us a pleasant surprise, and we left with a good impression of the elementary school students, at least as far as we could judge by this school. It was not a big sample, of course, but better than nothing.

On this visit to Russia we again attended a number of performances of opera and ballet—*Giselle* at the Bolshoi, the *Fountain* ballet at the Congress Theatre Hall, a Tchaikovsky concert at the Congress Theatre Hall, the opera *Peter Grimes* at the Bolshoi, and the Leningrad Ballet group doing *Chopiniana* and works by Khachaturian at the Congress Hall, all in Moscow. In Leningrad we saw the opera *Ruslam and Ludmilla*; an operetta entitled *One Hundred Devils and a Girl* at the Comedy Theatre; the Rimsky-Korsakoff opera, *The Vanishing City*; a Greig ballet; and *Raymunda* at the Kirov Ballet House. Incidentally, everyone seemed to go to opera and ballet, not just the long-hairs. You may say that everyone is brain-washed, since this is the same kind of music that one hears on radio and T.V. in Russia, and juke boxes are non-existent.

In Leningrad we visited the Hermitage Museum, and it really is as good as it is described to be; there are staggering collections of Picasso, Gaugin, the French Impressionists, Rembrandt, and Leonardo da Vinci, together with much early Russian and archeological material, furniture, jewellery, and so forth, in room after room. We walked until we were tired and then we left and came back the next day for more. Naturally these places cost money to support—large amounts of money—and this money is supplied by the state. It can easily do such funding, since in a controlled economy the state decides how much money goes into rockets, science, ballet, or hockey, and how much goes into extra pairs of nylon stockings, high-heeled shoes, or private cars. You pays your money and you takes your choice, but in Russia the state does most of the choosing rather than the average person.

As far as we know, we were completely free to come and go. We used public transportation as well as cars and taxis, and we did much of our sightseeing completely on our own. We took photographs freely. The only limitation was that we were told not to use the camera when we were in an aircraft. Mary left her camera in a taxi one day; later in the day it was returned by the taxi driver, who had gone to considerable trouble to track us down and return it personally. He wouldn't take a tip. People seem to move around freely inside Russia, although we were given to understand that travel outside Russia, and particularly outside the Iron Curtain, is fairly restricted. Travel by foreigners within Russia is controlled indirectly by having practically all foreign travel done through the state travel agency, Intourist. They book hotels, tours, guides, taxis, plane tickets, rail transportation, and everything else. Perhaps we had bad luck, but we found them most frustrating and exasperating. Of course we always got to where we were going eventually, or found accommodation, but usually we had a degree of delay and uncertainty that we are not accustomed to on this continent.

One trip which was lots of fun was an overnight journey from Moscow to Leningrad on the Red Arrow. We had had visions of sharing a sleeping car with a couple of bearded Russians, but we had been assured that we would have a two-berth compartment. When we arrived at the train we found that we had been assigned to a four-berth compartment. Visions of the two bearded Russians had us worried until a woman and her fifteen-year-old daughter appeared to claim the other two berths. The woman was a teacher of history, married to an airline pilot, and she and her daughter were going for a short holiday to Leningrad. We found them both quite charming. Came the time to go to bed. I was put in an upper berth and told to shut my eyes tightly while the ladies got undressed and into bed. The young girl was assigned the other upper berth. We slept well and were wakened in the morning by the porter bringing tea.

As I opened my eyes I saw, looking at me from what seemed to be ten or twelve inches away, two of the most sparkling blue eyes: "Good morning, Mr. Canadian," was the greeting.

When we got off the train we stood looking helpless, because the people we had expected to meet us did not appear. After a bit, a helpful porter came along, and we explained the situation to him.

"Don't worry," he said, "this happens more often than not! Just wait here." And he went to a waiting line of cars and soon found two distressed young women who had expected to meet us but had been given the wrong car number. Some little slip-up happened nearly every time, but everything always worked out all right eventually.

The many people whom we saw looked well-fed and happy, and they were fairly well dressed; there was a greater variety in the dress, we thought, than there had been five years earlier. There was no doubt that the general standard of living was a good deal higher than it had been five years before, although it was still a good deal lower than ours, with smaller living space, far fewer private cars, and so on. Again one would have to qualify things somewhat in that there are no unemployed, no one goes on strike and rents are absurdly low.

One of our friends told us a delightful story of a young man who thought that everything was done automatically, and so he just stayed at home. At the end of the week his usual cheque came, and others followed after two weeks, and three weeks, so by this time he thought that the bureaucratic system would let him live the life of leisure forever. However, at the end of the fourth week came a tap on the door. Outside stood a well-dressed man, notebook, hand, and pencil poised.

"Mr. Smith, I presume?"

"Yes, Mr. Commissar."

"I note that you were away from work for a week at the beginning of the month. I presume that you were sick and thought you would take sick leave, to which you are, of course, entitled?"

"Yes, Mr. Commissar."

"I note then that you were away another week—taking a week of your holiday, I presume?"

"Yes, Mr. Commissar."

"That is good," said the Commissar, making a couple of ticks in his note book. "I note then that you were away another week. I presume you were seeking to change your job to something more to your liking, as, of course, is your right?"

"Yes, Mr. Commissar."

"The next week is somewhat unusual, but I have no doubt that you were still trying to find suitable employment?"

"Yes, Mr. Commissar."

"Mr. Smith, I would advise that you find a job immediately—otherwise we shall find one for you. Good day, Mr. Smith."

We didn't know whether to be more amused by the story or by our guide's willingness to tell it to us.

Education, including higher education, is free. This statement again has to be qualified by the observation that the intake of students is determined by the state. So, to a large extent, is where they work on graduation. How far one can go in one generation under this sytem was illustrated by a charming young woman we met at Moscow University, just finishing a Ph.D. in chemistry. We were astonished to find that her parents had been nomads in central Asia, and that she had been born in a felt tent. Incidentally, most women work, many of them in the professions. For example, a far bigger number of doctors and engineers are women than in Canada.

We took Darla, the Ph.D. candidate, and a girl friend of hers, Tatiana, to Zagorsk, a monastery town about sixty miles outside Moscow. On the way we passed through a number of small towns and villages, all quite rural and countrified, with some of the old folk sunning themselves on benches outside their houses. Zagorsk is a monastery town with several magnificent cathedrals in an area surrounded by high walls, which must be the remains of an ancient fortification, I suppose. The cathedrals had the usual painted roofs and golden Asian domes. In one of the cathedrals a service was going on, so we pushed our way in. It was crowded with masses of standing people, mostly the very old or the very young. The music and the singing were magnificent and most moving. I must admit that as I stood there, tears came down my cheeks "and my heart was troubled."

Altogether, we enjoyed our five-week stay in Russia, and we found the Russian people we met to be very likeable. Just the same we were glad to go back to Saskatoon when the time came to return home.

Our third visit to Russia took place in September of 1969, the purpose of the visit being to attend the Mendeleeff celebrations as an official Canadian delegate. In 1869, the famous Russian chemist Mendeleeff enunciated his periodic law of the elements, and in celebration of this outstanding achievement a number of meetings and conferences were held. The main Russian celebration occurred in Leningrad, September 23 to 26, with approximately twenty-two hundred chemists present, mainly from the Soviet Union, but with a fair representation from the Western countries. There was a succession of scientific meetings, receptions, concerts, and tours. Tours were arranged to places of interest in the city of Leningrad and its surroundings. Many of the historical structures were badly damaged in World War II, but they have since been painstakingly restored. The public seems to be all in favor of these restorations, even though the cost has been immense and though most of the palaces obviously date from the czarist regime. Leningrad is by any standards a beautiful and fascinating city. We were provided with interpreters and guides. Among particularly pleasant memories are the ballet *Corsair*, the opera *Rigoletto*, and a visit to the circus. The conference was well organized and the hospitality overwhelming.

After a week of entertainment we thought we should try to repay our guides in some small way, so we asked one of them to get tickets for us to take them to the opera. On arriving at the theatre we were taken to a side door and ushered into a sumptuously decorated lounge which led on to a private box. The students explained that they had not been able to get seats all in a row, and that this was just as cheap anyhow. The opera was a delight, and when we went back to the lounge at the intermission there was a veritable feast of fruit, cakes, and wine, all beautifully served almost as in czarist times. I have to admit that we have never met such hospitality anywhere else.

On the return journey home, Mary and I stayed a day in Moscow and had the pleasure of dining with Academician Semenoff, then seventy-four but still very lively, and with his charming wife. As we met, his wife took hold of Mary by the arms and gave her a hug and a big kiss. Mary was always a favorite with Madame Semenova. Then she came and took hold of me, looked me over carefully, and gave me a couple of kisses, one on each cheek.

"With your little Mary, it was love at first sight," and then, after a pause, "but with you, it took a little longer!"

In 1978 Mary and I revisited the U.S.S.R. in company with Dr. R. J. Woods of the University of Saskatchewan. The visit was part of an exchange scheme between the N.R.C. and the Soviet Academy of Science, and it took us to Moscow, Tblisi, and Riga, where we met scientists interested in industrial radiation chemistry. As before we were royally treated, especially in Tblisi, where our hosts took us to various parts of Georgia. We were impressed by the obvious improvement in the standard of living since our previous visit. Streets were crowded with compact cars, people were well dressed and happy, and the atmosphere was very lively— things seemed to be on the move. Again we visited a number of private homes and we were pleasantly entertained. And we had the good fortune to get to the ballet, the opera, and the circus in Moscow.

We were particularly impressed by the way Riga had got on its feet again after the massive destruction and slaughter of World War II. The Latvians seem to have an endless capacity for survival and regrowth, and they have worked out a modus vivendi in relation to the rest of the U.S.S.R. One curious remark that we heard was that the terrible excesses of World War II had made them realise with full force how much they had been oppressed in the previous centuries. We on our part felt more and more deeply how lucky we were to live in Canada which has so far been spared the horrors of a holocaust and the excesses of a tyrannical dictatorship.

LOYAUTE ME OBLIGE

Top left: The house of the Spinks grandparents in Methwold. *(Photo courtesy the author)*.

Top right: The coat of arms of Thetford Grammar School. *(Photo courtesy the school)*.

Bottom: Thetford Grammar School; the old and new in the school's buildings. *(Photo courtesy the school)*.

Top: The Rev. Mr. Green often took John Spinks on archeological expeditions such as this one to Grimes Graves where flint was mined for the production of implements. *(Daily Mirror, London).*

Above left: Professor A. J. Allmand of King's College, London University, recognized John Spinks's talent and encouraged him to study further. *(Photo courtesy King's College archives).*

Above right: King's College, London University. *(Photo courtesy King's College archives).*

Top: An aerial view of the University of Saskatchewan, 1928—two years before John Spinks joined the faculty. *(Reproduced by permission of the University of Saskatchewan).*

Above left: Dr. T. Thorvaldson was Head of the Chemistry Department of the University of Saskatchewan when Dr. Spinks first came to the university. He presented John Spinks with research opportunities and thus helped to develop the young scientist's capabilities.

Above right: Four fishermen on Emma Lake: from left to right, John Spinks, Herman Ferns, Charlie McKay, and Dr. T. Thorvaldson. *(Photo courtesy the author).*

Top left: Dr. C. J. Mackenzie, former Dean of Engineering at the University of Saskatchewan and later president of the National Research Council, who involved John Spinks in his wartime research with the armed forces. *(Photo courtesy the National Research Council).*

Top right: Gerhard Herzberg, former professor of physics at the University of Saskatchewan and later winner of the Nobel Prize for chemistry. Dr. Spinks worked with Dr. Herzberg in Germany and later persuaded the president of the university to offer Herzberg the position in Physics. *(Photo courtesy the National Research Council).*

Above: The Commando: A Liberator aircraft in which John Spinks crossed the Atlantic in World War II. Winston Churchill often used this plane. *(Public Archives of Canada).*

Top left: Dr. Spinks's research had a great impact on agriculture around the world, particularly in his own prairie region. *(By permission of the Saskatchewan Wheat Pool: Photo by Gibson Photos, Saskatoon).*

Bottom left: Dr. Spinks's expertise in the use of radioactive tracers assisted scientists in other disciplines in developing equipment such as this Rube Goldberg original equipment for following an insect tagged with radioactive material. *(Photograph courtesy the author).*

Right: A radioautograph or self-portrait of some blades of wheat. By tagging substances with radioactivity, Dr. Spinks was able to assist agriculturalists in determining the exact nutrient uptake of plants. *(Photo courtesy the author).*

Top: The Canadian delegation to the Atoms for Peace conference at Geneva in 1955: Dr. Spinks, fourth from the right in this photograph, was a delegate to many such conferences. *(Photo courtesy Atomic Energy of Canada).*

Bottom: Ambassador Sol Rae and Mrs. Rae with Mary and John Spinks at Geneva in 1963 when John Spinks headed the U.N.C.S.T.A.D. delegation from Canada. *(Public Archives of Canada).*

President W. P. Thompson and his successor, John Spinks, at the installation ceremony, 1959. *(By permission of the university Alumni Association).*

Top left: The president's house at the University of Saskatchewan. *(Photo by Gibson Photos, Saskatoon).*

Top right: The coat of arms of the University of Saskatchewan. *(By permission of the university).*

Above: Dr. Spinks walking home down the blue spruce road leading to the president's house.

Top: The Wascana Group, overseers of the early development of the Wascana Project, in 1961: left to right: John Spinks, the Hon. A. E. Blakeney, Dr. E. C. Leslie, Mr. M. Yamasaki, and Dr. W. A. Riddell, first principal of the Regina Campus. *(By permission of the University of Saskatchewan).*

Bottom: Recipients of the Order of Canada, John Spinks and Frances Hyland, with Mrs. Spinks at Government House in 1971. *(Photo by Mike Kerr Photography, Ottawa).*

Top: The University of Regina campus.

Bottom: An aerial view of the University of Saskatchewan campus in 1972, three years before John Spinks's retirement. *(Photo courtesy of Gibson Photos).*

Overleaf:

Top: The Saskatchewan Institute of Pedology (Soil Science) recognized Dr. Spinks's valuable contributions to agricultural research with this award, presented in 1975. From left to right: Dr. J. E. R. Greenshields, Dr. Spinks, and Dr. D. A. Rennie. *(Photo courtesy the author).*

Bottom: John Spinks in front of the Thorvaldson Building, 1975. *(Photo by permission of the Star Phoenix).*

Chapter 18

Poland, Jamaica, and Geneva

During 1962–63 Mary and I were away on three rather extensive trips. The first was to Poland as part of a three-man team sent by the National Research Council to arrange an exchange of students between Canada and Poland at the postdoctoral level. The second was to Jamaica as part of a committee to review the three-year program and budget of the University of the West Indies, and the third was to Geneva where I was head of the Canadian delegation to a United Nations conference on scientific and technical aid to the developing countries. Looking back on the experience after the trips were over, I thought that on the whole it had been good for me and, I hoped, indirectly good for the university. When I was asked whether I would have agreed to three such strenuous trips had the invitations arrived at the same time, I replied: "Probably not, but as each one came up at rather short notice, it seemed important to say yes, if at all possible, and in each case the Board felt that I should accept."

After the visit to Poland short visits were made to the Universities of Bonn, Hamburg and West Berlin in West Germany. The universities seemed to be well equipped, and they were crowded with students. Massive support for research was evident; for example, at Hamburg University, a bevatron in course of construction had already cost over a hundred and thirty million marks (thirty-five million dollars) and the remark was made, "Now they've committed themselves to this much, they can't very well refuse to give us what else we need." These visits to universities in two countries which had suffered immense war damages convinced me that while we have every reason to be proud of our University of Saskatchewan, we have no cause to be complacent, and we shall have to make strenuous efforts to maintain our aim of excellence in higher education facilities.

The Jamaican trip was particularly memorable because shortly before taking off for Jamaica I had been offered the post of president of the National Research Council of Canada, at that time probably the top position open to a scientist in Canada. I thought about it carefully while I was in Jamaica and then regretfully refused the offer. I felt that it would scarcely have been fair to the university's Board of Governors to leave them after only two years as president, when a great many new projects had been started—a good many at my suggestion. My refusal did indicate that "for better or for worse" I had opted for academic administration and policy making rather than for scientific administration and policy making.

In the postwar period, two other job offers were more than usually attractive: one was to go to work on isotopes at the atomic establishment at Harwell, near Oxford, and the other was to go to Ames, Iowa, again to work in an atomic institute. The latter offer came as a result of a visit of Spedding to Saskatoon. Spedding was in charge of an institute at Ames, and he invited me to give some lectures there on isotopes in agriculture. On my return to Saskatoon I received an attractive offer which I turned down. I was enjoying myself where I was. A year or so later I was visiting a lab. in Beltsville, Maryland, and I met a young man whom I had met at Ames. He said that everybody at Ames had been astonished that I had turned down such a generous offer, and he asked how I could resist it. I said that where I came from it was quite cold in the wintertime and that as a result I was slightly cracked. He replied frankly, "Well, that is what we thought!" Out of the mouths of babes . . . .

Actually, I was enjoying my teaching and research and my life generally in Saskatoon. Without my ever lifting a little finger, Dr. Thorvaldson had seen to it that at the right time, the right kind of experience had come my way, and I had a host of friends, many slightly older than I was, who gave generously of their friendship and put up with my idiosyncrasies.

The trip to Geneva started out with an invitation to be part of the Canadian delegation to the U.N. conference on scientific and technical aid to the developing nations, to be held in Geneva in February of 1963. The invitation was received just before Christmas, so I enclosed the plane reservation for Mary in a Christmas card by way of informing her of the prospective journey. A few days before we were supposed to go I was told by an important personage that I was to be head of the delegation. When I suggested that it was perhaps not particularly appropriate for a university president to speak for Canada at such a meeting, I was informed that this had already been decided, and all I had to say was yes or no. So I said yes. On arrival in Geneva I met with the Canadian ambassador, Sol Rae, and discussed strategy with him.

As a general procedure I kept half a dozen draft speeches in my pocket, ready for all occasions, and checked out with both the ambassador and Ottawa. The method worked well. The other members of the delegation were highly competent in their respective fields. I tried not to be too officious as head of the delegation. In fact, even though I say so, things went rather well, helped on the social side by Mary's good social instinct and ability to entertain a group of conference delegates.

Two points were of interest. On any major question the U.S.A. felt bound to disagree in public with the stand taken by Russia and vice versa, although shortly thereafter the protagonists would meet over cocktails and chuckle about their public disagreements. In fact, both they and the other "developed" nations were more or less banded together, as were the "developing" nations. The latter were most anxious to set up a new and separate U.N. agency, whereas the former group felt that matters could be well taken care of by existing agencies.

Each noon hour a group of representatives of the "developed" nations would caucus in one of the corridors of the U.N. building, and as head of the Canadian delegation, I was invited to attend. I did so, usually keeping quite quiet, as befitted my station compared to the top American and Commonwealth brass, such as Ambassador Harriman and Lord Casey. One day, towards the end of the conference, I arrived at the caucus a few minutes late. I apologized for my late arrival and was told that in my absence I had been elected chairman. I protested, but my protests were to no avail. So I took the chair and asked what was the order of business.

"To get through a motion at the plenary session making it clear that one of the existing U.N. agencies will be given the task of implementing any recommendations arising out of the conference and approved by the U.N."

"You realize that if the U.S.S.R. or the U.S.A. brings in such a motion it will certainly be voted down."

"Yes!"

"O.K. Then we must get a highly respected person to address the plenary session and suggest such an idea. Whom do you suggest?"

"U Thant would be ideal, but he is ill."

"Who next?"

"Hoffman."

"Anyone know him well enough to get him to agree?"

I think Harriman agreed to phone him. To cut a long story short, Hoffman agreed, came to Geneva, made an excellent speech, and carried his point with unanimous approval. Thus ended my one incursion into international politics. It gave me an idea of the power of a country like Canada in making acceptable suggestions to an international group.

I should add that someone from Canada, and particularly someone from a relatively new province like Saskatchewan, can make a real contribution to developing countries, since there are still people in Saskatchewan who have been involved at first hand in the development process, for example in setting up research councils, establishing regulations for oil and gas developments, making the initial arrangements to establish research programs, and so forth. Many people in much larger countries have occupied important administrative positions, but they have still not had what one might call the grass-roots experience paralleling that required for a developing country.

Just to give some idea of the size of the conference, there were eighty-three nations, two thousand delegates, eighteen hundred and fifty papers, and ninety-five sessions crowded into two weeks—not to mention a continuous stream of luncheons and receptions which were also important in their own way. Most members of the Canadian delegation were housed in the Hotel de la Paix, a comfortable hotel looking out over Lac Leman. Using their facilities we were able to put on a good Canadian reception and to host a number of small luncheons. As always, Mary was a charming and competent hostess.

We made two other trips of more than usual interest to Israel and France in the latter part of 1963. The first was made in order to visit educational and scientific institutions, and the second was made to attend an O.E.C.D. meeting in Paris. The visit to Israel was made at the invitation of the Israeli government, and it gave us an overview of the universities and scientific institutes in Israel. On the way to these establishments we visited the historic places customarily seen by the usual tourist. Apart from their absorbing intrinsic interest, they form a necessary background to modern developments. The scientific developments showed some parallel to those which have taken place in Saskatchewan (which has similar size of population) in the last forty years.

High spots of the trip were the synagogue at Capharnum on the spot where Jesus preached—I stood there and wept—and the village of Ein Karem, home of John the Baptist, about six miles from Jerusalem—a charming spot with towers and bells, olives, cypresses and hills—the whole village conforming to and blending into the landscape. In retrospect, I was enormously impressed by what had been accomplished in fifteen to sixteen years. It is true the Israelis had received a good deal of outside help, but they had worked under the most difficult circumstances. I felt that we obtained a good overall view of the many and varied developments, and I was most grateful to the Israeli Government for making such a memorable visit possible.

In 1963, the O.E.C.D. (Organization for Economic Cooperation and Development) Committee for Scientific and Technical Personnel made a study of scientific and technical manpower problems in Canada and brought out a document entitled "Training of and demand for high-level scientific and technical personnel in Canada." It touches on such topics as factors influencing the development of higher education, expansion of higher education, development of postgraduate studies, research and development in industry and government, and manpower needs. The report was useful in that it gave us an idea of what outsiders think of Canada when given a chance to look in.

One of the main points to emerge was the French (and European) approach of "planification" or planning, which differs rather radically from most of our planning; for instance the French claimed that in determining the requirement for, say, engineers, they would set up an economic level for the next five, ten, or fifteen years, and then work back to how many engineers are needed at any given time, and from this figure they would determine the needed intake of engineering students in a given year, whereas we calculate how many students are likely to wish to come to university in the fall and take engineering, and then we try to make provision for them by way of buildings and faculty. Indications of job possibilities for our students are left pretty much to student counsellors in high school (who may or may not know what the real demand is) and to news media and similar sources of information. Obviously these are two quite different approaches. Canadian authorities have felt that at our stage of development we could "absorb" all the well-trained people our universities could produce for some time to come. There was also an interesting discussion concerning the relation of science and technology to government and concerning the importance of cultivating a few scientific statesmen.

Chapter 19

Alice in Ceylonland

Mary and I visited Ceylon for about a month at the end of 1969. I was member of a commission set up by the government of Ceylon to inquire into "the existing system of higher education in Ceylon and to make arrangements for the future development of higher education." The other members of the commission were Mr. Wilmot A. Perera and Mr. Alwin A. de Silva, both of Ceylon, together with Dr. Veni Shanker Jha of India, and Sir Brynmor Jones, vice-chancellor of Hull University.

We flew from Saskatoon to London by way of Winnipeg, stopped a few hours in London, and then flew to Colombo with a brief stop at Bahrein. The drive into the city from the airport was fascinating; the road was lined with coconut palms, and small huts, and many little fruit stalls. There seemed to be hundreds of thousands of people, all gaily dressed and looking well-fed and happy. We were taken to the Hotel Taprobane, where we had a huge airy room with a view overlooking the docks, which were crowded with shipping. The room had some air conditioning by huge fans mounted in the ceiling. The whole atmosphere was very much Somerset Maugham. We were thoroughly tired on arrival, and we slept about fifteen hours solidly. Tuesday was a poya day, the equivalent of our Sunday. We were taken by Mr. Kitto of the Canadian High Commissioner's staff to his home for a pre-Christmas party at which we met most of the Commission staff; it was all most enjoyable.

Next morning we breakfasted on delicious fresh pineapple and bananas, with toast and tea, before taking Mary out to a handicraft shop where she bought two lengths of batik cloth. We took the cloth immediately to a nearby shop where a tailor measured Mary and agreed to convert the cloth into dresses. I was greatly taken by the way in which the tailor took the measurements, and the resulting dresses were most attractive and just right for the hot weather.

Next day we started to work in earnest and visited the vice-chancellor of the University of Ceylon in Colombo. We interviewed various members of the faculty and toured labs. and classrooms. The faculty we met were impressive, but the facilities seemed inadequate. Some of the lectures, for example, were given in the grandstand at the race track. The next day was spent in discussions and in meeting people at a house which had been put at our disposal. On the following day, December 20, we visited Vidyodaya University and were involved in a particularly unpleasant incident.

Because of the known opposition of students and faculty groups to some of the members of the commission of enquiry, there had been some suggestion that we should postpone our visit to Vidyodaya until after the students had left for the vacation. However, when the secretary phoned on the nineteenth he was assured that it would be all right to make our visit, and certainly we were not told not to come. When we arrived shortly after nine o'clock in the morning, we were met by the vice-chancellor and taken up to his office, on the second floor of the building, to meet a number of deans and members of the administration. A few students standing around when we arrived greeted us politely when we greeted them. During the morning, a number of students gathered outside and from time to time made a sort of yelping or hooting noise. The vice-chancellor went out once or twice, presumably to see what was going on.

By the time we left at noon, there were about two hundred students standing around, and some of us went forward to speak to them. One or two were quite excited, saying they did not object to the foreign commissioners personally, but that they objected strongly to the local commissioners. I had a lively conversation with the student vice-president and felt that I got along quite well with him. There was a bit of good-natured pushing and shoving, but this was kept under control by the students. When we got into the two cars to leave, a monk tried to close the university gates, and this was the signal for a few unpleasant types to lie down in the path of the cars and for some in the rear of the crowd to throw coconuts and rocks at the cars. This was obviously a prearranged matter; even the photographers were there to record events at the right time. Bottles filled with sand were also used as missiles. Just for the record, it is not pleasant to be sitting in a car surrounded by a crowd that has suddenly turned hostile and is bombarding the car with heavy objects. One of the missiles broke the window in the rear of the car where I was sitting and we were covered with a shower of glass.

Almost immediately I noticed a great deal of blood on my trousers and jacket, and I saw that my left hand was covered in blood. I quickly found that most of the blood was coming from one spot where a vein had been cut at the base of the thumb. The bleeding stopped when I applied pressure to the spot. In the meantime, an administrative assistant had reopened the gate, and our driver seized the opportunity to push through. At some distance from the university we stopped at a Red Cross station and put an antiseptic dressing on my hand. From there we went to a hospital where my hand was cleaned up and I was given an anti-tetanus shot. We left after about an hour, and I am glad to say that the cut and a bruise on the wrist healed quickly. A window had been broken in the second car, and one of the passengers had received a bad cut and a bruise on the elbow which took some time to heal. Altogether, we got off lightly from what could have been an ugly affair.

We heard later that the office of the young man who had opened the gate had been completely wrecked. Luckily he had escaped to a police post just outside the gates. We also heard later that the police officer in charge of the post had inquired several times during the morning whether he might be needed and had been told not to come on the campus until he was asked. He could have been there with his men in a matter of seconds and I can't help feeling that somebody was to blame in not calling the police when the situation started to worsen. The public reaction, as expressed by the prime minister, the government and the opposition, the press, and numerous university people from vice-chancellors down was uniformly most sympathetic to us, and all were incensed that the traditional reputation of the Ceylonese for friendliness had been damaged.

After a careful assessment of the incident by the commission itself and by our High Commissioner, it was agreed that it would be advisable to continue with the work of the commission but to take additional precautions to avoid further incidents which might be forthcoming if the whole thing were part of a larger plan. It was agreed to move the commission's office downtown from the rather exposed building where it had been set up. We met in rooms in the hotel from then on, apart from visits to universities and other outside places of interest.

Next day we got down to business, using a room at the hotel for meeting purposes. Later in the day, Dr. Mendes, who had studied limnobiology at Saskatoon, took us out to Mt. Lavinia, a lovely resort spot a few miles outside Colombo. There were huge breakers coming in from the sea and graceful palms—just like a picture postcard. We finished the day at a beautiful carol service in Christ Church, which is a hundred and fifty years old.

Monday was spent discussing admission policies. We then went out to dinner at Mr. Perera's estate, about twenty miles from Colombo. The house was set on top of a hill in the middle of a rubber plantation. Darkness came with the usual tropical suddenness, and to our delight the garden was seemingly filled with fireflies. Mr. Perera had been ambassador to Pekin for a time, and he lived in a quiet but cultivated style, with magazines, papers, and books from all over, and coffee from gorgeous jade cups. Next day was a holiday—poya day, so Derrick Aluvehara took us to the zoo. It was outdoors, and it was the most beautiful zoo I have ever seen—well treed and watered, and stocked with all kinds of animals—zebras, elephants, rhino, bears—all in perfect condition.

In preparation for Christmas Mary picked up a beautiful bouquet of flowers, all for about a dollar. She used a potted plant for a Christmas tree and decorated it with some decorations which she found in a nearby store. It was rather different from the usual fir tree, but it still conveyed the right atmosphere. On Christmas Day we had breakfast with the Seymours and their children, who had a lovely time opening parcels. Parcels were also given to the children of the various members of the personal staff. It was a delight to see all the children playing together and enjoying simple things. Children's Christmas presents were almost nonexistent in the shops, but Mary had managed to find some pretty paper parasols in a store near our hotel, and she had wrapped them up as presents. When these particular parcels were opened there were squeals of delight, and the two girls immediately draped themselves in little saris and pirouetted with the parasols. In the evening we had dinner with the Canadian High Commissioner and his charming wife and their guests and had turkey and all the trimmings. The dinner was a pleasant ending to a lovely day, even though the temperature was ninety above instead of the usual twenty or thirty below in Saskatoon.

On the twentieth the commissioners met and sketched out a plan, including a list of major topics and a series of headings appropriate to each topic—a skeleton of a report without filling in the meat, if you like. Later in the day we had tea with the Pereras at Panadura, where they had a huge open house in spacious grounds leading down to the ocean. The setting was a perfect sandy beach with coconut palms and huge breakers rolling in from the Indian Ocean. The fifteen-mile drive gave an impression of endless humanity, of large houses, small shacks, endless small stores, piles of orange-colored coconuts, cows, bicycles, and buses, honking cars, pretty girls in school uniforms, and old people who looked poor.

Each day the commission continued with its work, and eventually a large number of people were seen, either at our request or at their request, from all levels of the university and from various sectors of the public. Seven major topics were recognized:

1. resources and enrolment policy
2. design for higher education in Ceylon
3. standards, methods of teaching and examining, and media of instruction
4. faculty problems
5. student problems
6. governance of universities
7. regional and international aspects.

Local working groups were set up, and each topic was further elaborated on. As a final step, joint meetings of a number of the working groups were held with the members of the commission. The local members of the working group were asked to hold further meetings which we hoped would lead to the production of the working papers that would form the framework of a report. While the faculty associations and students had declared that they would not cooperate with the commission (they objected to the members from Ceylon and to the failure to consult them about the commission), a number of faculty and students did express their personal opinions to the commission.

Eventually we visited the campuses at Vidyalankara and at Kandy, the ancient capital. Both sites were attractive, and members of the faculty seemed able. There were fine engineering labs. at Peredeniya but there was a lack of modern equipment. Kandy is a beautiful spot with small lakes and mountains, lush vegetation, and masses of gorgeous flowering trees and shrubs. The vice-chancellor was housed in a beautiful lodge. Not long before, the students had been on the rampage and had smashed the windows and wrecked the lower floor of the lodge, but luckily the police had arrived in time to rescue the vice-chancellor and his wife. We had lunch at a chalet, high above a small lake. On the way up to the chalet, on a winding road, we passed another car coming down and recognized J. B. Priestley and his wife. We were told that a number of writers spend part of the year in Ceylon. The road leading up to Kandy from Colombo was fascinating. We passed elephants, water buffalo, plantations of rubber and tea, and numerous paddy fields—all a rich green.

Another day we visited a tea plantation owned by Perera's son-in-law. The garden surrounding the house was a riot of flowers and fruits— banana, pawpaw, breadfruit, and so on. On still another day Mrs. Seymour took us to breakfast with Sir John Kotelawala, former Prime Minister of Ceylon, at his home near the local airport. We were there shortly before eight and watched as Sir John's car came roaring up to the front of the house and Sir John stepped smartly out, fresh from a dip in the sea.

Then followed an amazing ritual. First of all two pet elephants came forward to be fed stale bread, topped off with a bouquet of what looked like irises. It was fascinating to see with what grace the elephants took the proffered bunch of flowers and popped them in their mouths. Then we all walked around the grounds near the house while Sir John fed a variety of birds and animals, ducks, geese, peacocks, and fish. Behind him strode a man with a gun at the ready, in case a cheeky crow or other uninvited bird should try to horn in on any of Sir John's bounty. Eventually we came to a fair-sized aquarium containing a huge fish. It weighed twenty pounds at least, I would say. It eyed us with ill-concealed disdain, but when Sir John dropped in a banana it altered the angle of its head just enough for the banana to slide into its mouth. It looked for all the world like Winston Churchill swallowing a cigar.

By eight o'clock we were back at the house, where we had a sumptuous breakfast at a long table with various other members of the family. We were served many fruits, rice dishes, eggs, marmalade, and jams, and all the time

Sir John kept up a keenly intelligent conversation on all manner of things. In no time at all he had established points of common interest which he pursued with considerable skill. He was altogether an extremely impressive person. I have deliberately made this a rather disjointed account of the visit to Ceylon since confusion is the impression that we got: a country of great beauty and fabulous history, of teeming peoples and great contrasts in wealth, of warm likeable people with sunny smiles, and of a group that is intensely dissatisfied and ready for revolution.

At the end of the month it was agreed that Dr. Jha would stay in Ceylon to get the working groups going and that the Commission would reconvene about two months later to review progress and, if possible, proceed with the writing of a report. As a matter of history, before we could reconvene an election had been called. In June the government was toppled and Madame Banderanaike became prime minister. The commission was dissolved shortly thereafter and so it did not write a final report. It would appear, however, that the work done was not lost, and in fact the University of Ceylon has now been established, embracing the four original campuses and the Ceylon College of Technology. The change of government did not entirely satisfy the radicals, who staged an abortive coup in June of 1971 when some fifteen hundred people were killed and many thousands were arrested. Many students were sent to work camps to see the error of their ways.

Ceylon is now called Sri Lanka. It was unfortunate that the commission was set up at such a troublous time and apparently without much prior discussion with the official bodies representing faculty and students. The National Council for Higher Education and the Higher Education Act of 1966 were thoroughly disliked by the whole university community, and there had been a great deal of unrest involving violent confrontations, some incidents having occurred just a few months before our visit. Student groups were organized along political lines, and the student leaders at that time were extremely left wing and militant.

Another basic problem was the mismatch between higher education and the current needs of the country. As a developing country Ceylon can use large numbers of well-educated people, but it needs people educated in special fields. In these fields the graduates are in strong demand, but when we were there, there were fourteen thousand unemployed B.A.'s whose university training had not improved their job prospects appreciably. They formed a disgruntled and frustrated group as a consequence of their unrealized expectations. On inquiring we found that they all had the same three subjects: Buddhist philosophy, Ceylonese history, and Ceylonese geography.

There was an obvious reason for their choice of subjects. Shortly after Ceylon gained its independence after World War II, there was a reaction against the use of English, and its compulsory role in the high school was discontinued. Five or six years later the high school graduates no longer had English as a working language, and so they could take only subjects for which there were books in Ceylonese in the library: Buddhist philosophy, Ceylonese history, and Ceylonese geography. Practically all the chemistry books in the library were in English, with only a couple of elementary texts translated into Ceylonese. So while Ceylon needs well-trained professionals in all areas, it produces very few, and there is no market for much of what it does produce. This ironic situation points up in a dramatic way the need to match university output with manpower requirements as the French do. In Canada, we try to do this matching for the major professions, but we do it scarcely at all in the fields of arts and science. This failure could be serious when one remembers the large number of students in arts and science courses.

All in all, the visit to Ceylon reminded me vividly of *Alice in Wonderland*: everything was delightful, exciting, distressing, and frustrating. I'd love to take a second look into the Ceylonese looking glass; it is most revealing, since everything there points up in sharp relief, almost to the reductio ad absurdum stage, what troubles universities all over the world. Looked at from this point of view, the visit to Ceylon was by no means a waste of time for me.

On the way back from Ceylon to Canada we took a side trip to New Delhi to attend a vice-chancellors' meeting arranged by the Association of Commonwealth Universities. Apart from the value of the meeting itself, it did give us an opportunity to see at least one little bit of India, with its incredible millions and its terrible poverty. My niece Phyllis, the daughter of my sister Florence, came to visit us in New Delhi. She was teaching in a school for blind children, a hundred miles or so from New Delhi, in a true labor of love for which I greatly admired her. And naturally we spent a day visiting the Taj Mahal, which was just as beautiful as it is reported to be, but much bigger than we expected. On the way to Agra we passed through many small villages, all looking much poorer than their counterparts in Ceylon.

On the way back to Canada we stayed a day or so in Bangkok and saw the sights, including the Grand Palace, various Bhuddas, large and small, and some very precious—one of solid gold—six tons of it! We were particularly taken by the Floating Gardens and by the many homes on stilts along the canals. We stayed a day or so in Hong Kong and a couple of days in Tokyo. The highlight there was a visit with Father Fortin, who teaches Canadian studies at St. Sophia University, a stone's throw from the Hotel Otani, where we stayed. He gave us a graphic description of the troubles they had had with a handful of militant radical students who had completely wrecked a new residence in a matter of minutes. He took us to a very fine Japanese lunch, tempura style, which we enjoyed immensely.

And a day later we were back home in our own little beds and glad to be there. The trip had, however, been most instructive and worthwhile. Even nearly getting killed is all right too, provided it stays at the "nearly" stage.

Chapter 20

Northern Lights

My first extensive northern tour was in July of 1958 when I had the pleasure of accompanying Group Captain Carpenter on an inspection tour of R.C.A.F. facilities in Northern Canada. As I recollect, I joined the group in Ottawa. We flew first to Churchill, where we were outfitted with suitable clothing and given some background information about travel in the North. From there we travelled to Resolute by North Star. At Resolute there was an air strip and weather station and a small Eskimo village on the coast a few miles away. When we arrived on July 1, the temperature was zero Fahrenheit, and everything was still frozen up, including the sea. The sun shone twenty-four hours a day.

On the second day we were there I was taken by snowmobile to the Eskimo "village" which consisted at the time of five or six igloos. I was invited into one of them by the occupant. She was most friendly, but as her knowledge of English was zero and my knowledge of Eskimo was equally limited, conversation was difficult. The entrance to the igloo was through a passageway built of blocks of snow. It was cluttered with various pieces of equipment and with chunks of meat, all of which were frozen hard, of course. The roof of the igloo was too low for me to stand erect; the clearance was about five and a half feet, I should think. One part of the igloo was separated from the rest by a partition made of caribou skins. There was a ledge of ice about a foot from the ground, running around the inside wall of the igloo. This ledge was covered with skins so that it could serve as a seat.

After a minute or so the young woman, who was just over thirty but looked more than twice that age, brought out a small book and pointed to one of the pages. It was in syllabics. Then she sang a hymn to the familiar tune of "There is a Green Hill Far Away," slightly off key. I stood there stooped and weeping—my eyes still fill with tears as I think of it. I heard later that she had had ten children, two of whom were living. When one realizes that these courageous people housed in igloos live and move and have their being at a temperature below freezing point for the greater part of the year, to say that they could like their living conditions must be a slight exaggeration. Fortunately now most of them are at least in prefabs., except when they are out on the trail. Before I left the igloo I was given a mug of tea as a gesture of hospitality.

Outside the igloo half a dozen small children were playing, bundled up in fur parkas against the cold. When I appeared they clustered in front of me in a stooped position, digging at a small hollow in the ice with pieces of bone. Every now and again they would look up at me and laugh. Suddenly they all threw down their pieces of bone, ran around the igloo several times, and then settled down to digging and laughing again. Somehow I had the impression that they were having fun with me, but I couldn't quite fathom how.

Later in the morning, two Eskimos took me on a polar bear hunt using a komatik or large wooden sled, pulled by a dozen Husky dogs on a fantrace. The lead man saw after the dogs, encouraging them at intervals with a long whip. The other Eskimo and I sat on the back of the sledge and jumped off now and then to help the sled over patches of broken ice. The surface of the ice was covered with coarse snow, almost like granulated sugar. After a time one of the Eskimos said, "Stop!" and I said, "Stop." "Eat!" he said, and I said "Eat." So we stopped the sled and made tea, using ice chiselled up from the surface ice, which was free from salt, and heating it in a pot on a small oil heater brought along in a box at the back of the sled. I had carefully brought along my own thermos of tea and some sandwiches, since I didn't particularly look forward to a meal of seal meat. Then off we went back to the village, having seen nothing more than a white fox. There were frozen polar bear carcasses lodged on the top of a wooden framework, out of reach of the dogs, close by the igloos, and eventually I took a skin back with me to Saskatoon.

We heard later of two Eskimos who had been out hunting shortly before and had seen a bear near some pack ice. The dogs were loosed to circle the bear, and one of the Eskimos walked towards the bear and shot it. In the meantime the other Eskimo was making the usual tea, when out of the corner of his eye he saw another bear, which had been hidden in the pack ice, coming for him. He stooped to pick up his rifle from the sled, allowing the bear to reach him. The bear took a swipe at him and took off half of his sit-upon. The other Eskimo came and rescued his friend, who was flown to Churchill and lived to tell the tale. For my part, I was glad that we had not had any close encounter with a bear, friendly or not!

From Resolute we went north over Ellesmere Island to see some open water. A glacier fed into this open water, and every now and again a huge piece of an ice cliff would break off to form an iceberg. I was glad when we turned south again and were once more over the mainland. We landed at Inuvik on the MacKenzie Delta after seeing a number of pingoes or ice hills. From Inuvik we took a side trip to Aklavik, an old settlement which was also on the MacKenzie Delta. I met a good many Eskimos and Indians there and went into the Anglican Cathedral, a log structure with small stained-glass windows and a fine altar painting, "Our Lady of the Snows." It was the birth of Christ in a northern setting, with the babe wrapped in skins.

From Inuvik we went to Whitehorse on the Yukon, up to Dawson for a look at the gold-mining town of fabled history, on to Yellowknife, after flying over the spectacular falls on the Nahanni, and then to Edmonton and back to Saskatoon.

At the end of August, 1967, I had the pleasure of taking a further eight-day, eight-thousand-mile air tour of the North which took me six hundred miles into the Arctic Circle and included visits to Eskimo communities, DEW Line installations, research laboratories, and major mining operations. Some forty people made the tour as guests of Arthur Laing, Canada's Minister of Indian Affairs and Northern Development. They included representatives of business and industry, university person-nel, journalists, and government officials.

The first point to make is that since I had last visited northern Canada about a decade earlier, great developments had taken place. I should mention in particular open-pit mining operations, the exploration for minerals and oil, the provision of access roads and railways, greatly improved housing, and better educational facilities. Everywhere we went I met graduates of the University of Saskatchewan in such fields as geology, engineering, and education.

The tour started from Ottawa and included stops at Churchill, Resolute, Cambridge Bay, Tuktuk, Inuvik, Whitehorse, Dawson, and Yellowknife, with side trips arranged to other centres and points of interest. At Churchill the touring party visited the rocket range where rockets instrumented at the University of Saskatchewan have been sent aloft in studies of the upper atmosphere. On the way to Resolute, the northernmost point on the trip, the plane flew over Rankin Inlet, where the Institute for Northern Studies at the university had opened an arctic research and training centre under Professor Williamson's general direction. A class in Eskimo anthropology was given in the same summer of 1967.

Resolute, on Cornwallis Island, was the coldest point on the trip, the temperature having dropped to minus thirty-two degrees Fahrenheit, with a strong wind blowing. The touring party inspected an arctic weather station and visited an Eskimo community of more than a hundred. The community was served by a good school and was in striking contrast to the primitive community of eight or ten years earlier.

At Cambridge Bay the group saw the remains of the partially submerged *Maud*, the ship in which the explorer Amundsen made his famous drift through the Northwest Passage. Cambridge Bay has a DEW Line installation, a weather station, and an Eskimo village well served by schools, churches and recreational facilities.

At Inuvik, I was impressed by the excellent facilities, which include a large residential school, a one hundred bed hospital, and a research laboratory to serve the community and visiting scientists. Opened in 1964 to stimulate arctic studies, it is Canada's first permanent scientific research laboratory north of the Arctic Circle. From Inuvik, I made a side trip to Aklavik, which is still a healthy looking village with good trapping and hunting, although it was to have been phased out in favor of Inuvik.

I visited two open-pit mines during the northern trip. The first, at Whitehorse, was the New Imperial Mine, where copper is recovered and an ore concentrator is working at full capacity. The second, near Yellowknife, was the Pine Point operation, where one of the world's largest deposits of lead-zinc ore is located. A recently constructed concentrator treats five thousand tons of ore a day.

Altogether, I got the impression that enormous strides had been taken in the last decade but that much remained to be done. In particular, I felt that a massive attack needed to be mounted if the necessary research and development was to be accomplished, and furthermore, I felt that our university, with its related interests in the north of this province, had a major role to play in doing some of the pure and applied research.

In July of 1971 I visited Rankin Inlet on the west shore of Hudson Bay, where there is a sizeable Eskimo village and where the university had established an arctic research station under the direction of Professor Bob Williamson. At this time of the year the only access is by plane, first to Churchill via one of the usual airlines and then by a lighter plane, usually a DC3, which can land on the rough airstrip just outside the settlement of Rankin Inlet. The usual airport facilities are completely absent, so when the plane arrives it circles the settlement once or twice, lands, discharges people and cargo, picks up more people and cargo,and is off to its next stop, which may be up to Baker Lake or back to Churchill. If the plane is already full, and it usually is, passengers may have some trouble in getting on and may have to wait two or three days for the next flight.

On this occasion the reason for my visit was partly to take a look at the university facilities at Rankin and partly to attend a meeting of a small advisory committee which was considering the expansion of those facilities. At the beginning of July it was light twenty-four hours a day but a bit on the cool side. There was still a good deal of ice on the Hudson Bay and some of this, which had drifted inshore, tended to keep the air cool. Just at Rankin Inlet the terrain was rocky and rather rugged, but the country immediately surrounding the settlement was mainly flat tundra, with hummocks of grass and other sparse vegetation interspersed with boggy, wet, or damp patches. While I was there, a professor and his graduate student were studying the nesting habits of the Old Squaw duck, just a few miles away across the tundra. It was extremely handy for them to use our lab. as a base of operation.

Most of the Eskimos lived in prefabs. and did a good deal of art work: carvings in soapstone, handmade pottery, and beautifully decorated clothing such as parkas, mukluks and other garments. The prefabs. were connected by one or two meandering "roads," along which the proud possessor of a Honda motor bike was liable to tear at all hours of the day and night. The pay-off was to see this young Eskimo return in triumph from the tundra on his motor bike, with his rifle and half a freshly killed caribou slung across his back.

At the moment it is difficult to foresee what will happen to such a settlement. The people are charming and resourceful, but when taken away from their usual way of life, the members of the settlement are dependent on the government for about half their income. How to help them become self-supporting and more in charge of their own futures is a real problem.

In the meantime there is much that universities can do by way of researches related to almost anything: linguistics, literature, transportation, geology, geography, meteorology, communications, economics, history, and so forth. Eskimo concerns are truly a virgin field, except for sociology, an area in which the indigenous peoples have been researched almost to death. At one time it was said that the typical family unit consisted of father, mother, two children, a grandparent, and a sociologist.

This university laboratory at Rankin Inlet fits in well with the university interest in Indians and Metis, and it happens to fill a real national need when the federal government is grappling with the problem of what to do about the indigenous peoples. Bob Williamson, the former director of the lab., was a member of the N.W.T. Council for some years, as was President Barber of the University of Regina, who was formerly a member of the University of Saskatchewan faculty. This previous experience adds to the value of both men as members of the university community, and their university connection makes them valuable as consultants to the government. So having a laboratory eight or nine hundred miles away from the main campus is not as ridiculous as it might seem at first sight.

The whole art of the modern university is to have a feel for what will be important five, ten, or twenty years in the future. It is important then for the university to have key people or groups of people on its faculty who cover not only the usual areas of knowledge but who are exploring new areas of knowledge which may be of use in the future.

Chapter 21

Decade of Change: 1959-69

The University of Saskatchewan was founded in 1907 and began classes in 1909 with seventy students. Fifty years later there were some forty-six hundred students in attendance, and projections indicated that this number would increase rapidly. After a long and careful discussion of student population forecasts and of the desirable size of a campus, it was decided to start a second campus in Regina. The general principle was accepted that a modern university needs to be large enough to justify its having a faculty of sufficient size to give general coverage of all the major fields of knowledge. For a prairie university this implies a faculty of about seven hundred and a student body of about ten thousand. It was thought that once this critical size was reached, or was about to be reached, the province would be better served by creating a second campus rather than by allowing the original campus to expand indefinitely.

The concept of two autonomous academic groups was thus established, but it brought with it a new problem, that of the coordination of the activities of two institutions of higher learning which were supported from the same public fund. This problem, while new for Saskatchewan, has been met before and has been solved in various ways and with differing degrees of success in different parts of the world. Great Britain has had its Universities Grants Commission for many years; Manitoba has a commission; Alberta had a commission until 1974, when its commission was disbanded; and Ontario had its University Affairs Committee, which has now been replaced by a council of the universities of Ontario.

An alternative form of coordination is to have the activities of the separate campuses coordinated through what has been discribed as an "umbrella" university, which has well-defined fiscal and academic powers of a coordinating nature but no students or professors. This umbrella university provides liaison between the campuses and the government and preserves a maximum degree of autonomy for each of the constituent universities. It forms the common pattern of overall university governance in the United States of America, where it has been reasonably satisfactory and successful. What one needs is collective autonomy of independent corporations, which retain freedom of diversity among themselves but which present a common front on vital matters. In technical terms, such a collective autonomy uses a "systems approach"—a logically sound method. Like other systems, however, it depends on people for its successful operation. Any system will operate given good will and good people; even the best system will not work in the absence of good will or reasonably good people.

In 1959, then, the decision was taken to expand the university in Regina. The decision was taken by the University of Saskatchewan in Saskatoon, and it was agreed to by the provincial government. I inherited this decision and went on to implement it to the best of my ability. The concept envisaged the creation of an institution at Regina serving about five thousand students in the first instance, and eventually growing to eight to ten thousand. A site of about three hundred and thirty acres was secured on the southeast limits of the city of Regina, and a master plan for development of the site was prepared by Minoru Yamasaki, a noted American architect-planner.

The first buildings on the new campus were occupied in the fall of 1965, and buildings have been erected at a rapid pace since then. Initially there was much overcrowding and a lack of non-academic facilities, but by 1977 the campus had become slightly overbuilt, there being accommodation for about five thousand but an actual student body of less than four thousand. There is a fine physical education building, an elegant library, a good administration-humanities building, a student residence building, College West, and a number of others.

Academic developments in Regina have paced the physical developments; first came a College of Arts and Science, then the Colleges of Education, Business Administration, Graduate Studies, and Engineering. Federated colleges, Campion and Luther, were also added. In 1964, the Faculty Council at Regina was brought into being with full powers. Dr. Riddell, who had been dean of arts and science, had been appointed the first principal in 1962. Dr. Begg was appointed to the corresponding position of principal of the Saskatoon campus in 1967.

Gradually, the Regina Campus acquired an autonomy the equal of any other university, although the faculty in Regina would have questioned this claim. Many of them felt that the older sister university in Saskatoon exerted an undue influence in the overall Board of Governors and in the University Senate, although in fact, the Regina Campus was well treated financially—the Saskatoon campus was quite sure that Regina was too well treated.

Operating and capital expenditures increased enormously in the sixties: 1959–60 operational expenses were 8.63 million dollars, plus capital expenditures of 3.08 million, for a total of 11.7 million dollars; 1969–70 operational expenses had gone up to 46.68 million, plus capital expenditures of 12.61 for a total of 59.29 million. In the same period, full-time student enrollment had increased from 4,639 (1959–60) to 14,575 (1969–70). These additional funds were not obtained without a good deal of extra effort on the part of the Board and the Administration, something which is apt to be forgotten by those not directly concerned in the process.

In the case of capital grants, Premier Douglas agreed in 1959 to provide matching funds if the university would go on a fund-raising campaign. Two and a half million dollars was the amount set as the target, and the amount was realized. This initial success in fund raising served to raise the sights. Over the five-year period from 1959 to 1964, the rate of capital spending had been increased threefold, from about two million dollars a year to about six million a year. In 1967 a review of building requirements for the 1967–74 period indicated that a still higher rate of capital spending would be required. After a number of discussions, Premier Thatcher agreed to raise the government contribution to about 12.5 million dollars per year, provided the university would go on another fund-raising campaign.

The university raised about eight million dollars, a good deal less than had been hoped for, but still quite a substantial amount, and the government kept to its promise by providing somewhat over fifty million dollars in the four-year period. Persuading the government to raise the ante to this extent was not achieved without a good deal of hard bargaining, and there is no doubt that the continuous requesting of more and more money from the government served to erode the once ideal relations between university and government. No one likes to be put in the position of always being asked for more and more money year after year after year, particularly when it means diverting some funds from other pressing public demands. So inevitably the president, who has to bear the brunt of the attack, becomes less and less welcome. Naturally one tries to offset this deterioration of relations by making oneself, or rather one's institution, more and more indispensable, but there is a limit to the government's dependence on the university, and the store of good will is gradually eroded.

I must say, and I think I can say it with all honesty, that the relations between government and university in the 1959–69 period were excellent with both the C.C.F. and the Liberal governments. I trusted these governments, and I think that they trusted me. The situation was helped by a series of excellent and sympathetic ministers of education and by a number of excellent appointments to the university's Board of Governors. There was no doubt too that the university had the full confidence of the people of the province, who rightly regarded it as their university.

The full story of the enormous expansion in the sixties and the development in depth of a viable university system dedicated to satisfying the higher educational needs of the people of Saskatchewan is told in detail in *Decade of Change.* The story of the growth of the Regina Campus is related in a book by Dr. Riddell, *The First Decade.* A brief history of the university since its foundation is reproduced at the end of this book as Appendix B. It was a wonderful period in which to be associated with an academic institution, and I shall always be grateful to the Board of Governors of the university for appointing me president at that particular time and to the people of Saskatchewan for their support of the university in the sixties.

I am deeply indebted to a series of Chancellors, Dr. Auld, Dr. Culliton, and the Hon. John Diefenbaker for their help and friendship, and to a succession of Board chairmen, Messrs. C. H. Whiting, H. C. Rees, E. M. Culliton, E. K. Phillips, H. Pinder, E. C. Leslie, A. Tubby, and J. McFaull, for their unfailing and generous support. My warmest thanks go to a most loyal and cooperative staff who saw that things ran smoothly and efficiently. A special word of thanks is due to the senior administrative staff: Dr. Currie, Dr. Barber, Mr. Pringle, Mr. Wedgwood, Dr. John Bardwell, Mr. Lovell, and Mr. Saunders. The sum total of their academic-administrative expertise would be hard to match anywhere. To the students also, especial thanks are due. They, together with the faculty, contrived to make these years both exciting and rewarding. Last, but by no means least, a special thank you is owed to a very understanding and capable wife who did her best to keep me well and happy, who entertained friends and visitors alike, who accompanied me on trips abroad, and who, above all, shared my deep love for the university.

Chapter 22

Humpty-Dumpty

They say that all good things come to an end, and I suppose I should have realized that no exceptions are made to this rule, even for university presidents, and certainly not in a period of student unrest, faculty unrest, and world-wide disillusionment with institutions of higher learning. Even the evidence that universities have by and large responded well to the challenges of the times seems not to have helped much in refurbishing the current academic image. We have lived through an educational revolution much like the industrial revolution, in that for a generation education has been the driving force in transforming the life of modern man. It has provided the research and technical base of the technological revolution, and it has also provided much of the humanities base of the democratic revolution. The University of Saskatchewan has played an important role in these processes—often a pioneering role. How then did it happen that just when things seemed to be going so well at the university, members of the government should indicate in no uncertain terms that they were thoroughly dissatisfied with the leadership of the university?

In the summer of 1971, the Liberal government which had been in power for seven years in Saskatchewan was defeated by the N.D.P. party. Shortly after the new government took over, I made an appointment to see both the new Premier, Mr. Allan Blakeney, and the new Minister of Education, Mr. MacMurchy, to discuss university matters with them. The meetings went quite well, although I did feel that perhaps something was worrying the Premier. At the meeting I had, as a matter of form, suggested to the Premier that if he felt that a change in university leadership seemed desirable, I should be prepared to step down. He said that he certainly had nothing like that in mind, so, remembering that we had got along well some seven years earlier, when he had been Minister of Education, I assumed that relations between government and university would continue to be satisfactory.

I have to say with some reluctance that at this time there was a marked deterioration of relations between the university Administration and one or two of the government-appointed members of the Board of Governors. Until this time it had been true to say that the Board members acted in much the same way, regardless of whether they had been elected by the university Senate or appointed by the government. While this still held for most of the appointments, it was no longer so for all of them.

It was characteristic of the university climate of the times that the Saskatoon campus had a minor sit-in in 1970–71. I call it minor in that physical damage was negligible, but the political aftereffects were major. After the sit-in, the university was under continuous petty sniping. It would be charged that there was a lack of planning, lack of this, that, and the other, with a complete lack of substantiation of the charges. These charges would be duly reported in the press, and unfortunately no one thought it necessary to contradict them. Most people said, "Everyone knows that it isn't true," but saying that didn't help much. It appears that some dissatisfied people among students and faculty had the ear of the government. As is usual under such circumstances, the majority who were pleased with the way things were done did not go out of their way to offer their opinion.

Another factor which had a bearing on events was the price of wheat. In 1971 and 1972 the prairie economy was badly hit by what seemed to be a glut of wheat. Farmers were encouraged to grow less wheat and there was a dramatic exodus of people from the province—thirty thousand in one year—including many young people of university age. The result was a drop in university enrollment, and the government somewhat naturally expected this to be accompanied by a drop in faculty and budget at the university, but of course, it is difficult suddenly to fire fifty or sixty academics, particularly at a new university such as Regina.

In the event, the government actually increased the budget by quite a bit, but many academics merely saw that we were getting less than we would have liked to have had and complained long and loudly that the government had reduced our budget, a complaint which was not true. Naturally, the government did not appreciate this unwarranted bad publicity, and the Minister of Education did not enjoy the endless arguments about university salaries and university budgets. In retrospect, it would probably have been smarter had I fought less hard and had let the two campus principals and the government take the blame for any budgetary inadequacies. But at the time I would have considered such an approach to be dodging my responsibilities. Some people also found it convenient at this time to pass along all the unpleasant decisions to me, while at the same time complaining of their lack of decision-making powers.

It was particularly unfortunate that the main drop in enrollment occurred on the Regina Campus, which was about to expand its offerings in engineering from the first two years to the third and fourth years. Under the circumstances, the government allocated no capital funds for an engineering building which had been requested for Regina. It was also agreed that before any decision was made on further capital funding for engineering, an enquiry should be held. The Lapp Commission was set up, which recommended that engineering not be taught at all at Regina. The university Board took a slightly different approach. They agreed that the main effort in engineering should continue to be in Saskatoon, but they recommended that a modest program in engineering be continued in Regina for three to five years, during which alternative proposals could be considered. This compromise solution was actually suggested by the Deputy Minister of Continuing Education, and it was probably the only politically acceptable solution. It satisfied no one, and again it did not help the one-university image. It is ironic that now a College of Engineering has been established in Regina.

Then came the thunderbolt. On the day before the House opened, early in 1973, I was informed by the Minister of Education that major changes in the University Act were impending, involving the removal of the president's office and those of senior university administrative staff—Bill 90 it was called. I expressed my strongest disapproval to the Minister and later to the Premier. Both assured me that there was nothing personal about this, and that they had the greatest admiration for me and for my staff! Pressures from Regina and Saskatoon had, however, apparently convinced them that radical changes in university structure were required.

Both Senate and Board of the university objected strongly to the proposed changes, which would have replaced the Board of Governors by a Board of Regents, with the Deputy Minister of Continuing Education acting as Secretary of the Regents, thereby effectively transferring the coordinating power to the government. The appearance of Bill 90 stirred up a veritable hornet's nest of protest, as a result of which the bill was withdrawn and the Hall Commission was set up to advise the Government on university structure. The withdrawal of Bill 90 in April 1973 and the knowledge that a major change in university governance was imminent set in motion a number of power plays. A number of senior university people suddenly changed their attitude toward the one-university concept, and a surprising amount of hard feeling between the two campuses came to the surface. Many people in Regina still felt aggrieved that the University of Saskatchewan had been placed in Saskatoon in 1907, and a number fought long and hard to get their own university in Regina.

The Hall Commission produced its report in December of 1973, recommending that "the campuses at Saskatoon and Regina be established as independent universities" and "that there be a body to be known as the Saskatchewan Universities Commission which shall be comprised of nine part-time members, all of whom shall be appointed by the Lieutenant-Governor in Council."

Eventually, in June 1974, three acts were passed, setting up two independent universities and a coordinating commission. Thus ended the one-university approach, started in 1959 with the blessing of the government, which had accomplished so much in the fifteen years of its existence. It had had within it the possibilities of further evolution, and it is somewhat ironic that a university committee, chaired by Dr. Riddell, brought in a report in the fall of 1972, which, had it been adopted, would have given legislative recognition to the de facto autonomy of the campuses and set up a coordinating board. The changes were not pressed at that time largely at the suggestion of the Minister who already had "plenty of things on his plate to see to."

With the disappearance of the one-university concept went a number of highly desirable features: one salary scale for academics, one union negotiation, one pension scheme, uniform administrative procedures, automatic review of competing plans, and the development of overall provincial plans for higher education under strong academic leadership. I emphasize strong academic leadership since it is this which distinguishes the one-university approach from the commission approach. The executive director of a universities commission is usually recognized for his administrative ability, but he is not usually picked for his outstanding qualities of academic leadership. It is perhaps significant and even ironic that the commission structure was in 1978 modified by the appointment of a full-time paid chairman, Dr. Sibley, former academic vice-president of the University of Manitoba. A large degree of academic freedom is now lost, since as a result of the acts, a number of senior positions, including those of the president, the vice-president, the controller, and the assistant to the president, have been legislated out of existence. Appointment and dismissal of university officers has since the beginning of the University of Saskatchewan, been in the hands of the Board of Governors, and retention of this power of appointment and dismissal has properly been regarded as the keystone of the arch of academic freedom. For the government to usurp this authority under the strategem of a legitimate major change in the University Act seems to me to attack the very foundations on which a university must stand. To my knowledge an action such as this has never been carried out in any other Canadian university, or for that matter in any university of the Commonwealth. The proud boast in this university of sixty years of freedom from political interference is no more.

A few faculty expressed their disapproval in print, and I admired their courage. Most of them apparently did not appreciate what was happening under their noses.

"Humpty Dumpty sat on a wall, Humpty Dumpty had a great fall. . . ." I can't help feeling a bit sad that things should have turned out in this way, but on the other hand, I'm now reasonably philosophical about it. I was already close to retirement and the Board kindly granted me leave for the

1974–75 year, after which I retired. They gave me the title "President Emeritus," but I am now back in my old office in the Chemistry Building, where I am rapidly becoming a chemist again and bringing out another edition of the book *Radiation Chemistry*, in collaboration with a colleague of mine, Dr. R. J. Woods.The "emeritus" role does not really suit me.

Of the other senior administrative officials, Principal Begg became president of the University of Saskatchewan in Saskatoon, while Principal Archer became the first president of Regina University. Vice-President Barber resigned from his position and spent two years as chairman of the Indian Claims Commission. On the resignation of President Archer at the end of 1975, Dr. Barber was appointed president at Regina, an excellent if somewhat surprising appointment. Mr. Pringle became vice-president, finance, in Saskatoon; Drs. Haslam and King were appointed vice-presidents; and Dr. Bardwell remained in the position of assistant to the president, although with considerably changed duties. Mr. Wedgwood, the director of planning, was appointed executive head of the Saskatchewan Universities Commission. In Regina, Dr. Tinker was appointed vice-president.

Looking back over 1959–74, I realize that some things were done which ought not to have been done, and, equally, some things were not done which ought to have been done, but by and large, considering the world-wide handicaps of the 1960s, I still think that the people of Saskatchewan can be proud of the accomplishments of their university in the fifteen-year period. A whole new university campus was built in Regina, capable of handling five thousand students, complete with faculty, colleges, and organizational structure. A vastly expanded campus arose in Saskatoon, which is still one of the most beautiful in Canada and is continuing to give the lead in its acceptance of an increased responsibility for meeting the needs of the community.

Regina, of course, blamed me for what they felt was a lack of progress under my direction. However, now that I have taken all the kicks and am out of the way, they are ready to claim full credit for what they previously blamed me for doing. And they are apt to overlook the key role played by the university in the development of the Wascana project.

Many faculty of the Saskatoon campus gradually came to feel that I was in some way responsible for the creation of the Regina campus, although in fact the academic decision was taken by the university Council under the late President W. P. Thompson. And like academics everywhere, the academics in both Regina and Saskatoon refused to accept that coordination of higher educational facilities within a province is here to stay and will be effected in one way if not in another.

I'm still too close to the events of the last few months to have a really clear idea why things happened in the way they did. My brother suggested somewhat cynically that if I wanted to know who my friends were, I should see who finished up in the top positions. Perhaps after all, the great change of the past decade was not the rise of student power, which hit the headlines, but the quiet increase of public power, by legislatures, coordinating councils, and by ministers of education. This is a country-wide, indeed a world-wide phenomenon. Yet campuses need a large measure of independence for their effective performance, and no academic worth his salt could stand idly by and watch a major assault on academic freedom. Of course, so long as the universities themselves are preserved, it matters little that university presidents come and go, for one reason or another.

PART IV

A SYSTEMS APPROACH TO SCIENCE

Chapter 23

The Infrastructure

In 1962, a book by T. S. Kuhn appeared entitled *The Structure of Scientific Revolutions*, published by the University of Chicago Press. Among other things it drew attention to the changes in approach of philosophers and historians of science who now favor perceptions of the scientific enterprise that take human factors into account as well as the purely logical structure. According to Kuhn, science consists of a series of peaceful interludes, punctuated by a set of theories, standards, and methods, which he refers to as a *paradigm* 'a pattern, an example'. Actually, what Kuhn is doing is exploring the process of arriving at a theory. He is constructing a sociological theory of scientific theory construction. In modern parlance he is describing the "infrastructure" of one part of science, the theory construction part. Kuhn has written a second book on these matters, *The Essential Tensions: Selected Studies in Tradition and Change* (University of Chicago Press, 1977).

Obviously there are many parts of science: doing experimental work, making observations, putting forward tentative hypotheses, testing these hypotheses, applying scientific knowledge to everyday life, and so on, and each of these parts will have an infrastructure. The actual infrastructure which evolves will depend on the goal to be achieved, but whatever the goal, assuming that there is a goal, reaching the goal will certainly be helped if one knows something about the matter in hand. This description begins to sound suspiciously like the description of a systems approach, and of course that is exactly what it is.

The building up of a more general infrastructure to pure and applied science as a whole is a worldwide phenomenon. In Canada, this growth has occurred gradually over the last fifty or sixty years and is a matter of considerable national interest and importance. I had the good fortune to be involved in the growth of some of the elements of this infrastructure. Some would say that I gradually fitted in with the bureaucratic process and became a science bureaucrat.

I suppose my first introduction to the science bureaucracy was at the university level as a member of the university Council's Committee on Graduate Studies. The Council committee was transformed into a graduate faculty, with Dr. T. Thorvaldson as its first dean, in 1946. There were seventy-three students enrolled in the Graduate College, all working towards a master's degree. In 1947–48, the university's Council and Senate agreed to a limited expansion in Ph.D. work, and two Ph.D. students were admitted. It took a lot of hard arguing to get the Council to agree to this expansion, and my involvement in these arguments probably constituted my first brush with the research bureaucracy. I became dean of graduate studies in 1949, and it quickly became clear that the level of research activity in the university was almost directly dependent on the funds available, so when I was asked to serve on research bodies such as the National Research Council, I did not say no. Each time I learned quite a bit, and gradually I acquired a feel for the organisation of research.

By 1959 the enrollment in the Graduate College had increased to a hundred and fifty-five, and the number of Ph.D. candidates to thirty-five. Research grants had grown to 1.58 million dollars. By 1970, the graduate enrollment had risen to five hundred and fifty, and research grants to 6.84 million dollars. Grants doubled again in the next eight-year period. This growth was certainly helped considerably by my membership and that of a number of other professors in various research bodies. My ideas about graduate studies were helped considerably by my participation in 1966, with Drs. Hare and Arlt, in a commission to study the development of graduate programmes in the Ontario universities. The report created quite a furore, largely because the ideas it expressed were about ten years ahead of their time.

Organisations and commissions with which I was connected in the 1945–78 period included the National Research Council, the Saskatchewan Research Council, the Defense Research Board, the Canada Council, the Western University Presidents, I.P.C.U.R., the Oil and Gas Conservation Board, the Canada West Foundation, the P.O.S. Pilot Plant Corporation, the Centre for Community Studies, S.E.D. Systems Ltd., the Institute for Northern Studies, the Institute of Pedology, NewStart, Atoms for Peace, U.N.C.S.T.A.D., the Chemical Institute of Canada (as past president), I.U.P.A.C., A.U.C.C., the Banff School of Advanced Management, and the commission on graduate studies in Ontario Universities. The significance of these baffling clumps of initials will become clear in the rest of the chapter. My impressions of a few of them are worth recording, together with an indication of the impact that a person such as myself was able to make on them.

In 1958, members of the N.R.C. (National Research Council) included fifteen top scientists from universities across the country, together with C. J. Mackenzie, a former academic, C. C. Cushing of the Canadian Labour Congress, and Dr. Jane of Shawinigan Chemicals. The chairman of the council was Dr. E. W. R. Steacie, who exerted a strong leadership role. The Council acted on a consensus basis. If, after discussing a new topic, everybody seemed agreed, the matter would go through. If one or two people seemed unconvinced, the matter was shelved and brought up again at another meeting, possibly with minor modifications. During the whole time that I was connected with the Council, it was solidly behind the president.

Much of the Council's business was occupied with the distribution of funds by way of scholarships and grants in aid. Such matters received preliminary screening in numerous committees, subcommittees, and associate committees. Two major things that I was involved in were the introduction of major equipment grants and the forecasting of grant requirements. I have already described how we got the first major equipment grant at the University of Saskatchewan for the purchase of a Linear Accelerator. Subsequent grants to the other universities were all much larger, so everybody benefited from our trail breaking.

In the Forecasting committee, appointed in 1963, I was chairman. We spent some time finding out what the researchers would have liked to have had as distinct from what they had applied for, which was usually modified very considerably by what they thought they might reasonably expect to get. That the needs were three times the money available came as no surprise, but having exact figures did help the N.R.C. in the annual battle with Treasury Board. The National Research Council has played a major role in the development of science in Canada as a whole and in the universities in particular, and largely as a result of its efforts, Canada now has a respectable reputation in world science.

In the last few years science has been under attack by bodies such as the Senate's Lamontagne Committee, and the funding of science has suffered correspondingly. In 1978, the federal Cabinet seemed to have become aware of this shabby treatment and to be trying to improve the financial support of science. Estimated as a percentage of the gross national product, Research and Development in Canada is about half that of the major industrialized nations. Catching up will take a huge effort. As a general criticism, one would have to say that the minister in charge of science has usually been very bright but relatively ignorant of science and rather low on the cabinet totem pole. He or she has usually not stayed long enough as minister to make much of an impact. Elsewhere I have described the growth of science on a provincial scale and the need for coordination and rationalization on a national scale. (For an inside and perceptive description of the evolution of a power structure for Canadian science, see F. R. Hayes, *The Chaining of Prometheus*, U. of Toronto Press, 1973.)

Other memories of my association with the N.R.C. include acting as a member of a team which visited Poland, and serving as associate editor of the *Canadian Journal of Chemistry*. (A recent history of the N.R.C. has been written by W. Eggleston: *The N.R.C.: 1916–1966*, Clarke-Irwin, 1978).

The S.R.C. (Saskatchewan Research Council) was started in 1947 with the objective of supporting research that would be of interest in the development of industry, based on provincial natural resources. In 1954 a brief was presented to the government proposing the establishment of research laboratories with a full-time director. This proposal was approved in 1955, and a building on the university campus was completed in 1958. Dr. Warren was director from 1956 to 1972. I was a member of the S.R.C. from 1950 until 1974, and for a number of years I was chairman of the Technical Committee of the Council, which is largely responsible for the organization and direction of the research programme. There were numerous advisory committees on topics such as lignin, lignite, soil mechanics, geological studies, uranium recovery, and so forth. In the first twenty-five years, the budget increased from about a hundred and eighty thousand dollars a year, to over two million. Having the S.R.C. labs. on campus was of great value to the university in developing its scientific research potential and, in turn, the S.R.C. benefited by being on campus, with convenient access to university staff and facilities. The easy interrelationship was helped considerably by the first chairman, Dr. Woodrow Lloyd (1947–61), who had a great feel for the university and for its capabilities.

Later on, the rapport between the S.R.C. and the provincial government seemed to be less satisfactory, and I felt that the government was not getting as much out of the S.R.C. as it might have done. I felt that the Cabinet needed to have someone on hand who had a good knowledge of scientific developments, to give information and advice as needed on a confidential basis. Eventually, in 1977, the Saskatchewan Policy Council was set up with a science secretariat under Dr. Katz. Dr. Katz has now retired and his group has apparently been disbanded. What is quite clear is that governments, whether federal or provincial, still have a lot to learn about their role in the science-industry-government relationship.

The D.R.B. (Defense Research Board) was established shortly after World War II, with Dr. O. Solandt as its first director. D. G. Goodspeed has written its history (Ottawa: the Queen's Printer, 1958). I was a member of the Board from 1958 until 1962. At that time Dr. A. H. Zimmerman was chairman. The main responsibilities of the D.R.B. were to provide scientific advice to the Minister of National Defense and to the Chiefs of Staff and the Armed Services; to add to the pool of scientific knowledge; and to develop in Canada a well-trained group of scientists in those fields of science of vital importance to defense. My wartime experience in operations research and atomic energy gave me a useful background, as did a number of contacts I had with the armed forces in the 1945–58 period, doing "jobs" for them and attending symposia from time to time. Membership of the D.R.B. in 1959 included the following: the chairman, D.R.B.; the vice-chairman, D.R.B.; the chief of the Naval Staff; the chief of the General Staff; the chief of the Air Staff; Deputy Minister of National Defense; the president of the National Research Council; the Chief Scientist; the Chief of Establishments; the Chief of Administration; the defense research member of the Canadian Joint Staff, London; the defense research member of the Canadian Joint Staff, Washington; and the private secretary to the Minister of National Defense.

I already knew many of the members of the D.R.B. and I soon got to know the services and government representatives. I grew to respect their abilities and characters. Just to be with these people every few months was a rewarding experience, and it helped me a great deal in getting a better idea of what went on in another facet of Canadian life, that to do with defense. I like to think also that my rather broad scientific background made me of some use in general discussions as well as in performing bread-and-butter tasks on appointment committees and review committees. It was only in 1966 that an Annual Report was made available to the public.

The Canada Council was established in 1957 with the Hon. Brooke Claxton as chairman and G. H. Levesque as vice chairman. Dr. A. W. Trueman was the first director, followed by Jean Boucher in 1965, with Peter Dwyer as associate director. Its general aim was to support the arts and its initial funding was the interest from a capital grant of fifty million dollars, then about two million a year. I was a member from 1960 until 1966. Claude Bissel, then president of the University of Toronto, was chairman in 1960, and he was succeeded by Jean Martineau. Included among people who served on the Board during my term were Sir Ernest Macmillan, Mme. A Paradis, Miss Vida Peene, and E. P. Taylor.

The members of the Canada Council brought a wide range of expertise and experience to the Board, and they provided a broad geographic distribution of opinion from St. John's to Victoria, B.C. In no time at all new members of its Board learned to act as part of a team. Everyone had ample opportunity to have his or her say, and decisions of the Council were carried out competently by the administrative staff. Council meetings were held mostly in Ottawa, but from time to time meetings were held in other centres across the country, giving an exposure of Council members to regional problems. Members usually gathered at the appointed place on the evening before the meetings were to start, and they got to know one another at a social gathering. Dr. Trueman's voice and Sir Ernest's playing on the piano acted as effective catalysts in breaking the ice.

My particular role on the Canada Council was to represent the university graduate studies point of view and to bring the necessity of grass roots support of the smaller orchestras to the attention of the Council. I also pushed the absolute necessity of getting an annual grant from the federal government. An application for such a grant was made in 1963, and thereafter the budget grew successively to seven million in 1965, eleven million in 1966, and twenty-one and a half million in 1967. I like to think that my earlier experience as a member of various granting agencies was helpful. Certainly my contact with the broad membership of the Canada Council was most helpful to me. (Curiously enough, I had been invited to prepare an essay on the natural sciences for the Massey Commission in 1950, whose report led to the setting up of the Canada Council). Husbands and wives were invited to some of the Council's social functions and these further contacts were helpful to the whole operation of the Canada Council.

When I became president of the University of Saskatchewan I automatically became a member of a number of groups such as the Western University Presidents, the A.U.C.C. (Association of Universities and Colleges of Canada), the Banff School of Advanced Management, and the Association of Commonwealth Universities. These organizations served in different ways to keep university presidents informed of what was going on in other universities and provided them with a forum for discussion of matters of common interest.

In 1959, the Western presidents' group was small—one president from each of the western provinces—but with the rapid expansion of higher education in the 1960s, the group quickly expanded. A typical agenda for a meeting would include exchange of information on enrollment, budgets, faculty salaries, university-faculty relationships, tenure, sabbatical leaves, student funding, new program developments, and university grants commissions. From time to time, a particular item would appear on the agenda; for example, in 1962, an item appeared at the end of the agenda: "Possible establishment of a veterinary college in the West." The meeting of the Western presidents was an informal arrangement between the Western presidents, and it served a useful purpose in the early days. Eventually the membership became so large and the business so heavy that a minimum structure seemed called for.

At the same time, university budgets were escalating astronomically, and calls for coordination and rationalization became more and more insistent. So in 1965 the P.P.E.C. (Prairie Provinces Economic Council whose members were the premiers of Manitoba, Saskatchewan and Alberta) asked that Manitoba invite the deputy ministers of education and the chairmen of the universities commissions or similar bodies to form I.P.C.U.R. (the Interprovincial Committee on University Rationalization). I.P.C.U.R. was established as a standing committee of the P.P.E.C., with two members from each province named by the ministers of education, and with the president of each university and the two principals from the University of Saskatchewan as members.

The purpose of I.P.C.U.R. was to study means of developing and coordinating opportunites for higher education in the prairie provinces. Among the studies made in the 1965–72 period were: indexes for comparable student expenditures, interlibrary cooperation, an inventory of academic programs, the development of national reporting forms, and an inventory of graduate programs and research. Proposals for new programs, such as a new faculty of architecture, and schools of library science and of mining engineering were examined in detail. Dr. Riddell, who became secretary to I.P.C.U.R. in 1970, prepared an excellent summary of the activities of I.P.C.U.R. in the 1965–72 period (the First Annual Report of I.P.C.U.R.).

I.P.C.U.R. has now disappeared. Its functions are now performed by the Council of Western Presidents and by the Council of Ministers of Education. The latter was established in 1966 and now has a relatively large secretariat. Its growth parallels the realization that while the B.N.A. Act states that education is a provincial right, in a country such as Canada, which has ten provinces, some attempt at rationalization is imperative if its people are to have any identity as Canadians living in anything that can be called a country. The relatively wishy-washy attitude taken by successive federal governments to an overall educational policy for Canada has not helped the cause of Canadian unity.

The Oil and Gas Conservation Board was set up in the early fifties by the Saskatchewan government. Its membership consisted of Mr. James T. Cawley, Deputy Minister of Natural Resources, Professor Edmunds, a geology professor interested in oil and gas, and myself. We reported to the minister, Mr. Brockelbank. One of our first tasks was to draw up suitable regulations, and in doing this we had the help of industry and other boards. Eventually we sat down with industry to hammer out the final draft. Sometimes a dispute would arise over some rather trivial matter of wording, and often I was able, as a relatively disinterested party, to suggest a minor change which would be accepted by both government and industry. My role as mediator indicated to me how important it is for university people not to be publicly committed to ideologies or "isms." Naturally, members of the Board did not have a direct financial interest in any oil companies and did not accept gifts, Christmas or other, from oil companies. We were much helped in our technical discussions by Dr. Herman Kaveller, a professor and consultant from Oklahoma. My own experience in teaching classes in chemical engineering and physical chemistry was helpful to me in understanding the matters brought to the Board.

The Oil and Gas Conservation Board had a pleasant and easy relationship with the Hon. John H. Brockelbank, who had to bear the ultimate responsibility for any decisions taken. Having a relatively independent Board, with access to the necessary data and expertise, was helpful to him, and I think the whole arrangement worked out well. It avoided confrontations between the minister and industry, and yet it gave industry every opportunity to have its say, both privately and at public hearings. The Board, on its part, recognized that a number of the matters brought to it, particularly policy matters, often had a political component which quite properly had to be settled at the Cabinet level.

As a bonus to me, I went on a number of trips to the oil and gas fields in Saskatchewan and Alberta in order to get background. This background has been useful to me in assessing the energy crisis of 1973 and the subsequent actions of the federal and provincial governments. It has also provided a framework into which to fit assorted bits of information that have come my way in the last twenty years and which otherwise would have long since gone into limbo.

The C.W.F. (Canada West Foundation) was founded in 1973 with the objective of strengthening the position of the Canadian West within confederation. I was invited to become a member of its council in 1975. It is an independent, non-profit organization engaging in studies, research, and the development of policy. It has made studies on Canada's mining and petroleum resources and is presently engaged in studies on Canadian confederation, coal, agricultural policy, and water supply. The membership covers a broad cross section of the population of western Canada and includes senators, former M.L.A.'s and M.P.'s, a retired general, an economist, a newspaperman, lawyers, business executives, researchers, academics, and so on—a pretty lively crowd!

Meetings are held in Calgary two or three times a year and each meeting is most stimulating. My role is to act as devil's advocate for anything related to science or research. I prepared a number of papers on regional research rationalization, and eventually I published a paper on "A research strategy for Western Canada." It may be worth giving a brief outline of the contents of my report in order to show the role of the Canada West Foundation as a forum for ideas that may benefit the future life of the whole region.

My main theme was the importance of cooperation in a region where the common interests are served by the four governments of the western provinces and the administrative bodies of the Yukon and the North West Territories, and where there are several universities and a variety of industries. This cooperation must necessarily extend outside the region to working with the federal government and other bodies. One example of a field in which such cooperation is needed is, of course, in the diversification of the economic base of the western region.

My report emphasized the importance of new initiatives that are essential to cooperation and success in planning the development of the West. One is the setting up of data bases for dissemination of information about scientific research and about social programs throughout the region. Such data bases are essential in that they make the fruits of successful work on one particular problem known and readily available over the whole region, where the same problems may be expected to arise. Thus time-wasting duplication of effort can be avoided, and the benefits of the effort can be maximized.

The second new initiative I advocated in my report was the setting up of an organization to coordinate scientific research and to develop scientific policy throughout the region. Such an organization would focus on the general problem areas such as energy, water, and atmospheric pollution, and on such specific problem areas as optimum coal utilization, potash development, land inventory (and the associated problem of a coordinated national system of mapping land), transportation in isolated areas, and protein production and utilization.

My brief description of some of the administrative bodies with which I was associated over a thirty-year period serves both to illustrate my evolution as a science bureaucrat and to flesh out some of the bones holding together parts of the infrastructure underpinning scholarly and research activities in Canada. It indicates briefly, too, some of the connecting links between science and the arts and the community. Some general thoughts on the relationship of science to the community, arising from fifty years as a scientist and thirty years' participation in the administrative aspects of science are put together in the next chapter.

Chapter 24

Two Blades of Grass

The technique of optimization is of wide applicability. Wherever or whenever groups do somewhat the same thing under somewhat different circumstances, one can analyse the actual operating experience and come up with suggestions on how to improve or optimize the operation. The system may be an agricultural system, which one tries to improve for the overall benefit to the farmer (or the community), very much as Swift envisioned it, "to make two blades of grass to grow where only one grew before," or it may be a system of hospitals, where one tries to get the optimum service for a given expenditure of money, supposing that to be the limiting parameter.

On one occasion, when I was a member of the University Hospital Board, I had a long conversation with Dr. Wendell McLeod, Dean of Medicine, about wartime operations research and its possible application to a hospital system. With his usual enthusiasm, Dean McLeod seized on the idea and arranged to appoint a young doctor who was familiar with the concept of systems analysis. Unfortunately, at that time most of the practitioners of the hospital had not heard much about systems analysis and thought that someone was trying to push them around. Next time something fairly neutral was done—I think that an attempt was made to improve the medical records system, and it was done under the supervision of an engineer rather than a medical man, so none of the doctors felt particularly threatened. The Hospital Systems Study Group gradually evolved, first of all as a strictly University Hospital effort, and then extending its contacts to the whole province of Saskatchewan's hospital system.

Operations research can be used to optimize a social situation too, as for example in the NewStart program initiated by the federal government in cooperation with the provincial governments some ten years ago. The federal government was interested in setting up experimental programs of assistance to disadvantaged groups of people. I happened to meet one of the federal administrators of the program, Mr. Garnet Page, who had been a student of mine in chemistry and who was for some years executive director of the C.I.C. (Chemical Institute of Canada). Over a luncheon, he told me about the program, and I reminded him of my wartime operations research experience. Out of this conversation grew the highly successful Prince Albert NewStart program.

The Prince Albert NewStart program was applied in an urban-rural situation in which a large number of Indians and Metis had drifted into the outskirts of Prince Albert and had found difficulty in adjusting to the general way of city life. Many of them had dropped out of school in grades five or six and had been discouraged in any attempts they had made to improve their academic standing later in life. This low academic standing in itself made it difficult for them to obtain jobs, even though they might have been quite capable of handling the jobs. Generally, they suffered from a complete lack of confidence. The method adopted was to get a group of about fifty people together by means of the employment service and put them on a three-pronged program, first bringing up their academic standing by using the most recent techniques of programed instruction in which they just concentrated on the thing they did not know. Most of them were thirty years old or so, and they obviously knew much more than the grade five standing which they had on paper. In fact, it proved possible to get them up from grade five to about grade ten in ten months' to a year's time. A sympathetic attitude was taken by the instructors—no one told the students that they were stupid or made derogatory suggestions. At the same time as they did academic work they studied a trade—carpentry, bricklaying, small business, store clerk, and so forth, depending on their inclination. The third branch of study was called "socanics"—social behavior—and it was just a course in general behavior: how to talk to a stranger, how to open a bank account, how to get on a bus, how to clean up the mess if one accidentally spilled a cup of coffee, and similar matters. Most people learn these things automatically at home, but those who do not, for whatever reason, are under a tremendous handicap and find it difficult to develop any degree of self-confidence.

The whole operation was checked systematically, changed to eliminate weaknesses and to make improvements, and after four or five run-throughs, a very satisfactory program was developed. It was an example of the method of successive approximations, measuring the progress or lack of progress and adjusting the system accordingly. After about five years the program was taken over by Manpower. The director, Stu Conger, deserves full marks for his successful handling of a difficult problem. One valuable spinoff from the program was the use of the NewStart project as an instructional instrument to let people, including members of the federal government, know what operations research or systems analysis was all about.

It goes without saying that the experiment has to be carried out under natural conditions and on a fair scale if one is to get significant results. Getting significant results from NewStart required the training of successive groups of about fifty people for five successive years. Supporting these people (and their families) cost quite a bit, although most of this cost could be offset against welfare and unemployment payments. These payments, salaries, equipment, and the rest amounted to about a million dollars a year, for a total of five million. It is most unlikely that a professor would ever have been given this kind of money to do a social science experiment, but the federal government could find such sums and they did so, much to their credit.

One system of particular interest to the scientist and to those who employ scientists, is that of science itself. How does one optimize the work of scientists in a given province or a given country, or for that matter in the world, keeping in mind the limitations of money, equipment, and scientists, and not forgetting that the scientists are themselves a peculiar breed of people? Many of the scientists are suspicious of anyone who tries to tell them what to do, and yet all would agree that they do need some system of support—in modern lingo, there needs to be some kind of an "infrastructure."

In Canada, a positive step was taken towards the development of an infrastructure with the establishment, in 1916, of the National Research Council. Some decades later, the Science Policy Council was set up, and in keeping with the political structure of Canada, the provinces eventually set up provincial research councils and even provincial science policy councils of their own. However, in spite of the many advances made in applying new discoveries to the benefit of Canada, the Committee of the Senate on Science Policy "deplored the weakness of the research and development (R and D) effort and innovative performance of Canadian industry" (Vol. 4 of the committee's *Report* (1977), p. 40).

The committee complained (ibid., p. 68) that "there was no ... inventory of the research programmes being carried out, even in the public sector." The Lamontagne committee had stated earlier (Vol. 2, 1972) that a coherent science policy requires a better understanding of the relationship between research, discovery, and invention, and an appreciation of the conditions leading to successful innovations.

Many researchers, including myself, have attacked some of the findings of the Lamontagne committee, but it remains true that there is a good deal of dissatisfaction in Canada with the degree of support of research on the one hand and the seeming inability of industry as a whole to take full advantage of the advances in technology on the other. Part of the problem is that besides science and scientists, pure and applied, there are also social scientists to be considered. The two groups often do not even speak the same language, let alone understand each other. In the scientists' terms, we are trying to optimize physical processes through the process of scientific discovery, whereas the social scientists seek to optimize the whole process, paying particular attention to human behavior and human wants as expressed through political systems. The satisfaction of these wants leads eventually to social changes, and thus leads one to define the problem as an examination of the infrastructure relating creativity to social change. It will be realised that different infrastructures of varying degrees of sophistication are possible, but even a brief examination of the problem helps to define the legitimate areas of interest of the researcher and the politician and suggests parameters which might be used in assessing the adequacy of a given infrastructure at a given time and place. In what follows, examples will be taken mainly from the prairies in the last half century.

Anyone who has been around the region for any length of time will readily admit that many changes have taken place on the prairies in the last half century, some good, some bad. Some changes are obviously the result of causes outside our control, such as the weather; some, such as the growth of the health care system, are the result of actions taken by people and governments, and therefore at least to some extent they are within our control. Obviously the growth of the health care system has depended on many things: ideological factors, the results of elections, the state of the economy, and the state of the arts of medicine and nursing. In a general way, the overall development of the health care system is the result of overall government policy. The development of particular aspects of the system, such as the building of the Plains Hospital in Regina or the payment of a fee for each drug prescription, is a matter of strategy, and strategies are developed as a part of policy implementation. A practitioner of the natural sciences will probably already have drawn a parallel with the optimization of a chemical or physical process—the chemist varies the temperature and pressure in the ammonia synthesis in order to get the optimum yield of ammonia. Methods have been worked out for obtaining the optimum yield in a chemical process, even when several variables are involved.

Those in the social sciences realize full well that systems involving peoples aren't quite as predictable as chemical systems. On the world scale a Hitler may come along, on a national scale there may be a Churchill or a Trudeau, or on the provincial scale, a Levesque. In spite of this element of chance people do wish to know what may happen, and subjects such as "futurology" now have a great vogue, as do the Club of Rome, the Delphi method, and the scenarios lingo. The object of futurology is to forecast the future. It helps one's forecasting if one has some way of influencing what will happen. One technique for controlling change, within certain limits, is operations research. The object of operations research is to carry out the operation in hand in the best possible way with the means available. Optimization techniques have been developed, including the sequential method and the method of steepest ascent. Essentially operations research may be thought of as the application of scientific and mathematical methods to the analysis of any administrative system which contains an improvable operation. From a mathematical point of view, one takes a systems approach. If one understands the system and the interrelationship of the various parameters controlling it, one can then adjust the parameters so as to make the system move in the desired direction. From the point of view of decision theory, one is helped in making the right decision so as to achieve the desired goal.

The speed of social change is quite often controlled by the rate of spread of a new idea, and one might speak of the half-life of an idea—how long it takes for half the people to hear about a new idea. This used to be quite a long time when communication was solely by word of mouth, and it has been speeded up greatly by the printed word, the telephone, and now by radio and T.V. This speedup, which has some advantages, is subject to an odd kind of drawback—there is nothing to guarantee that the information passed along is accurate or well thought out. When you heard by word of mouth you soon learnt whether Joe Doe was to be trusted or not, and you treated his information accordingly. The printed word requires a different form of expertise. Language and literature classes at the university spend a great deal of time teaching students how to abstract the truth from the written word. However, we still don't have classes on how to abstract the truth from radio or T.V. We know that much of what we hear or see on T.V. is propaganda, straight lies, or perhaps harmless bamboozling. Sometimes T.V. even acts as a strong deterrent to some desirable change. We must find ways to overcome the increasing knowledge gap. Not everyone can be an economist or a scientist, but we cannot have too big a gap between the average and the leadership.

When we ask where is creative science located, we think of the obvious places—universities, government laboratories, both federal and provincial, and industry. Anyone who wants a comprehensive account of the creative science on the prairies, however, whether annually or for a particular area of science, by and large won't find it. Of course, bodies such as the university and the Saskatchewan Research Council bring out annual reports which list areas of research, and recently the Canadian Agricultural Research Council has published an inventory of agricultural research projects. It has in it a short analysis in terms of geographic locale and relative emphasis in terms of man-hours. But by and large, comprehensive summaries and analyses are lacking. Such summaries would obviously be useful to anyone wishing to pick out areas where research needs to be expanded.

From an historical point of view, some of the earliest research on the prairies was done at the dominion experimental farms and at the university. The 1909 *President's Report* for the University of Saskatchewan mentions the preparation of experimental plots on the university farm. By 1915 results of research in plant breeding received mention, as did some of the late W. P. Thompson's early plant-breeding experiments. The 1917 report contained specific references to pure and applied research at the university, and from then on, comments about research appeared with increasing frequency. The circumstance that Dr. Murray, the first president of the University of Saskatchewan, was an early member of the N.R.C. probably had a bearing on this increased research. We are all familiar with the late W. P. Thompson's genetic approach to rust research, the work on the production of alkali-resistant cement by Thorbergur Thorvaldson, the development of the cobalt therapy unit, and, more recently, the development of a grain loss monitor.

A look at the annual reports for the universities of Regina and Saskatchewan covering recent years reveals a large number of fields of research, in the social sciences as well as in the natural sciences, occupying a large number of students and professors and requiring a good deal of money—the last item now approaching ten million dollars.

In a general way, the sixty-year period from 1916 to 1976 has been a period of growth in research effort—slow but sure in the first thirty years and accelerating in the thirty-year postwar period. Key factors as far as the universities are concerned have been the development of colleges of graduate studies—later to become colleges of graduate studies and research, the development of Ph.D. programs in the 1950s, the development of institutes such as the Institute of Pedology, the Institute for Northern Studies, and the Canadian Plains Research Centre, and the acquisition of major research tools such as the Linear Accelerator. Of major importance has been the development of the National Research Council itself, with its heavy emphasis on support of university research, and the location of a number of research centres, such as the Canada Department of Agriculture Laboratory, the Prairie Regional Laboratory, and the Saskatchewan Research Council on the University of Saskatchewan campus. Seemingly more remote but eventually having a major impact is the development of a national science policy with a Science Council and now a provincial science policy with a Provincial Science Policy Council.

To the outsider it might seem that the influence of all aspects of creative science on prairie development has been rather haphazard, but this impression would be wrong, even though a number of the individual events may have had an aspect of chance. Backing a winner at the race track may be a matter of chance to the average racegoer and it may so appear to him—he is lucky or not—but the knowledgeable owner of race horses eliminates a good deal of the chance as far as he is concerned by having good horses in his stables, by treating them well, and by having good jockeys. And the owners of race tracks help by putting up valuable and prestigious prizes—everyone has heard of the Grand National and the Kentucky Derby.

One can draw a parallel between this and a modern university. In a university there are specialists in many areas of knowledge, and their expertise can be brought to bear with a good chance of success on almost any kind of problem that comes to their attention. In the absence of this diversified group of specialists it might take quite a long time, let alone a great deal of money, to develop the appropriate research group from scratch, and, in fact, by the time the problem was solved it might be too late.

One dramatic example of the successful efforts of groups of specialists is the development of the cobalt therapy unit at the University of Saskatchewan shortly after the war. It had its origins twenty years earlier, when Dr. Harrington of the physics department built a piece of equipment for making radon "seeds", used in cancer treatment. Dr. Johns was taken on staff as a biophysicist, to work in conjunction with the Cancer Clinic, and he and a number of his students, such as Sylvia Fedoruk and Dr. Cormack, made a notable contribution in elucidating the complicated subject of just what happens when radiations are absorbed by tissue. Many hundreds of these cobalt therapy units have now been sold at a hundred thousand dollars apiece, but unfortunately they were not made in Saskatchewan.

The art of the university is to have a fabulous group of race horses who will win races. Naturally someone (the government) has to pay for the horses and their riders, and someone has to house and feed them and keep them up to scratch. When the stable is a university, it helps to have a bright and understanding president with some knowledgeable deans and heads of departments. Dr. Walter Murray's understanding helped the University of Saskatchewan to get Nobel Prize winner Herzberg on staff in the dirty thirties. When the stable is a research institute, a first-class director is of paramount importance. You don't expect one of your stable boys to tell you about horses in faraway provinces, although they may have good ideas about local prospects.

The modern university has assumed an obligation to help the community, whether local, provincial, national or international, to realize its goals, and this aim is accomplished by the university's acting as an agent of change. Change is effected partly through the teaching process, by turning out the required professionals, by anticipating what new kinds of professionals will be required, and by fostering the continuing growth of these professionals in subjects such as veterinary medicine and dentistry. The university effects change partly by the information it provides. Some of this information will be general, such as material about the environment and the energy crisis; some of it will be particular, such as advice about crops and fertilizers. Some of this information will educate the public so that it can take advantage of a changing world and of its changing opportunities. The university does continual research to supply new information—about new crops such as rape and new types of grains, for example. It also does research in economics, transportation, and social problems. There is area research, too, of the kind done by the Institute for Northern Studies in Saskatoon, and by the Plains Area Research group in Regina. The university provides not only information, but methods of information retrieval, computerization, and the like.

The university can set up such units as an hydrology division or the Institute of Pedology, the Institute of Space and Atmospheric Studies, and even applied groups such as S.E.D. Systems Ltd. on the University of Saskatchewan campus. It can also encourage laboratories such as the P.O.S. Pilot Plant Laboratory to locate on campus. There is a general pattern for setting up such units, but the systematic application of the idea still needs some development. One stage at the University of Saskatchewan was marked by the change in structure from Graduate College to Graduate College and Research. Under its extended mandate, the college takes a general interest in contract research, in new areas of research, and in the appointments to the position of vice-president, research, at the university. There is also the necessity to coordinate the work of the universities in a province where there is more than one university. The principle can be extended to a region such as Canada West or to a country.

In trying to anticipate the future demands of the community, the university will often be put in the position of doing things which the community does not quite understand and of which it may not even quite approve, and yet the university would be remiss if it did not do those things which it felt to be in the best interests of the community. Thus an increasing amount of time must be spent on communications, so that no big gap develops.

Naturally there are a number of built-in mechanisms for keeping the university informed of the needs of the community and vice versa, keeping the community informed about the needs and work of the university.

The modern university is increasingly concerned with matters outside the boundaries of the province and even outside the boundaries of the country. For example, in Saskatoon there is a strong nuclear physics group. Many of the people trained in this group have assumed leading positions in the nuclear industry, and this relationship between Saskatoon and industry has had a direct effect in stimulating demand for Saskatchewan uranium. There is an indirect effect in keeping the people of Saskatchewan, as well as the university, au fait with one of the most important developments of our times, nuclear research, which has led to literally thousands of unexpected discoveries, such as the use of atomic radiations, isotopes, and so on, which have had million-dollar effects upon the economy. To mention only two things, experiments using isotopes as tracers have led to a better understanding of plant and animal nutrition, with related dollar benefits, and the neutron moisture meter has played a dominant role in studies of optimum water utilization in irrigation programs in Saskatchewan and in countries such as India and Pakistan.

The university upper atmosphere research program has similarly kept up to date with space research. While this seems at the moment to be only remotely related to the interests of Saskatchewan, weather satellites give us for the first time the possibility of understanding the forces producing different types of weather, something which cannot help being of eventual interest and benefit to the farmer. Remote-sensing satellites also provide information of value to the farmer. The upper atmosphere program led to the setting up of S.E.D. Systems Ltd., a nonprofit research company, set up by the university to do applied and contract research. This type of approach has been further encouraged by the establishment of a research park in Saskatoon. Research in the south of the province should receive stimulation through the Research Board of the Canadian Plains Research Centre.

An interesting side effect of all of these studies is that people gradually adopt the attitude that problems are meant to be solved and usually can be solved if we tackle them in the right way. People discover that we can, in fact, organize for development. Basic to the whole operation of organization for development is, of course, the creative process, and this is a fascinating topic in itself, about which many books and articles have been written and many symposia held, but of which there is still no satisfactory explanation. We have ideas about what helps creativity, but the basic process still eludes us. The question arises as to what conditions favor creativity, other things being equal. I would say that one's surroundings are most important—for me Professor Allmand's lab. at King's College in the Strand, Dr. Herzberg's lab. in Darmstadt, Germany, Dr. Thorvaldson's chemistry department in Saskatoon, the Operations Research group of the R.C.A.F. under wartime stimulus, the Montreal atomic energy laboratory under the stimulus of the exciting discovery of fission (director, Sir John Cockcroft), and the University of Saskatchewan campus in Saskatoon as a whole. In each place there were interesting and capable colleagues, a good atmosphere, good traditions, reasonably good facilities, and most important—a complete absence of a negative approach.

Although one wasn't cocky to the point of thinking that one could always solve the problem, one certainly didn't ever think that one couldn't possibly do the problem.

As far as I was concerned, the critical period occurred when I came from England to Saskatoon, thousands of miles from my professor, and was faced with the need to do some research on my own. I thought up some new problems, got some new results that were considered interesting by my colleagues, and I was away to the races. I kept a file of problems to be tackled and added to it any time I had a new idea—sometimes while walking home or before going to sleep at night.

Going to Darmstadt to work in spectroscopy after a few years in Saskatoon was quite a challenge, since I was not a physicist. With Dr. Herzberg's understanding approach I soon got going, and it didn't hurt my ego one bit to find that I could get to the production stage in a new field (for me) in a few months. Of course, I was lucky to be with such a brilliant person as Herzberg—who was just chockablock with ideas—and to be in a fairly new field that was just dying to be cultivated.

A few years later I was again extremely lucky to get in on the ground floor with operations research and later with isotope and radiation research. In both I was working with some extremely able people in relatively new areas of discovery.

In each of these situations one has to have time to think—blocks of time when nothing else is important. I suspect that it is also helpful if one doesn't have to spend too much time thinking about other difficult matters such as debts, family problems, difficult colleagues, and so on.

Universities have traditionally been good places in which to do research and to have creative ideas, and quite often one can create the right conditions to get research done—the establishment of a research institute is an example of creation of the right conditions to optimize group creativity. It would take a long time to get together a group expressly for the purpose of solving any one particular problem, but the university provides a setting in which suitable people are to be found, often already working on various aspects of a problem. Its resources remind one of Dr. Gamow's story of hunting in the quantum jungle, which I reproduce here in a somewhat modified form to fit hunting in the quantum research jungle:

> Once upon a time there was a jungle, full of all sorts of interesting animals, and every now and again, hunters would venture into the jungle and come back with the most amazing tales. A celebrated hunter would go in on an elephant hunt with many beaters who would flush out magnificent tigers. The hunter would take aim through a telescopic sight, and to his horror not only would he miss the tiger but he would have sworn that what he had seen in the sight was not a tiger but a lion, or sometimes even an ape. Another would go in shooting pheasants and do no better. However, one day a chap went hunting elephants in the jungle and came back with a fantastic story about how he had tried to shoot many elephants and had had no luck. Then in sheer frustration he had fired off half a dozen shots at random. To his astonishment a huge tiger had dropped at his feet, shot through the heart. A physicist living in the neighborhood, who happened to be an expert in quantum theory, realized that the chap had been hunting in a quantum jungle where there was just a certain probability that a hunter might hit something, and so he organized a quantum hunt in which an assortment of good hunters went in with elephant rifles, tiger rifles, and so on. They shot off at random, and as they left the jungle after a seemingly fruitless day, a veritable shower of game fell from the sky.

The art of the university is to have a fabulous group of hunters who will develop weapons to bring down as-yet-unthought-of animals who are lurking in our quantum jungles. Of course, one has to be careful to avoid the situation of a group of hunters who are armed with everything from a slingshot to a Sten gun, firing off at random for some hours, and suddenly being deluged with a shower of butterflies' wings, a pheasant's tail, a rabbit's paw, a lion's whisker, and an elephant's trunk. Such bags have fallen into a ready waiting pot, which on inspection has been found to contain alphabet soup!

PART V
A SCIENTIST'S PHILOSOPHY

Science, Language, and Truth

We get our perceptions of the outside world through the senses: sight, smell, hearing, taste, and touch. For example, we "see" with the eye. It is thought that a quantum of light is absorbed by a dye-stuff called visual purple, which is present in the rods and cones of the retina of the eye, and that this light bleaches the molecule of visual purple. This bleaching produces an electric impulse which travels along the optic nerve and is received by the axons and neurons of the brain. The signals which result from a beam of light coming from an object produce impulses which are interpreted by the brain as coming from a man's face, a car, or perhaps a flower. Computers have been programed that like the brain can carry out pattern recognition, and since their mode of operation is essentially an on-off operation like that of the neurons (using little magnets which are either one way up, $\frac{N}{S}$, or the other, $\frac{S}{N}$), one is tempted to draw a parallel between the brain and the computer. The question will be asked, how does the eye continue to see when one continues to look at an object. Actually, the eyeball is subject to minute movements, from one side to the other, at a rate of about 50 per second, which means that the stream of photons coming from a particular point on an object will hit first one rod or cone and then one near by, so that successive impulses can be produced. In the meantime, the bleaching process in the visual purple is reversed chemically, by reagents in the rods and cones, and the visual purple molecules are once again ready for action. A recent article in *Science* (Oct. 1978, p. 174) suggests that the mechanism involves proton transfer and an intermediate compound which has a lifetime of less than six picoseconds.

In a similar way, when sounds reach the ear, impulses are sent to a particular part of the brain, there to be recognized by the brain as sounds of a particular kind—such as the sounds represented by the words "a" or "cat" or "dog". Of course, it took many years of evolution for a primitive amoeba, responding to some simple chemical activation, to evolve into an animal with a brain, capable of attaching a name to a particular thing such as the word *dog* to the thing dog. And it was relatively recently, a few thousands of years ago, that one of our bright ancestors thought of representing a word with symbols scratched on a piece of clay tile, and thus produced hieroglyphics, or that a still smarter ancestor thought of using letters, which together formed words that related to spoken words and things. And in time there were sentences connecting words according to certain rules of grammar. Scientists developed particular languages of their own, which were at first crude and designed more to mystify than to inform, like the writings of the alchemists.

The modern attitude in science is that the true meaning of a term is to be found by observing what a man does with it, not what he says about it. Thus scientists, by performing operations which can be repeated by scientists, can reach agreement. All scientists know what is meant by the names *oxygen* and *hydrogen* and what is meant by the statement that "oxygen and hydrogen combine to form water," since each of the terms can be operationally defined.

Chemists have gradually elaborated a chemical language in which symbols are put together in equations to represent chemical reactions. Thus $2H_2 + O_2 = 2H_2O$. The symbol H stands for hydrogen, O for oxygen, and H_2O for water. The hydrogen molecule contains two hydrogen atoms and is written H_2; the oxygen molecule contains two oxygen atoms and is written O_2. The equation tells us that two hydrogen molecules will combine with one oxygen molecule to form two molecules of water. If we know the relative weights of the atoms we can also interpret the equation in terms of weights. The atomic weights of hydrogen and oxygen are 1.008 and 16 respectively, so we can deduce that 4 x 1.008 parts by weight of hydrogen will combine with 32 parts by weight of oxygen to form 36.032 parts by weight of water.

Before arriving at this relatively sophisticated language, the subjects of chemistry and physics were developed as sciences over the course of some hundreds of years, using the so-called scientific method. In this method there are a number of basic steps. First of all there are concepts or constructs such as velocity, mass, chemical element, and chemical compound. These form the main ideas which the particular sciences use in their vocabulary. The ideas are defined by operational definitions which tell us how to measure something. Since the results of the measurement are expressed in numbers, mathematics is involved, and here we should keep in mind the Peano demonstration that the whole of mathematics can be deduced, given the one axiom that there are two distinguishable states, say eecki and weeki. The next step is to examine the relationship between the constructs, supplementing known knowledge with experiments. In this way we arrive at physical laws which are usually mathematical relations such as Boyle's Law: the product of pressure times volume for a given amount of gas at a given temperature is constant; $PV = $ a constant, or, including the temperature T, $PV = RT$, where R is a constant. The third step is to put forward a tentative hypothesis or explanation for the observed behavior. This hypothesis is tested by further experimentation, and if necessary minor adjustments may be made in the hypothesis, or on rare occasions the hypothesis may be discarded altogether. In trying to arrive at a hypothesis that would account for Boyle's Law, the kinetic molecular hypothesis was developed, and it gradually assumed the status of a theory. The reader is no doubt familiar with the idea of a gas consisting of molecules in rapid, random motion.

Modern science has developed so many independent ways of measuring the sizes and shapes of molecules that most scientists would say that the molecules are "real"—as "real," say, as the desk on which one writes. It is not too much to say that one of the aims of a chemist is to develop constructs which will eventually emerge as things which can be measured and counted in an unambiguous fashion. About fifty years ago physical chemists started talking about extremely reactive particles, formed in some reactions, which they called "free radicals." This term denoted OH radicals, for example. These free radicals have now been measured, using sophisticated techniques of optical spectra, electron-spin spectra, pulse radiolysis and so on, and as a result, they are accepted as being as "real" as molecules. Thus they are no longer in the category of convenient hypotheses but are in the category of established theory. The existence of an enormous worldwide chemical industry, based on chemical principles, gives support to the general soundness of fundamental chemical theory.

Sometimes even a well-established theory has to be modified in the light of new discoveries, as when it was found that the atomic weights of nitrogen obtained from air and nitrogenous chemical compounds differed slightly. The discrepancy was found to be a result of the existence of small amounts of impurities in the nitrogen obtained from air, the impurities being rare gases, such as helium and argon, which were unknown until that time. (Actually, the existence of helium had been suspected from studies of the sun's spectrum.)

Science, then, attempts to reach the truth by a series of successive approximations, or, as Bronowski says, "Science is an attempt to represent the known world as a closed system with a perfect formalism." In other words, science is a relatively stable body of knowledge which at any moment is closed but is always changing. The impact of science on society depends in part on scientific ethics, a subject of increasing concern to the public and to the scientists themselves. The scientists themselves belong to a worldwide society with intercommunications by way of scientific societies, journals, and meetings. By and large, when a scientist writes a paper, scientists all over the world will believe that the scientist is writing the truth as he sees it. This confidence is not extended to many non-scientific subjects; thus in political pamphlets, even supposed facts may be highly suspect. In the last decade or so the social science of science has become a subject of some interest and has given rise to controversial books such as Kuhn's *Structure of Scientific Revolution*, in which he tries to develop a "paradigm" or pattern for the development of a new theory. This interest in the human aspects of science leads us to consider the relationship of science to such basic topics as language and to consider what one might call the philosophical aspects of science.

The interest of scientists in language is a relatively recent phenomenon, but reflection on language is not new. In fact, reflection on language is one of the oldest and most constant preoccupations of the human mind. It appears that this preoccupation has been deepened at all critical points in human culture: at the time of the Greek sceptics, at the time of the medieval scholastics, at the time of the espistemologists of the eighteenth century, and finally now.

In the Upanishads we read: "If there were no speech, neither right nor wrong would be known, neither pleasant nor unpleasant; therefore, meditate on speech." Locke expresses the same thought: "When I first began this discourse on understanding, I had not the least thought that any consideration of words was necessary—but later—I found that unless their force and signification were well understood, there could be little said pertinently and clearly concerning knowledge." In science also, language is of great importance since what science says can only be said in words, even though at times science has recourse to graphs and equations.

In considering what language is, we may say in the first instance that it is meaningful communication between man and man. The question of using a language to express the meaningful rather than the unmeaningful, the true rather than the false, raises the question of linguistic validity. As to what is meant by the meaning of an assertion, Carnap says that it is the way in which "it may be verified," that is, the meaning is the verification. A consequence of this interpretation would be that all uses of language to which the question of truth and falsity is irrelevant are meaningless. While many would object that this interpretation is too rigid, it does approach the operational viewpoint, a viewpoint which has proved to be very useful in science and which does not necessarily exclude other branches of knowledge such as art or poetry.

The operational approach makes everything relative and also everything verifiable. If a concept is defined in terms of actual operations it will not be necessary continually to revise our attitude to nature. We may, for example, consider the word *length*. What is meant by the length of anything—for example, the edge of a post card? The card can of course be measured, and its length might come to, say, 5 inches. With a more accurate rule it might measure 5.1 inches, and still more accurately, 5.11 inches. Using a traveling microscope would add still more decimals, and using a traveling electron microscope, still more decimals, but by this time the edge of the post card would be magnified so much that it would look quite irregular, and with a still further stage of magnification the observer would start to see the molecules constituting the edge of the card. Now these molecules are oscillating back and forth, and it becomes hard to say what constitutes the exact end of this post card. The observer might take the average position of the end atom, as it oscillated back and forth like the pendulum of a grandfather's clock, as constituting the edge of the card. However, at this point his physicist friend would tell him that there are electrons revolving about the end atom. The observer might then decide to take the extreme position of the electron in its orbit as being the "edge" of the post card.

But now he is caught because, in order to see the electron, he has to look at it with a light bundle or photon, and since he sees the electron, the light bundle must have collided with the electron, and the electron is therefore no longer where he thought he saw it. This means that the observer cannot possibly measure the length of the post card to any desired degree of accuracy. The same difficulty comes up any time an attempt is made to measure very small things exactly, and since this is so, it would be better not to speak of lengths at all. Rather they should be called *lingths* or *langths* or *lungths*—anything which would avoid associating with the word the usual attributes of length.

Ordinarily the area of anything circular is given by $\pi r^2 = \pi \times radius^2$, but if the cross-sectional area of the nucleus of an atom is calculated in this way and then checked by bombarding the nucleus with neutrons, it is sometimes found that the calculations are out by a factor of 20,000. Now if $\pi \times linth^2$ or $\pi \times lungth^2$ had been taken, an *irrea* or *urrea* would have been obtained, certainly not an area, and the properties of this *irrea* would have been investigated operationally before anyone jumped to any rash conclusion about it.

Similar effects appear when measurements are extended to interstellar space where, for example, a star is said to be a certain number of light years away. Here the question of simultaneity comes in. Ordinarily there is no difficulty in deciding that a ruler has its two ends on the two points whose separation is required at the same time. However, it is quite otherwise in the case of interstellar distances, and an analysis of the question of simultaneity for such measurements led Einstein to his famous relativity theory with its concept of space-time. Quite obviously, then, language is of considerable importance in science.

It would thus appear to be of particular importance that our concept be so ordered that our present experiences do not place obstacles in the path of further inquiry. For example, Newton's definition of time, "Absolute, true and mathematical time, of itself and from its own nature, flows equably without regard to anything external, and by another name is called duration," shut the door on an examination of the concept of time, and it took an Einstein to force the door open. Quite obviously, then, in order to understand the world and our lives, a language must be used whose structure corresponds to physical structure.

One language that represents things rather well is mathematics, and a good understanding of it can be of help in grasping the relationship between things. By contrast, the language inherited from our primitive ancestors is such that it often provides separate terms for factors which are inseparable in fact and vice versa, for example matter and energy, space and time. As a result, an attempt is made to split in our minds what is unsplittable in the real world. In optics the continual reference to light "waves" retarded the introduction of quantum theory, and even now speaking of wave and particle properties of photons and electrons introduces many difficulties. If a new experiment is not too far beyond the margin of known ground it can be explained with concepts derived from past experience; if not, an explanatory crisis develops, as in explaining the quantum theory and the theory of relativity. It is then advisable to adopt the operational approach, rather like a cautious kitten approaching a hot stove.

Many people still think that all experience must conform to familiar types, and of course language helps to confirm such tendencies. Even in quantum theory it is tempting to ask, why does the electron emit energy when it jumps? The talk of "probability" in quantum mechanics similarly proved irresistible to many of the philosophically minded and led some of them to indulge in wild speculations about causality and free will. The difficulty is again mainly one of language. Probability was introduced into wave mechanics in an attempt to interpret the wave function ψ. "ψ^2 represents the probability of the electron's being found at that point at any instant." Operationally it is just something which is proportional to ψ^2, and at best it is just in the category of an hypothesis. This probability is very different from probability in everyday affairs, as in throwing dice, where "probability" has an experimental meaning (statistics of large numbers of observable events).

Even in discussions of the scientific method some people have had difficulty in distinguishing "scientific" from "experimental," "laws" from "theories," "explanations" from "statements." For example, Boyle's law is considered as explaining his observations. This is understandable, as we commonly use the word *law* as the name for absolute truth, whatever that may be. The situation is not helped by using *law* in two fundamentally different ways, as in Newton's "law" of gravitation and Kepler's "laws." Kepler's "laws" were experimental. Newton showed that they were what one would expect if there were a force of attraction between bodies, without saying what this force is. His "laws" of motions are axiomatic. Maxwell's "laws" fall in the same category.

In talking about the operational approach, it should be noted that many constructs are very valuable, such as the idea of an atom, the idea of stress in a beam, or the idea of an electric field. However, one should always be careful to distinguish between constructs and the direct data of experience. An electric field is determined by placing a charge there and measuring the force. The idea is an extremely valuable one, but many physicists go further and imagine the field as being real, and imagine, furthermore, that its existence involves the existence of a medium. The problem of the ether is thus largely a problem of language.

An operational approach indicates that energy is possibly not entitled to the pre-eminent position that physical thought is inclined to give it. The interconversion of matter and energy is now well known, as is also Einstein's equation relating to this "interconversion." It would seem that Einstein could have simplified matters considerably by coining a word such as *mattergy*, matter and energy merely being different forms of mattergy, mattergy I and mattergy II. Their interconversion appears then as something to be expected and rather matter-of-fact, rather than as a modern form of black magic.

In a few years' time our children will be verbally conditioned to such ideas, and one can imagine coming up behind one of them and hearing him recite a little nursery rhyme on the way home from kindergarten:

Little Miss Muffet in Anti-Matter Land
Little Miss Muffet
Sat on an anti-tuffet
In a Diracian sort of way.
Down came an anti-spider
And sat down inside her
And vaporized Miss Muffet away.

It should be explained that Dirac, a Cambridge professor, was prominent in the development of the theories of matter and anti-matter.

Actually, one does not need to go as far as mattergy to find linguistic difficulties in thermodynamics. If in thermodynamics one thinks of heat content as being literally "content of heat," one soon gets into difficulties. These are avoided (at least partly) by talking about enthalpy and noting that enthalpy $H = E + PV$. The pressure, P, and volume, V, are operationally well understood, and some people claim to know what the internal energy, E, is. However, when E is examined operationally, it is found that it is never measured absolutely, but that only changes in E, ΔE, are measured (equals $q - w$, which can be measured). So an operational point of view would talk about "changes in energy" going past the boundaries of a system. The first law of thermodynamics is then reduced to saying that as "change in energy" crosses the boundary surface, the increase inside equals the amount which crosses, and therefore it is conserved. Instead of stating the first law of thermodynamics as "The energy of the world remains constant," a statement which is a theory and not a law, we could state it as a law: "In any change, chenergy (change in energy) is conserved." This first law of thermodynamics is an experimental law and could be brought up to date by stating it in the form, "In any change, chmattergy is conserved." (Chmattergy equals change in mattergy.) One difficulty about speaking of energy is that there is a tendency to extend the verbalization and think of energy as analogous to matter. It is possible to detect changes in mass passing a boundary surface, as when adding a pound of iron. There is operational meaning in saying, "There is so much matter in this enclosure, say two pounds of iron," but the same statement is not true for energy.

Another language difficulty arises in the use of the word *isotope*. Isotopes have the same atomic number but different atomic masses, and it is, therefore, correct to speak of U^{238} and U^{235} as isotopes of U. It is, however, not correct to speak of a table of isotopes any more than it is to call a telephone directory a table of brothers and sisters. Such a table should be called a table of nuclides or, according to a recent suggestion, a table of monobars. (A nuclide or monobar is a species of atom characterized by a definite type of nucleus, that is one having a definite number of protons and neutrons.)

Everyone is familiar with the so-called "normal" curve. Many attempts have been made to establish a law of nature known as "the normal law of errors," the name of which implies that errors ought always to be distributed in this way. The use of "normal" implies more than is justified by the facts, the adjective *normal* being one which is established by custom and which provides a convenient label for a distribution of this type. To quote Poincaré, "Everyone believes in the Gaussian error curve because the mathematicians think that it is a natural law and the scientists think that it has been proven mathematically."

Science has been defined by some as any verifiable and communicable knowledge. Others seek to define it in terms of method, the method of science being that of framing wider and wider generalizations based upon observation and experiment. There is no doubt that since the days of Galileo there has been an attempt to bring all science into a mathematical form. The ideals of a scientific language are definiteness and exactness. In fact, some have claimed that "science is language well made," and this claim closely parallels the idea of science as being "organized common sense." Its language would then be, in principle, the language of common sense. Unfortunately, recent developments in quantum mechanics get so far from the usual idea of common sense that even a person like H. G. Wells exclaims that "in the heights or depths of modern physics" his mind "sinks down exhausted!"

Physical science began with a literal or copy theory of concepts. With Galileo, secondary qualities were stripped off, leaving only the primary qualities of extension and motion. Even in the nineteenth century the understanding of a physical happening was thought to be equivalent to the ability to make a mechanical model or physical picture of it. With electrodynamics, the copy theory was abandoned. The ideal of science was no longer to picture but to predict.

The function of the scientific concept is now to symbolize reality and not to picture it, mathematics supplying the fundamental symbolism; *e, g.,* the concept of light has progressed through Newton's corpuscles, Huygens' waves and Planck's quanta to a wave-mechanical ψ. To speak of wave and corpuscle properties then becomes nonsense.

Of course, not all constructs of modern physics are of this type. In fact, one physicist has distinguished three classes of constructs or symbols: (*a*) the sensible, such as physical models; (*b*) the pseudo-sensible, such as atoms and electrons; (*c*) the abstract or wholly insensible, such as the quantum mechanical, in which the electron and any other physical system is replaced by an abstract construct.

Before leaving the question of language, one should of course point out that in poetry, for example, certain aspects of reality which are perhaps otherwise inexplicable are sometimes expressed best by deviations from the real—as in T. S. Eliot's:

> They are rattling breakfast plates in basement kitchens
> And along the trampled edges of the street
> I am aware of the *damp souls* of the housemaids
> Sprouting despondently at area gates.

While this verges on the grotesque, it is revelatory to an extraordinary degree.

While the exact significance of what poets say may be questioned, there is no doubt that poetic and artistic symbols do awaken within us powerful feelings. Another writer has said:

> Art in all its forms, asserts the reality of the experienced qualities of things. The poet hears the rippling brook, and unlike the physicist, he does not abstract the atoms and sound waves and forms of running water. . . . That which the poet catches and the physicist misses is the bare indeterminate experienced quality which the psychical contributes, and this has its roots neither in observed nature nor in man, but in the ultimate atomic elements out of which both are constituted.

Actually, that which he catches is not physics but metaphysics.

Naturally one does not wish to dispense with poetry, fiction, fantasy, or emotions, since life would indeed be duller without them. But more and more in science the philosophy of the operational approach should be adopted, for even in science words are not always what they seem, and an eloquent but wrong use of words has often "lent an air of verisimilitude to an otherwise improbable hypothesis."

Science and Creativity

The pure sciences concern themselves with so-called scientific principles, laws, and theories which apply to matter in general and which do not
usually require that one have a certain amount of the matter in order to
observe the phenomenon in question. However, in the applied sciences we
are interested in having a certain amount of the material and in having it in
a certain configuration. For example, the engineer is interested in having a
rod or a sheet or even a cylinder of metal which he uses to fabricate
machines and other useful devices. A whole new set of laws and theories
applies to material en masse. These things which the engineer has created
are used in different arrangements to build houses and cities, which are in
the field of subjects such as architecture and town planning. We start
talking about one design as being more "economical" or more "elegant"
and we get into a whole new world of values, which eventually involves us
in ethics and in the humanities generally.

Actually, engineers built houses and bridges long before the chemists
knew anything about the chemical behaviour of mortar. The humanists and
philosophers expressed their views about man and his world for a still
longer period of time. It is only rather recently that the relationship between
science and the humanities has been seriously discussed.

The natural sciences as is well known, are concerned with the
knowledge of objects in nature, with the changes occurring in these objects,
and with the laws governing such changes. Not all branches of science are
studied with equal intensity, and it can be said in a general way that those
branches of science which are likely to yield returns of immediate interest
are likely to be the most intensively studied. For example, about two

centuries ago, when improvements in navigation were of prime importance, much attention was paid to the study of the heavenly bodies and to the development of mathematics applicable to such studies. Similarly, in the last century, much attention was paid to physics and chemistry and to their applications to industry, while in the last decade, an equal attention was paid to electronics and nuclear phenomena and to their application to war.

While the practical aspects of science may seem to have received undue stress, it is worth emphasizing that science has proved itself to be a particularly powerful way of dealing with certain aspects of our experience—those aspects exemplified by the so-called natural laws, such as Boyle's Law and Ohm's Law. It has also had a considerable success in dealing with the more subtle and complicated phenomena of astrophysics and nuclear physics. Even in the realm of animate nature, biochemistry has been able to deal with the happenings within the individual cells of living creatures. It is, perhaps, not too much to claim that science has given us an understanding and control of the forces of physical nature.

An important corollary of the progress of science is that it justifies the unspoken belief of the scientist in the rational faculty of the mind and in the ability of man to arrive at a reasonably coherent picture of the universe in which he lives. To quote Cassirer, "We may dispute concerning the results of science, but its general function seems to be unquestionable. It is science that gives us the assurance of a constant world." Science is often thought of as dull fact-grubbing, but this contemptuous assessment is surely indefensible, for the conceptual universe depicted by science is a product of the creative imagination. Research in science means the objective discovery of new things and new phenomena and the building up of a body of adequate theory. In this last aspect it is closely related to the composing of a piece of music, to the writing of a great novel, or to the execution of a great painting—all involve creativity of a high order. Scientists such as Galileo, Lavoisier, and Einstein are characterized by the genius exhibited at the beginning of their investigations and by the economy of thought through which they achieve their results.

A consideration of the human and creative aspects of science leads one naturally to ask how the practitioners of science get ideas. How did Lucretius first get his concept of an atom? How did Dalton develop his atomic theory? How did Rutherford first get the idea of a nuclear atom? In what way can the scientist claim to be creative? Two important books on the subject of creativity are *The Creative Process in Science and Medicine*, by H. H. Krebs and J. H. Shelley (New York: American Elsevier, 1975), and *Facing Reality* by J. C. Eccles (New York: Heidelberg Science Library, 1970).

In 1939 I had a very bright student working with me on the reactions of a red liquid, dichlorine hexoxide (Cl_2O_6), formed by the interaction of ozone and chlorine dioxide, the ozone being formed by the action of a silent electric discharge on pure oxygen. One day, instead of getting the expected red liquid he obtained some white crystals which fumed in moist air and exploded in contact with organic materials. On analysis these turned out to be a new compound, $NClO_6$, later named nitroxyl perchlorate. It was formed purely accidentally; there was a leak in the ozonizer equipment, letting in some air which formed nitrogen dioxide (NO_2) in the ozonizer and it, with O_3 and ClO_2 formed $NClO_6$. A possible sequence of reactions might be:

$$NO_2 + O_3 \rightarrow NO_3 + O_2$$
$$ClO_2 + O_3 \rightarrow ClO_3 + O_2$$
$$NO_3 + ClO_3 \rightarrow NClO_6$$

As far as I am concerned, this was straight luck and not creativity, although I suspect that a painter who put a dab of this here and a dab of that there and came up with a masterpiece would take full credit for creativity.

This discovery for nitroxyl perchlorate may be compared with the discovery of a new method for making Cl_2O_6 that I chanced upon while investigating the photosensitized decomposition of ozone in the presence of chlorine. When light is absorbed by a mixture of chlorine and ozone, the ozone is decomposed into oxygen, the chlorine apparently remaining unchanged. For low concentrations of ozone, two molecules of ozone are decomposed for each quantum of light (q) absorbed. This reaction is explained by the scheme:

$$Cl_2 + q \rightarrow 2Cl$$
$$2(Cl + O_3 \rightarrow ClO_3)$$
$$2ClO_3 \rightarrow Cl_2O_6$$
$$Cl_2O_6 \rightarrow Cl_2 + 3O_2$$

For high ozone concentrations there was a chain reaction, quantum yield approximately 100. This reaction is explained by the scheme:

$$ClO_3 + O_3 \rightarrow ClO_2 + 2O_2 \qquad)$$
$$\qquad\qquad\qquad\qquad\qquad)\text{chain}$$
$$ClO_2 + O_3 \rightarrow ClO_2 + O_2 \qquad)$$

The last equation was tested, and in fact, when ClO_2 and ozone were mixed in a suitable glass chamber, a red liquid Cl_2O_6, formed by $2ClO_3 \rightarrow Cl_2O_6$, was deposited on the sides of the vessel. This little piece of research did, to my mind, involve creativity of a high order.

Shortly after World War II, radiation sources became available, making it possible for relatively small chemical laboratories to launch into studies in radiation chemistry. Radiation chemistry formed a natural extension to my early work in photochemistry, so I encouraged one of my students, Bill Hummel, to make preliminary studies on a well-known system, the oxidation of ferrous sulfate solution. All we did was to vary the energy of the radiation using X-rays, cobalt gamma rays, and rays from a betatron (20 Mev), but we had the advantage of close relations with a group of physicists, Harold Johns and Dr. Katz in particular, who were well up in the experimental and theoretical aspects of energy absorption. So we got some meaningful results. Other students worked on other systems covering liquid, gaseous, and solid phases. Each time the results were quite original, and occasionally we hit on something interesting. In photochemistry intermittent light radiation was used to determine the mean life of free radicals. We were able to do the first intermittent gamma ray experiments using a powerful cobalt γ ray source and a rotating slotted steel cylinder. Later we had the idea of pulsing the material instead of the radiation, and we obtained similar results—a very simple idea but quite imaginative—at least no one else had thought of it at that time. I later investigated free radicals using electron-spin techniques. The method involved placing some of the material in a glass tube and irradiating it with gamma rays. Naturally, the glass was irradiated at the same time, producing free radicals in the glass itself which themselves gave an electron-spin pattern that formed an undesirable background to the electron-spin pattern of the material being investigated. We were able to avoid getting this background for certain materials by carrying out the irradiation with soft β particles from tritium, the tritium being added to the specimen in the form of tritiated water. The betas were absorbed by the liquid and not appreciably by the glass walls of the containing vessel. Not an earthshaking idea but still quite original!

During 1950 I worked with Dr. Armstrong on the synthesis of ethyl bromide from ethylene and hydrogen bromide, using gamma rays as the initiator of the reaction. Some years later the method was used by Dow Chemicals as the basis for making ethyl bromide on an industrial scale. While the initial idea was not of the kind that makes headlines, it was quite original, and to that extent it satisfied some of the criteria for creativity. Indeed, Harmer ("Industrial Uses of Large Radiation Sources," IAEA, Vol. II, p. 207, Vienna, 1963) suggests that our publications stimulated additional interest in the United States in the possibilities of a radiation-chemical route to produce ethyl bromide.

In spite of the glowing picture which I have painted of the scientist as the imaginative artist and as the material benefactor of this modern age, there is still a tendency to look down upon the scientist as a barbarian. Ortega declared, "The new barbarians are the highly competent professional men—lawyers, physicians, engineers, etc., more learned than ever before, but at the same time more uncultured."

Hardly more complimentary is Churchill, who once declared that the scientist "should be on tap but not on top." He started a memorandum setting up the atom bomb project with the words, "Although personally I am quite content with existing explosives...." This bland phrase is a monument to a non-scientific education. Everyone knows of the debt which the western world owes to the massive Churchillian phrases which kept England going in the dark days of 1940, but we are also not unaware of the major part played by radar and by the physicists who had developed radar in the 1930s. It is of some interest that Britain entered the 1939 war without a single scientist or person with any degree of scientific training in the Cabinet—a war which she would almost certainly have lost but for a handful of scientists.

One of the former chairmen of the Parliamentary and Scientific Committee for the United Kingdom, Sir Henry Tizzard, has been much worried about the lack of scientific background in high places and has stated in a public lecture: "There still remains the problem of ensuring that the majority of our future administrators, if not all, shall have had a broad scientific education. The fact that most arts students at universities have now had education in the natural sciences up to a low prescribed standard at school does not meet the need at all. Much more than that is needed for the education of higher ministers . . . I can foresee even greater changes in society within the next hundred years than in the past . . . the changes will all be due, directly or indirectly, to the advance of science and technology. The great need of government will be to avoid the social dangers that the changes will involve, even in times of peace, without losing the benefits. How this can be done without forethought based on a real knowledge and understanding, I do not know."

Where many matters of national importance are of a scientific nature, it is essential that the public have a general understanding of science, for in a democracy it is upon the popular attitude towards science that the attractiveness of the profession, the resulting selectivity for those entering the profession, and the degree of support obtained for their work will depend. There is a real danger at the present time that scientific information may come to be regarded as something separate from what the layman calls common-sense knowledge, and that science itself may be treated as something outside the scope of, or even antagonistic to the humanities. The member of parliament who, when asked his opinion of the atomic energy film which he had just seen, replied that it was interesting but scientific, and therefore he could not be expected to understand it, was adopting an attitude which is still common among people who would never admit to a lack of appreciation of art or music, or to an inability to understand the complex jargon of the race course or the stock exchange. One of the main tasks is to break down this barrier by showing that science is not an esoteric cult but an important component in the structure of our common affairs and that scientific ideas form an integral part of the pattern of our thoughts.

In spite of this lack of understanding of science by the general public, there is an increasing demand for scientists and technologists to satisfy the requirements of our modern civilization. Many of these scientists and technologists receive their training in our universities, and it is of some interest to examine the impact of science itself and the teaching of science on the universities. It is also of interest to examine the compatibility of the aims of science with the traditional aims of the university, long the stronghold and bastion of the humanities.

About a hundred years ago Newman expressed the ideal of the

university as that of being a repository of knowledge and ancient wisdom, and he stated that the university fulfilled its duty if it kept this wisdom alive and handed it on from generation to generation. He thought that research was better done in academies and institutions, and that in fact, a good teacher was unlikely to have time to do research. However, universities like other institutions are subject to change, and nowadays the universities have as one of their major aims the extension of the boundaries of knowledge. It has even been said that for a modern university to stop doing research is for it to commit academic suicide. Similarly, in choosing new staff one usually looks for the productive person, on the grounds that the head of a department who is well known for research will be able to attract lively young researchers, and between them, the burden of teaching can be well taken care of. One of the main objectives in teaching at the university level is to inspire students to work and think for themselves. Who can do this better than the academic who is still actively contributing to the production of new knowledge? The nightmare of a president is to have unproductive heads of departments, for it soon becomes evident that, with an unproductive head, the whole department loses interest in furthering knowledge, too. Universities have proved, for their part, to be ideal places for doing fundamental research; they provide time to think, an opportunity to work and talk with keen minds in other disciplines, the stimulus of contact with bright students, and the lack of being prodded to some close and fixed goal.

It is often claimed that science students specialize too narrowly and take little interest in the humanities, and unfortunately this criticism is often true. However, it should be pointed out that a scientific education does have this advantage—it succeeds to a remarkable degree in its primary aim, that is in producing scientists. It should be added, too, that the scientist has a fair idea of what constitutes truth, and of how it should be sought and taught in his field of endeavor.

It has been suggested quite seriously in some quarters that science and the humanities resemble Tweedledum and Tweedledee, and that at the present time, they are in the process of changing places. In the past, classics reigned throughout the whole sphere of higher education. There were no rivals. There was a large demand for classical scholars, and there was a classical tone in all learned walks of life, so that aptitude in classics was a synonym for ability. However, all this is gone, and gone forever. There are now other disciplines, each involving topics of widespread interest, which often exhibit in their development veritable feats of genius, both in stretch of imagination and in philosophic intuition. Almost every walk of life is now a learned profession and demands one or more of these newer disciplines as the substratum for its technical skill. In the old days, scholars at the colleges of Oxford and Cambridge were trained for positions in and around the Court, and one of the reasons why the colleges expanded was that more such people were required as secretaries, scribes, notaries, and teachers. It is, therefore, quite appropriate that nowadays, when people are required in large numbers in the scientific professions, universities should train them.

In spite of the seeming rivalry between science and the humanities there is much to be said in favor of the view of Father Levesque of Laval University who recently expressed himself as preferring the word *humanism* to *humanities*. He went on to say that "Science, technology, even the humanities, should be regarded as the products of man and at the service of man. A scientist may be a humanist and vice versa; there is not necessarily or essentially a conflict between the two." Science has, of course, strong ties with a number of the humanities subjects and is often largely dependent on them.

The scientist can get quite excited about history and particularly about archaeology, disciplines in which the evidence is meticulously sifted and weighed in reaching conclusions about early civilizations. History has an important part to play in the teaching of science, which should be not just the bare recital of the dates when certain laws were propounded, but a humanistic approach to the interplay of new techniques and discoveries and to the growth of technology and its influence on the spread of knowledge and on the development of civilizations.

The use of logic in examining the coherence of a scientific theory and in testing the deductions made from its postulates is so obvious that it need not be stressed here. In addition, science is becoming more and more interested in symbolic logic, which can be particularly valuable in testing constructs in rapidly developing theories such as the gene theory of heredity, or in testing neurological theories. In spite of this interlocking, there is a regrettable lack of liaison in most universities between science and logic. A few science students do take courses in logic, but it must be admitted that logic taught in the classical manner does not appeal to them. Some slight sympathy on the part of the teachers of logic for the problems of the science student would seem highly desirable, since the science students have much to gain from a thorough grasp of logic. It would be most valuable if a few of the illustrative problems in elementary logic could be placed in the field of science.

There is, of course, a strong interdependence between science and philosophy, but one has to admit that some scientists find difficulty in following certain so-called philosophic approaches or in swallowing certain philosophies. The extreme view on the one hand is represented by one local scientist who defined philosophy as "largely what the scientists haven't got around to yet." He also said that "the problems of philosophy were largely those which could be speculated about or reasoned about with insufficient facts or proven theory. Alternatively, they involved taking scientific conclusions and trying to carry them further than scientists would go on the available information."

An equally extreme view is taken by some of the modern philosophers, such as Heidegger and the existentialists: "Truth, the Real or Being, is an elusive thing like rare game. It reveals itself to him who offers his mind to it, who stalks it secretly without disturbance. The scientist uses brutal methods to attack the real; he forces it into traps, overpowers and captures it. What he finally possesses is not living truth but the corpse of truth."

In spite of these extreme views, science and philosophy can be mutually helpful. Thus modern physics, for example, holds a message for philosophy. As a matter of fact, the first effect of Einstein's theory of relativity was philosophical rather than technical. Philosophers and theoreticians had to review their conception of the universe as a result of his work. Einstein's discoveries gave us a new way of conceiving the observable raw data of our experience.

A paragraph from Ortega's *The Modern Theme* will emphasize the point:

> The science of today is the magic vessel into which we have to look to obtain a glimmering of the future. The modifications, which may appear to be only technical, that modern biology, physics, sociology or prehistory are producing, through their experimental work, in the whole fabric of philosophy, are the preliminary gestures of the new age. The extremely delicate subject matter of science . . . is capable of acting at the present moment as a register, on a very small scale, of phenomena which will, with the passage of years, loom gigantic upon the stage of public life. . . . Unless our generation desires to lag behind in its own destiny, it must adopt some kind of orientation towards the general character of modern science. . . . On what men are beginning to think today, depends how they will live in the market places tomorrow.

If the philosopher can profit from modern science, equally there is no doubt that men engaged in the development of physical theory can profit from philosophical reflection about the meaning of their research. It is of interest that while science starts in dealing with what we may define as pure fact (that which is known by immediate apprehension alone), it soon gets away from this approach. Thus the astronomer who examines the sun sees as a pure fact the beauty of the sunset. The scientific object, the sun, which is a three-dimensional spherical mass of atoms, is a theoretically inferred object or a construct. The instrument for showing the sun as pure fact is that of the impressionist artist.

There is another philosophical problem in that some things are not observable all the time, and yet we attribute to them continuing properties—for example color to the flowers at night. So, quite obviously, there are metaphysical elements in physics; science will tell us what things are real but it will refuse to say what is reality. We should not expect science "to put salt on the tail of the absolute," as Aldous Huxley puts it.

The structure of scientific knowledge is a mental structure, a conceptual tapestry woven from the gossamer threads of thought. Who is bold enough to say what relationship the tapestry has to the reality behind it? That there is some regular relationship may be inferred by the success of prediction. Science as well as the arts is an expression of man's effort to bring order and beauty and understanding into his life.

In addition to problems of fact, there are problems of value, paramount in the humanities and the social sciences. It is characteristic of a problem of values that, in part at least, it raises the question of what ought to be rather than of what is. It is important to distinguish, in the humanities, between problems which require factual social theories for their answer and problems which require normative social theories. One critic has pointed unkindly "to the failure of the traditional methods to solve a single specific normative problem of our world, notwithstanding the fact that the proposed traditional methods have been known for centuries." He also said that "If the methods for handling problems of fact in the natural sciences could evidence in their support only talk about their adequacy, while never solving a specific scientific problem or verifying a specific theory, so as to remove it from the realm of controversy and debate, experts studying nature would most certainly reject them. It is time for social scientists, moral philosophers, and humanists to do the same with the traditionally proposed methods for solving ethical and normative social problems." When the humanities people are inclined to chide the scientists for their failure to say anything about values, they should remember that while science may not create values, it does provide many of the means for their realization.

It seems that at present science is insufficient for the representation of human experience in at least two major fields, the areas of feeling and of value judgment. This deficiency is not necessarily a consequence of fundamental limitations of the scientific method, although possibly it may be. A comparison of scientific and ethical postulates seems to indicate a strong contrast. The former are initially tentative and are confirmed with use. For the latter we are strangely practical. We often display for them an irrational insistence on *a priori* evidence; we demand that they come to us accredited with absolute certainty or with divine sanction. This contrast leaves one with the feeling that a wholesome scientific attitude might be useful in trying to assess certain ethics and in sorting out the various aspects of an ethical problem.

As late as the seventeenth century there was a fierce intolerance about minute details such as the permissibility of surplices, the status of lecterns, or the sound of church bells. And there was equally a violent dislike of witches. That such matters no longer rouse any great passions is at least in part a result of the spread of rational science. It does not, unfortunately, follow that we are much better off for losing old superstitions, for in chasing out the one devil we seem to have let in seven more at least as bad as the first. Man's prejudiced nature has merely found other outlets for his aggression, outlets typified by the words, *rich* and *poor, nationalist* and *imperialist, colored* and *white, communist* and *bourgeois,* and so on.

In strong contrast to the inability of science to say much about ethics, science itself does raise many ethical problems. These are not the common problems related to truth and honesty which plague some professions, since the scientist commonly would not dream of falsifying his results. They are, rather, problems raised by the use made of some of the fruits of science, as for example, in weapons of mass destruction. Should a scientist work on the development of such weapons? Should he work on those aspects of a science which might lead to improvements in such weapons?

The advent of science brings with it perplexing difficulties, but with the advance of science a host of favorable forces will operate in mankind's behalf, as a result of his ever increasing power and his wider and deeper understanding of his environment and of himself and the social organism. It has been claimed that science is uniting the world intellectually as has nothing since the early Church sent its missionaries and disciples abroad. While this claim may be somewhat exaggerated, it is true that science has become a great international cooperative enterprise, transcending, for the most part, racial and political barriers. The interchange of scientific information is so necessary and advantageous that science is a powerful factor in promoting international good will and the realization of the unity of the human race.

In a recent speech, a Nobel Prize winner has suggested that an epoch in history, our own, which has produced one of the greatest achievements of the human race, may be passing into a twilight which does *not* precede the dawn. Science, the triumph of the intellect and the natural faculties, has resulted in the hydrogen bomb; the glib conclusion is that science and the intellect are false guides. We must seek elsewhere for hope and salvation, but, say the same people, we must keep ahead of the Russians. Incidentally, there is little likelihood of the Russians and us getting together on the basis of a purely humanistic philosophy since in this sphere our respective doctrines flatly contradict one another. However, there may be the possibility of an agreement based on a philosophy of the natural sciences, since the Russians do believe in the scientific method and in the natural sciences, Lysenko notwithstanding.

What educated people are really looking for today is wisdom. Wisdom is knowledge plus understanding, a quality which is within the human being. Without it, knowledge is dry and almost unfit for human consumption. The humanities preserve and create values. They express the symbolic, poetic, and prophetic qualities of the human spirit to the highest degree. Without the humanities we would not be conscious of our history. We would lose many of our aspirations and the graces of expression that move men's hearts.

The humanities discern a part, a vital part, of the life of man, but that is not all by any means. Man lives in a universe of which he is a part. To learn to understand himself he must also learn something of the universe. There is no scientific basis for the classical axiom that the proper study of mankind is man. The value of science or literary scholarship lies not in subject matter alone. It lies chiefly in the spirit and living tradition in which these disciplines are pursued. Science and the humanities are not the same thing. The subject matter and the spirit and the traditions are different. Our problem in the search for wisdom is to blend these two traditions in the minds of individual men and women.

The greatest difficulty which stands in the way of a meeting of the minds of the scientist and the non-scientist is probably the difficulty of communication. The mature scientist can listen with pleasure to the philosopher, the historian, the literary man, and even to the art critic. He reads, listens to music, and generally enjoys the arts. Unfortunately, this channel of communication is almost a one-way street. Despite its universal outlook, its unifying principle, and its splendid tradition, science seems no longer to be communicable to the great majority of educated laymen. To many of them, the scientist seems to be a creature scattering antibiotics with one hand and H-bombs with the other.

All in all, in spite of these difficulties of communication, there are many possible bridges between science and the humanities, and one may even wonder why the practice of placing science and the humanities in juxtaposition has arisen. The apparent contraries are not exclusive but interdependent. The relationship between science and the humanities can be summarized in a sentence from Heraclitus: "Men do not understand how that which is torn in different directions comes into accord with itself—harmony in contrariety, as in the case of the bow and the lyre."

Chapter 27

Epilogue: Zero–One

I am now over seventy, having spent one-third of my life in England and two-thirds in Canada, mostly on the prairies—a Norfolk Dumpling has been transformed by some strange alchemy into a Prairie Gopher—a fairly big gopher but a gopher none the less! Many forces have been at play in my life. Some have been purely physical, such as the weather and natural events; some have been historical, such as the events which have taken place, including the two world wars and the many other extraordinary events of the last half-century; and some of the forces in my life have been spiritual.

My reaction to these forces has been partly physical (a cut finger, a bruised knee, a slice of roast beef transformed into muscle and energy) and partly mental. These latter effects are triggered by physical happenings. I look at this piece of paper and see the letter **I,** formed by the arrangement of a few specks of colloidal carbon on a sheet of paper. For the letter to appear on the paper, the colloidal carbon had to be obtained by the partial oxidation of hydrocarbon gases coming from strata a few thousand feet below the surface of the prairie, where they had been deposited by the decay of living substances from the earth some millions of years ago. The paper, consisting of a layer of cellulose fibres ($C_{12}H_{22}O_{11}$) had to be obtained from a Douglas Fir which had been carrying out a photosynthetic reaction, $CO_2 + H_2O + light \rightarrow C_{12}H_{22}O_{11}$, for five hundred years or so, within sight of the Pacific Ocean. Light, in the form of photons, had to be reflected from the paper and the carbon so as to fall on the rods and cones in the retina of my eye, there to bring about a slight chemical change, resulting in an electric impulse from my eye to my brain by way of the optic nerve, which arrived there and fired the axons and neurons, much as in a super-duper computer, so that the neurons acted to give pattern recognition, or what we call memory and thought. These memories will be stored and will later result in further electric messages to other parts of the body and in subsequent biochemical and physiological reactions. All this complicated account of how the brain works leads me to the modern parable of the computer:

> The computational analyst went out to solve problems using computers, and some of his problems were fed into computers by means of incorrectly structured programs, while others were fed into computers which had inadequately filled data banks. But some of his problems were fed into computers which had well-filled data banks and correctly structured programs. These computers produced satisfactory print-outs in short periods of time, and the computational analyst went on his way rejoicing.

It seems to be generally agreed nowadays that the brain consists of a complicated assemblage of axons and neurons which can be triggered by electrical impulses reaching the brain through the intermediary of the various senses of sight, hearing, taste, smell, and touch. The brain acts in many ways like a giant computer, and this reflection leads us then to make the following observations—all, may I say, from a rather simplistic point of view. These observations have a bearing on my ideas about education and on my personal philosophy.

First, if nothing is fed into the computer, it won't matter how pretty and shiny the computer is or how often you press the correct buttons, for nothing can possibly come out. Thus a certain amount of basic information must be fed into the computer before anything can happen. A corollary of the parallel drawn between computer and human brain is that a student must be given certain basic information which should be as accurate and as up-to-date as possible. Not all of the information needs to be in the particular computer being used. The student can tie into a much more extensive computer system, and this tying in corresponds to learning how to make use of information stored in libraries, computers, other people's heads, and similar sources. In short, information retrieval, in one form or another, should be taught at an early stage in the student's education.

It should be recognized, of course, that an enormous amount of guff and downright misinformation is fed into the student's computer every day, and for that matter into everyone else's computer, by way of television and other communications media. Instilling a healthy scepticism of all information and teaching the young how to arrive at the truth is a must. The Communists are not the only ones to indulge in brainwashing.

Secondly, no matter how much information is available in the data bank, if the computer is incorrectly programed or the wrong buttons are pressed, "incorrect" answers will be obtained. Thus the student needs to be taught how to think logically, so that he may arrive at a fairly logical conclusion even if an inadequate amount of information is available, and even if these items of information have conflicting significance. This teaching is, of course, a tall order, and it will tax the skills of even the best of teachers. Fortunately, our everyday common-sense approach to things is basically a scientific approach: we assume that there is a basic orderliness to nature and that natural phenomena follow certain relatively simple basic rules or laws.

The deterministic approach of the natural sciences is an Aristotelian approach—a thing either is or it is not, and of course the elements in a computer work in the same way—the little magnets in the memory drum are either up or down. A computer can thus, as is well known, act as a simple logic board and make the correct deductions from a given set of assumptions. The brain, consisting of axons and neurons which can either fire or not fire, can operate similarly in accordance with Aristotelian logic—in fact, apart from secondary factors, it can hardly do anything else. One might quip that given the type of brain we have, it is hard to think of Aristotle's arriving at anything but Aristotelian logic. The amusing thing is that Aristotle arrived at his form of logic without the modern knowledge of brain structure.

One could elaborate on this approach to memory and learning at great length, but to do that would take too much space. There is still another point to make. Using the methods of science we can find out about nature—the why of things—however, science tells us nothing about what we should do. Science does not help us with ethical problems, that is, problems of value. For guidance we must turn to the accumulated record of all human experience, to the understanding revealed by the study of human behavior, and to the ethical teachings of our religious faiths. These are the strands that through education must be interwoven with science and technology to form the fabric of a single culture and the life of a peaceful and harmonious world.

What educated people are looking for today is wisdom, and perhaps the greatest challenge to the teacher is to teach the young the ideas of right and wrong, a love of country, and a love for one's fellow man. This may sound old-fashioned, but I feel sure that without such teaching our much vaunted modern approach with new math, chem-study, and all the rest will lead to naught. Thus the wise should be asked to indicate what should be taught, the researchers should help determine how best to do the teaching, the teachers should continuously update their teaching methods, and the operations researchers should help to optimize the overall educational process.

Having been educated for the future we may ask, to what purpose? I would suggest that we should use this education to help solve a few of the many problems awaiting us in the strange world in which we live.

In spite of the advances in the last sixty years or so, we have to admit that in this period we have been singularly inept in dealing with social and political problems. People still starve, and people still fail to realize the perils associated with getting a kick out of the latest drugs such as L.S.D. There have been two major world wars in my lifetime, each getting more destructive and more inhumane, as we see by the gas chambers of Auschwitz and the hundred thousand dead at Hiroshima. And there has been a major war in Vietnam. We don't know how to live amicably with our neighbors, we don't know how to deal with poverty and crime, and most of our citizens have no idea how to make profitable use of the growing amount of leisure that our modern civilization provides. We need, then, an adequate number of broadly educated men and women who are both imaginative and creative, and who can help solve some of our social and spiritual problems. "To everything there is a season, and a time to every purpose under the heaven: a time to be born, and a time to die; a time to plant, and a time to pluck up that which is planted."

Appendix A — List of Publications

List of Abbreviations and Sources.*

*Only publications appearing more than three times have been abbreviated; all others appear in full in the text. Publication data on publications with a limited circulation is entered here, rather than in the text.

Can. Chem. Processing (Canadian Chemical Processing). Formerly Canadian Chemical and Process Industries. Toronto.

Can. J. Chem. (Canadian Journal of Chemistry) Ottawa.

Can. J. Res. (Canadian Journal of Research) Ottawa.

Can. J. Tech. (Canadian Journal of Technology) Ottawa.

Chem. Can. (Chemistry in Canada) Ottawa.

J. Am. Chem. Soc. (Journal of the American Chemical Society) Easton, Pa.

J. Chem. Phys. (Journal of Chemical Physics) Lancaster, Pa.

J. Chem. Soc. (Journal of Chemical Society) London.

Nature, Lond. (London).

The Rotunda. Published annually 1927–1961 by Emmanuel Theological College, University of Saskatchewan.

Sci. Agric. (Scientific Agriculture) Ottawa.

The Sheaf. Published weekly by the Students' Representative Council, University of Saskatchewan.

Z für Phys. (Zeitschrift für Physik) Braunschweig.

CHRONOLOGICAL LIST OF PUBLICATIONS

1929   1.   A. J. ALLMAND and J. W. T. SPINKS: Photosensitized decomposition of ozone. *Nature, Lond.* **124,** 651. 1929.

1931   2.   J. W. T. SPINKS: The analysis of chlorine-monoxide-chlorine mixtures. *J. Am. Chem. Soc.* **53,** 3015-3016. 1931.

       3.   J. W. T. SPINKS: Photosensitized decomposition of ozone by bromine. *Nature, Lond.* **128,** 548. 1931.

       4a.   A. J. ALLMAND and J. W. T. SPINKS: The action of light on mixtures of ozone and chlorine. Part I. Experimental. Results with low ozone concentrations. *J. Chem. Soc.* 1652-1666. 1931.

1932   4b.   A. J. ALLMAND and J. W. T. SPINKS: The action of light on mixtures of ozone and chlorine. Part II. Results with high ozone concentrations. Discussion. *J. Chem. Soc.* 599-612. 1932.

       5.   J. W. T. SPINKS: Gaseous photo decomposition of chlorine dioxide. *J. Am Chem. Soc.* **54,** 1689-1690. 1932.

1933   6.   J. W. T. SPINKS: Bromo-sensitized photo-decomposition of chlorine dioxide. *J. Am. Chem. Soc.* **55,** 428. 1933.

1934   7.   G. HERZBERG, F. PATAT, and J. W. T. SPINKS: Brands of "heavy" acetylene in the near infra-red. *Nature, Lond.* **133,** 951. 1934.

       8.   J. W. T. SPINKS and J. M. PORTER: Photodecomposition of chlorine dioxide. *J. Am. Chem. Soc.* **56,** 264-270. 1934.

       9.   G. HERZBERG and J. W. T. SPINKS: Absorption bands of HCN in the photographic infra-red. *Proceedings Royal Society of London,* A, **147,** 862, 434-442. 1934.

      10.   G. HERZBERG and J. W. T. SPINKS. Ueber das Rotationsschwingungsspektrum des Acetylens (C_2H_2). *Z. für Phys,* **91,** 5-6, 386-399. 1934.

      11.   G. HERZBERG and J. W. T. SPINKS: Photographie der zweiten Oberschwing des HCl bei 1.19u mit grosser Dispersion. *Z. für Phys,* **89,** 7-8, 474-479. 1934.

      12.   J. W. T. SPINKS: Ueber ein ultraviolettes Bandensystem von AsN. *Z. für Phys,* **88,** 511-514. 1934.

      13.   G. HERZBERG, F. PATAT, and J. W. T. SPINKS: Rotationsschwingungsspektren im photograpischen Ultrarot von Molekulen, die das Wasserstoffisotop der Masse 2 enthalten. 1. Das C HD-Spektrum und der C.C. und C.H. Abstand im Acetylen. *Z. für Phys,* **92,** 1-2, 87-99. 1934.

1936.   14.   G. HERZBERG, J. W. T. SPINKS, and W. W. WATSON: Pressure broadening of the HCN band lines and intermolecular forces. *The Physical Review* **50,** 12, 1186. 1936.

1937.   15.   J. W. T. SPINKS and H. TAUBE. Photodecomposition of chlorine dioxide in carbon tetrachloride solution. *J. Am. Chem. Soc.* **59,** 1155. 1937.

      16.   A. G. BROWN and J. W. T. SPINKS: The bromine sensitized decomposition of chlorine monoxide in green light. *Can. J. Res.* **B, 15,** 113-123. 1937.

      17.   J. W. T. SPINKS and H. TAUBE: Photodecomposition of chlorine dioxide in carbon tetrachloride solution. *Can. J. Res.* **B, 15,** 499-524. 1937.

      18.   J. W. T. SPINKS: *Atomic Spectra and Atomic Structure* (translated from the German of G. Herzberg). Prentice-Hall, New York. 1937.

1938   19.   F. H. EDMUNDS, J. L. JACKSON, J. W. T. SPINKS, and V. A. VIGFUSSON: Some skeletal remains in Saskatchewan. *American Antiquity* **3,** 3, 244-246. 1938.

      20.   J. W. T. SPINKS and M. KALINA: Dichlorine hexoxide. *Can. J. Res.* **B, 16,** 381-389. 1938.

1939   21. J. W. T. Spinks: *Molecular Spectra and Molecular Structure*, Part I. (translated from Herzberg's German Edition) Diatomic Molecules. Prentice-Hall, New York. 1939.

1940   22. J. W. T. Spinks: Photoreactions sensitized by the halogens. *Chemical Reviews* **26**, 1, 129-139. 1940.

23. W. E. Gordon and J. W. T. Spinks: Nitroxyl perchlorate. *Can. J. Res.* **B, 18**, 358-362. 1940.

24. R. Mungen and J. W. T. Spinks: The bromine-sensitized photo-decomposition of ozone. *Can. J. Res.* **B, 18**, 363-371. 1940.

25. L. M. Watson and J. W. T. Spinks: The separation and identification of the compounds present in a Turner Valley crude oil. *Can. J. Res.* **B, 18**, 388-404. 1940.

1942.   26. J. W. T. Spinks: Rotational structure of the Birge-Hopfields bands of N_2. *Can. J. Res.* **A, 20**, 1-5. 1942.

27. L. G. Hendrickson, A. T. Hutcheon, and J. W. T. Spinks: Aromatics in Turner Valley crudes. *Can. J. Res.* **20**, 231-239. 1942.

1943   28. W. G. May, K. A. Miners, and J. W. T. Spinks: Preliminary examination of some Turner Valley crude oils. *Can. J. Res.* **B, 21**, 73-79. 1943.

1945   29. B. C. Green and J. W. T. Spinks: Equilibrium diagrams for binary mixtures of aniline, ethylaniline, and diethylaniline. *Can. J. Res.* **B, 23**, 269-274. 1945.

30. J. W. T. Spinks: *Science as a force in world order study*, University of Saskatchewan Extension Dept,. 415-45.

1946   31. K. L. Knox and J. W. T. Spinks: Tracer experiments with radio-active indium. *Can. Chem. Processing*, 85-88. 1946.

32. J. W. T. Spinks and S. A. Barber: Study of fertilizer uptake using P-32. *J. Am. Chem. Soc.* **68**, 2748-2749. 1946

33. J. W. T. Spinks: Tracer applications. *National Research Council Division of Atomic Energy Summer Series*, N.R.C. No. 1682. 1946.

1947   34. W. Graham, A. T. Hutcheon, and J. W. T. Spinks: Catalytic aromatization of Turner Valley crudes. *Can. J. Res.* **B, 25**, 108-117. 1947.

35. J. W. T. Spinks (as told by R. MacDonald); Atomic research aids farm scientist. *Saskatchewan Farmer* **38**, 5, 1. 1947.

36. J. W. T. Spinks: Atomic research and agriculture. *Agricultural Institute Review*, **2**, 3, 213-220. 1947.

37. J. W. T. Spinks and S. A. Barber: Study of fertilizer uptake using radioactive phosphorus. *Sci. Agric.* **27**, 4, 145-157. 1947.

38. S. A. Barber, J. Mitchell, and J. W. T. Spinks: Soil studies using radioactive phosphorus. *Can. Chem. Processing*, **31**, 757-759. 1947.

39. J. W. T. Spinks: The use of radioactive tracers in chemistry of plant nutrition. *Proceedings of Conference on Nuclear Chemistry*, Chemical Institute of Canada, Hamilton Meeting, 134-152. 1947.

1948   40. J. W. T. Spinks and S. A. Barber: Study of fertilizer uptake using radioactive phosphorus: II. *Sci. Agric.* **28**, 2, 79-87. 1948.

41. J. W. T. Spinks and C. I. Tollefson: Adsorption measurements on flour using radioactive isotopes. *Cereal Chemistry* **25**, 2, 139-145. 1948.

42. T. J. Arnason, E. Cumming, and J. W. T. Spinks: Chromosome breakage in plants induced by radioactive phosphorus (P-32). *Science*, **107**, 2773, 198-199. 1948.

43. J. B. O'Neil, J. R. Jowsey, C. C. Lee, M. A. Reade, and J. W. T. Spinks:

Determination of the fate of phosphorus in the laying hen by means of radiophosphorus (P-32). *Science* **107**, 2777, 295-296. 1948.

44. J. W. T. SPINKS, H. G. DION, M. A. READE, and J. E. DEHM: Study of fertilizer uptake using radiophosphorus: III. *Sci. Agric.* **23**, 7, 309-314. 1948.

45. T. J. ARNASON, E. CUMMING, and J. W. T. SPINKS: Chromosome breakage induced by absorbed radioactive phosphorus, P-32. *Can. J. Res.* **C, 26**, 109-114. 1948.

46. J. W. T. SPINKS, J. B. O'NEIL, J. R. JOWSEY, C. C. LEE, and M. A. READE: The use of radiophosphorus, P-32, to measure phosphorus utilization by laying hens. *Can. J. Res.* **D, 26**, 163-176. 1948.

47. J. W. T. SPINKS, E. CUMMING, R. L. B. IRWIN, and T. ARNASON: Lethal effect of absorbed radioisotopes on plants. *Can J. Res.* **C, 26**, 249-262. 1948.

48. J. W. T. SPINKS: Halogen sensitized photoreactions. *Can. J. Res.* **B. 1**, 26, 629-642, 1948.

49. J. W. T. SPINKS: What atomic energy means to the prairies. *The Western Producer*, November 4, 1948.

1949   50. H. G. DION, J. W. T. SPINKS, and J. MITCHELL: Experiments with radiophosphorus on the uptake of phosphorus by wheat. *Sci. Agric.* **29**, 3, 167-172. 1949.

51. R. H. SINGLETON and J. W. T. SPINKS: A comparison of the direct and indirect radioactive methods for determining the surface area of a strontium sulfate precipitate. *Can. J. Res.* **B, 27**, 238-257. 1949.

52. J. B. O'NEIL, J. R. JOWSEY, C. C. LEE, and J. W. T. SPINKS; Distribution of P-32 in chick embryos. *Can. J. Res.* **D, 27**, 223-232. 1949.

53. J. W. T. SPINKS, C. C. LEE, and J. B. O'NEIL: The use of P-32 labeled glycerophosphate in the study of yolk phospholipids. *Can. J. Res.* **B, 27**, 629-637. 1949.

54. H. G. DION, R. BEDFORD, R. ST. ARNAUD, and J. W. T. SPINKS: Plant injury from phosphorus-32. *Nature, Lond.* **163**, 906-909. 1949.

55. R. M. STOW and J. W. T. SPINKS: Exchange of ions between the surface of crystals and solutions. *J. Chem. Phys.* **17**, 8, 744. 1949.

56. T. J. ARNASON, R. L. IRWIN, and J. W. T. SPINKS: Some effects of P-32 on the development of *Drosophila*. *Can. J. Res.* **D, 27**, 186-194. 1949.

57. J. W. T. SPINKS and H. G. DION: Study of fertilizer uptake using radiophosphorus. *J. Chem. Soc.* Suppl. Issue No 2, S410-S415. 1949.

58. J. W. T. SPINKS, M. R. BERLIE, and J. B. O'NEIL: Determination of the fate of calcium in the laying hen by means of radio-calcium (Ca^{45}). *Science* **110**, 2857, 332-333. 1949.

59. H. G. DION, J. E. DEHM, and J. W. T. SPINKS: Study of fertilizer uptake using radio-active phosphorus. IV. The availability of phosphate carriers in calcareous soils. *Sci. Agric.* **29**, 512-526. 1949.

60. J. W. T. SPINKS: Mr. Atom meets the Farmer. *Proceedings of the Royal Canadian Institute.* **14**, 70. 1949.

1950   61. J. W. T. SPINKS and L. B. JAQUES: Tracer experiments in mammals with Dicumarol labelled with carbon-14. *Nature, Lond.* **166**, 184. 1950.

62. J. W. T. SPINKS, V. A. VIGFUSSON, R. L. EAGER, W. GRAHAM, and T. THORVALDSON: Preliminary Report on the variation in the viscosity of stannic chloride, titanium chloride and of a mixture of chlorosulfonic acid and sulfur trioxide with temperature. Declared OPEN August 1950 by N.R.C.

63. J. W. T. SPINKS and G. A. R. GRAHAM: Preparation and characteristics of a polonium-beryllium neutron scource. *Can. J. Res.* **A, 28,** 60-66, 1950.

64. J. W. T. SPINKS: Artificial radioactivity. *The Canadian Medical Association Journal,* **62,** 120-122. 1950.

65. J. B. O'NEIL and J. W. T. SPINKS: Application of radioisotopes to a comparative study of calcium and phosphorus metabolism in the laying hen. *Chem. Can.,* 23(91)-25(93). 1950.

66. L. B. JAQUES, C. C. LEE, L. W. TREVOY, and J. W. T. SPINKS: Tracer experiments with radioactive Dicumarol. *Can. Chem. Processing.* **34,** 821. 1950.

67. L. B. JAQUES and J. W. T. SPINKS: Dicumarol labeled with C-14. (Abstract of Paper No. 133 printed from the *Proceedings of the International Society of Hematology).* 1950.

68. A. P. ARNASON, R. A. FULLER, and J. W. T. SPINKS: An electronic method of tracing the movements of soil-inhabiting insects. *Science* **111,** 2871, 5-6. 1950.

69. C. C. LEE, L. W. TREVOY, L. B. JAQUES, and J. W. T. SPINKS: The synthesis of 3, 3'-methylene-C^{14}-bis (4-hydroxycoumarin). *Can. J. Res.* **B, 28,** 170-171. 1950.

70. C. C. LEE, L. W. TREVOY, J. W. T. SPINKS, and L. B. JAQUES: Dicumarol labelled with C-14. *Proceedings of the Society for Experimental Biology and Medicine.* **74,** 151-155. 1950.

71. H. G. DION, J. E. DEHM, and J. W. T. SPINKS: Tracer studies with phosphate fertilizers. *Can. Chem. Processing.* **34,** 11, 905-909. 1950.

72. R. L. B. IRWIN, J. W. T. SPINKS, and T. A. ARNASON: Deposition of P-32 in developing *Drosophila. Can. J. Res.* **D, 28,** 137-142. 1950.

73. L. B. JAQUES and J. W. T. SPINKS: Factors affecting the prothrombopenic action of Dicumarol and related drugs. *Transactions of the* 3rd. *Macy Conference,* "Blood clotting and allied problems." 68. January 1950.

74. J. W. T. SPINKS: Tagged atoms, an aid to agricultural research. *The Saskatchewan Engineer,* **5,** 43. 1950.

75. R. A. FULLER, J. W. T. SPINKS, A. P. ARNASON, and H. MCDONALD: Use of radioactive tracers in investigations on soil-inhabiting insects. *81st Annual Report of the Entomological Society of Ontario,* 7-15. 1950.

1951   76. J. W. T. SPINKS: The Natural Sciences. An essay prepared for *The Royal Commission on National Development in the Arts, Letters and Sciences,* 1949-1951 (*The Massey Report),* 261-288. 1951.

77. J. W. T. SPINKS, D. A. LANE, and B. B. TORCHINSKY: A new method for moisture determination in soil. *Can. J. Tech.* **29,** 371-374. 1951.

78. T. J. ARNASON, R. L. IRWIN, and J. W. T. SPINKS: P-32–induced lethal mutations in *Drosophila. Canadian Journal of Zoology* **29,** 234-239. 1951.

79. J. M. NAYLOR, G. W. R. WALKER, C. O. PERSON, D. MURRAY, T. J. ARNASON, and J. W. T. SPINKS: Uptake of P-32 by some cereals. *Canadian Journal of Botany* **29,** 329-338. 1951.

80. J. W. T. SPINKS, MARGUERITE EAGER, and ERICA LEPP. The application of radioactive tracers to chemical analysis. *Chem. Can.* 47 (211)–50 (214). 1951.

81. A. M. KRISTJANSON, H. G. DION, and J. W. T. SPINKS: Hollow cylinder method of measurement of P-32 in plants. *Can. J. Tech.* **29,** 496-501. 1951.

82. J. W. T. SPINKS: Science and mass media in Canada. Editorial in *Chem. Can.* **3,** 21. 1951.

1952   83. J. W. T. SPINKS, H. W. BALDWIN, and T. THORVALDSON: Tracer studies of diffusion in set Portland cement. *Can. J. Tech.* **30,** 20-28. 1952.

84.   J. E. BURKELL and J. W. T. SPINKS: Measurements of self-diffusion in aqueous solutions of sodium dihydrogen phosphate. *Can. J. Chem.* **30**, 311-319. 1952.

85.   H. R. EISENHAUER, J. M. PEPPER, L. B. JAQUES, and J. W. T. SPINKS: Dicumarol-2-C^{14}: Synthesis and metabolism studies. *Can. J. Chem.* **30**, 245-251. 1952.

86.   P. F. SOLVONUK, J. E. LEDDY, L. W. TREVOY, L. B. JAQUES, and J. W. T. SPINKS: Experiments with C^{14}-menadione (Vitamin K$_3$). *Proceedings of the Society for Experimental Biology and Medicine* **79**, 597-604. 1952.

87.   D. H. MURRAY and J. W. T. SPINKS: Synthesis of P^{32} labelled parathion. *Can. J. Chem.* **30**, 6, 497. 1952.

88.   J. W. T. SPINKS: What's in a length? *Chem. Can.* **4**, 6, 52(112). 1952.

89.   R. W. HUMMEL and J. W. T. SPINKS: Oxidation of aqueous ferrous ammonium sulfate solutions by betatron radiation. *J. Chem. Phys.* **20**, 6, 1056. 1952.

90.   J. MITCHELL, A. M. KRISTJANSON, H. G. DION, and J. W. T. SPINKS: Availability of fertilizer and soil phosphorus to grain crops, and the effect of placement and rate of application on phosphorus uptake. *Sci. Agric.* **32**, 511-525. 1952.

91.   R. V. PHILLIPS, L. W. TREVOY, L. B. JAQUES, and J. W. T. SPINKS: Synthesis of 2-methyl-C^{14} naphthoquinone. *Can. J. Chem.* **30**, 11, 844-846. 1952.

1953   92.   D. A. LANE, B. B. TORCHINSKY, and J. W. T. SPINKS: Determining soil moisture and density by nuclear radiations. (A paper presented at a meeting of Committee D-18 of the American Society of Testing Materials, Cleveland, Ohio, Mar. 5, 1952). *The Engineering Journal* **134**, 23-34. 1953.

93.   C. C. LEE and J. W. T. SPINKS: The pyrolysis of calcium salts of carboxylic acids. *Can. J. Chem.* **31**, 103-106. 1953.

94.   J. MITCHELL, H. G. DION, A. M. KRISTJANSON, and J. W. T. SPINKS: Crop and variety response to applied phosphate and uptake of phosphorus from soil and fertilizer. *Agronomy Journal* **45**, 1, 6-11. 1953.

95.   P. ROTHERY, J. M. BELL, and J. W. T. SPINKS: Cobalt and Vitamin B^{12} in sheep. I. Distribution of radiocobalt in tissues and ingesta. *Journal of Nutrition* **48**, 1, 173-181. 1953.

96.   R. W. HUMMEL and J. W. T. SPINKS: Betatron irradiation of aqueous ferrous sulfate solutions. *Can. J. Chem.* **31**, 250-261. 1953.

97.   F. J. H. FREDEEN, J. W. T. SPINKS, J. R. ANDERSON, A. P. ARNASON, and J. G. REMPEL: Mass tagging of black flies (*Diptera:Simuliidae*) with radiophosphorus. *Canadian Journal of Zoology* **31**, 1-15. 1953.

98.   G. R. FREEMAN, A. B. VAN CLEAVE, and J. W. T. SPINKS: Betatron irradiation of water saturated with benzene. *Can. J. Chem.* **31**, 448-457. 1953.

99.   C. C. LEE and J. W. T. SPINKS: Rearrangement in the reaction between 2-phenylethylene-1-C^{14} and nitrous acid. *Can. J. Chem.* **31**, 8, 761-767. 1953.

100. C. C. LEE, F. C. G. HOSKIN, L. W. TREVOY, L. B. JAQUES, and J. W. T. SPINKS. Vitamin K, labelled with C^{14}. *Can. J. Chem.* **31**, 8, 769-772. 1953.

101. J. A. SHEMANCHUK, J. W. T. SPINKS, and F. J. H. FREDEEN: A method of tagging prairie mosquitoes (*Diptera:Culicidae*) with radiophosphorus. *The Canadian Entomologist* **85**, 7, 269-272. 1953.

102. C. C. LEE and J. W. T. SPINKS: The mechanism of the ketonic pyrolysis of calcium carboxylates. *The Journal of Organic Chemistry* **18**, 9, 1079-1086. 1953.

103. J. B. O'NEIL and J. W. T. SPINKS: The relationship between the density of the fresh egg and calcium uptake in the chick. *Poultry Science* **32**, 818. 1953.

104. J. B. O'NEIL and J. W. T. SPINKS: A simple method for determining percent uptake of Ca^{45} in tibiae of chicks. *Poultry Science* **32**, 5, 877-878. 1953.

105. G. R. FREEMAN, A. B. VAN CLEAVE, and J. W. T. SPINKS: Irradiation of one molar aqueous chloral hydrate solution with Co⁶⁰ gamma rays and betatron x-rays. *Can. J. Chem.* **31**, 1164-1172. 1953.

106. R. W. HUMMEL, A. B. VAN CLEAVE, and J. W. T. SPINKS. Betatron irradiation of aqueous ceric sulfate solution. *Can. J. Chem.* **31**, 1203-1210. 1953.

107. F. D. F. TALBOT and J. W. T. SPINKS. Studies on Saskatchewan Ores. *The Precambrian* **26**, 12, 11-16. 1953.

108. J. W. T. SPINKS: Training for research at the university. *Scientific Research in Saskatchewan*. Published by authorization of the Saskatchewan Research Council, Government of Saskatchewan (CBC radio talk, 1953). 1953.

1954   109. C. C. LEE and J. W. T. SPINKS: The isotope effect in the synthesis of 3,3'-methylene-C¹⁴-bis (4-hydroxycoumarin). *Can. J. Chem.* **32**, 327-330. 1954.

110. G. R. FREEMAN, A. B. VAN CLEAVE and J. W. T. SPINKS: Irradiation of aqueous chloral hydrate solutions with Co⁶⁰ gamma-rays: Average lifetime of the free radical chains. *Can. J. Chem.* **32**, 322-326. 1954.

111. R. W. HUMMEL, G. R. FREEMAN, A. B. VAN CLEAVE, and J. W. T. SPINKS: Rotating sector method applied to reactions induced by Co⁶⁰ gamma-rays. *Science* **119**, 3083, 159. 1954.

112. D. V. CORMACK, R. W. HUMMEL, H. E. JOHNS, and J. W. T. SPINKS: Irradiation of ferrous ammonium sulfate solutions: Energy absorption and ionization calculations for cobalt 60 and betatron radiation. *J. Chem. Phys.* **22**, 1, 6-12. 1954.

113. C. J. KRAUSS and J. W. T. SPINKS: Temperature coefficients for self-diffusion in solution. *Can. J. Chem.* **32**, 2, 71-78. 1954.

114. W. A. G. GRAHAM, J. W. T. SPINKS, and T. THORVALDSON: The mechanism of the hydration of tricalcium silicate and β-dicalcium silicate. *Can. J. Chem.* **32**, 2, 129-142. 1954.

115. R. W. HUMMEL, A. B. VAN CLEAVE, and J. W. T. SPINKS: Irradiation of chloroform-water systems with Co⁶⁰ gamma-rays and betatron x-rays. *Can. J. Chem.* **32**, 5, 522-531. 1954.

116. F. C. G. HOSKIN, J. W. T. SPINKS, and L. B. JAQUES: Urinary excretion products of menadione (vitamin K₃). *Canadian Journal of Biochemistry and Physiology* **32**, 240-250. 1954.

117. J. W. T. SPINKS: Language and science. *Journal of Chemical Education* **31**, 7, 348-351. 1954.

118. L. B. JAQUES, G. J. MILLAR, and J. W. T. SPINKS: The metabolism of the K-vitamins. *Schweizerische Medizinische Wochenschrift* **84**, 29, 792-807. 1954.

119. R. A. FULLER, P. W. RIEGERT, and J. W. T. SPINKS. Persistence of radio-activity in grasshoppers (*Acrididae*) tagged with phosphorus-32. *The Canadian Entomologist* **86**, 5, 201-203. 1954.

120. J. W. T. SPINKS: Impact on the university of special projects undertaken for government and industry. *Proceedings of National Conference of Canadian Universities*, 60-63. 1954.

121. C. C. LEE and J. W. T. SPINKS: Rearrangement studies with C¹⁴. II. The preparation of 2-phenylethyl halides. *Can. J. Chem.* **32**, 1005-1011. 1954.

122. J. W. T. SPINKS: Chemical industry in Saskatchewan—present and future. *Chem. Can.* **6**, 11, 27-30. 1954.

123. K. J. JENKINS, J. M. BELL, J. B. O'NEIL, and J. W. T. SPINKS: The effects of antibiotics in the synthesis of Vitamin B₁₂ in the chick. *Canadian Journal of Biochemistry and Physiology* **32**, 628-635. 1954.

124.   J. W. T. SPINKS: Green Cheese Research. *Culture* **15**, 395-403. 1954.

125.   J. W. T. SPINKS and T. THORVALDSON: Steward Basterfield: 1884–1954 (obituary notice). *Proceedings of the Royal Society of Canada*, 61-62. 1954.

1955   126.   D. V. CORMACK, R. W. HUMMEL, H. E. JOHNS, and J. W. T. SPINKS: Irradiation of ferrous ammonium sulfate solutions: Energy absorption and ionization calculations for Cobalt-60 and betatron radiation. *J. Chem. Phys.* **23**, 1, 162. 1955.

127.   R. M. STOW and J. W. T. SPINKS: Simultaneous surface exchange studies using both cation and anion. *Can. J. Chem.* **33**, 938-946. 1955.

128.   J. W. T. SPINKS: Where is Young Canada Going? *Trade and Commerce*, 18, Nov. 1955.

129.   J. W. T. SPINKS: Wartime Operational Research. *Chem. Can.* **54**, 1955.

130.   L. KATZ, T. M. KAVANAGH, A. G. W. CAMERON, E. C. BAILEY, and J. W. T. SPINKS: Photofission of U^{238}. *The Physical Review* **99**, 1, 98-106. 1955.

131.   B. C. GREEN and J. W. T. SPINKS: Automatic plotting of the position of a moving radioactively tagged object. *Can. J. Tech.* **33**, 307-316. 1955.

132.   J. W. T. SPINKS: Studies of special problems in agriculture and silviculture by the use of radioisotopes. Paper No. A/CONF./8/P/10, *Proceedings of the International Conference on the Peaceful Uses of Atomic Energy* **12**, 75-88. Geneva, August 1955. Also in *Canadian Chemical Processing*, **63**, Oct. 1955.

133.   J. W. T. SPINKS, T. THORVALDSON, H. W. BALDWIN, and F. W. BIRSS: Etudes sur le ciment avec traceurs radioactifs. (Communication presented to the 26th Congress of Industrial Chemistry, Paris, June 1953). *La Revue des Matériaux de Construction*, **476**, 138-144. 1955.

134.   B. C. GREEN and J. W. T. SPINKS: An automatic crab traces wireworms. *Design Engineering*, 19-20. December 1955.

1956   135.   J. W. T. SPINKS: Use of radioactive tracers in research and instrumentation in the mineral industry. *The Canadian Mining and Metallurgical Bulletin*, 308-371, May 1956; and The Canadian Institute of Mining and Metallurgy. *Transactions* **59**, 232-235. 1956.

136.   J. W. T. SPINKS: Atoms for Peace—Some impressions of the Geneva Conference. *The Green and White* **2**, July 1956.

137.   RUTH E. KREBIEL and J. W. T. SPINKS: Surface studies using ion-exchange autochromatography. *Science* **124**, 3220, 487. 1956.

138.   J. W. T. SPINKS: Radiation chemistry. *Chem. Can.* **8**, 46-51. 1956.

139.   A. L. RIEGERT, H. E. JOHNS, and J. W. T. SPINKS: Ag-phosphate glass needles for measuring gamma dose. *Nucleonics* **14**, 11, 134-137. 1956.

140.   J. D. TAYLOR, G. J. MILLAR, L. B. JAQUES, and J. W. T. SPINKS: The distribution of administered vitamin $K_1 C^{14}$ in rats. *Can. J. Biochem. and Physiology* **34**, 1143-1152. 1956.

141.   J. R. JOWSEY, M. R. BERLIE, J. W. T. SPINKS, and J. B. O'NEIL: Uptake of calcium by the laying hen, and the subsequent transfer from egg to chick. *Poultry Science* **35**, 6, 1234-1238. 1956.

142.   J. W. T. SPINKS: Harmony in contrariety. *Culture* **17**, 348-363. 1956.

1957.   143.   J. W. T. SPINKS: Chemistry in Canada (in Russian). *Chemical Industry* **1**, 51-60. 1957.

144.   J. W. T. SPINKS: Utilizaton of scientific manpower (contribution to the Sarnia Imperial Oil Symposium, October 30, 1956). *Research and Engineering*, 123-127. 1957.

145. C. C. LEE, G. P. SLATER, and J. W. T. SPINKS: Rearrangement studies with C¹⁴. IV. The absence of rearrangement in the Schmidt reaction with 3-phenylpropionic acid-2-C¹⁴. *Can. J. Chem.* **35**, 276-278. 1957.

146. RUTH E. KREHBIEL and J. W. T. SPINKS: Surface studies using ion exchange autochromatography. *Can. J. Chem.* **35**, 294-300. 1957.

147. J. PAWLIW and J. W. T. SPINKS: Neutron moisture meter for concrete. *Can. J. Tech.* **34**, 503-513. 1957.

148. A. G. BRICKNELL, L. W. TREVOY, and J. W. T. SPINKS: A study of sulfate in nitrocellulose using S³⁵O₄ as tracer. *Can. J. Chem.* **35**, 704-714. 1957.

149. L. B. JAQUES, ERICA LEPP FROESE, R. O'TOOLE, and J. W. T. SPINKS: Relation between duration of hypoprothrombinemia with Dicumarol and the level of the drug in the liver. *Archives Internationales de Pharmacodynamie et de Thérapie* **111**, 4, 478-489. 1957.

150. C. C. LEE, G. P. SLATER, and J. W. T. SPINKS: Rearrangement studies with C¹⁴. V. The solvolysis of 2-phenylethyl-1-C¹⁴ *p*-toluenesulphonate. *Can. J. Chem.* **35**, 1417-1422. 1957.

151. A. FONTIJN and J. W. T. SPINKS: Addition of *n*-butyl mercaptan to 1-pentene on irradiation with x-rays or gamma rays. I. 140 kvp. x-rays. *Can. J. Chem.* **35**, 1384-1396. 1957.

152. A. FONTIJN and J. W. T. SPINKS. Addition of *n*-butyl mercaptan to 1-pentene on irradiation with x-rays or gamma rays. II. Effect of rigorous drying degassing. *Can. J. Chem.* **35**, 1397-1409. 1957.

153. A. FONTIJN and J. W. T. SPINKS: Addition of *n*-butyl mercaptan to 1-pentene on irradiation with x-rays or gamma rays. III. Energy dependence, 140 kvp. to 24.5 mevp. *Can. J. Chem.* **35**, 1410-1413. 1957.

154. R. J. WOODS and J. W. T. SPINKS: The action of Co⁶⁰ gamma rays and of Fenton's Reagent on aqueous bromal hydrate solutions. *Can. J. Chem.* **35**, 1475-1486. 1957.

155. J. W. T. SPINKS: Modern scientific development in Canada. *Journal of the Royal Institute of Chemistry* **81**, 789-804. 1957.

156. J. W. T. SPINKS: Radioisotopes in agriculture and silviculture research. Chapter 1 in *Nuclear Radiation in Food and Agriculture*, ed. Ralph Singleton, 3-71. The Geneva Series on the Peaceful Uses of Atomic Energy. D. Van Nostrand Co., Inc. 1957.

1958   157. B. C. GREEN and J. W. T. SPINKS: Lapse-time motion picture studies of soil-burrowing insects. *Nature, Lond.* **181**, 434-435. 1958.

158. J. W. T. SPINKS: The design of chemical experiments. *Chem. Can.* **10**, 3, 36-40. 1958.

159. B. C. GREEN and J. W. T. SPINKS: A free-moving isodose-tracing machine. *Nucleonics* **16**, 4, 92-94. 1958.

160. J. W. T. SPINKS: Radioactivity and its biological implications. *The Western Producer*, April 3, 10, and 17. 1958.

161. A. L. RIEGERT AND J. W. T. SPINKS: Energy dependence of silver phosphate glass dosimeters. *International Journal of Applied Radiation and Isotopes* **3**, 125-130. 1958.

162. J. W. T. SPINKS: Nuclear energy in agriculture and biology. (An address to the Annual Meeting of the Agricultural Institute of Canada, Wolfville, N.S., June 1958.) *Agricultural Institute Review* **13**, 5, 12. 1958.

163. J. W. T. SPINKS: Some recent applications of isotopes in research and control in industry. Paper No. 15 P/216; A.E. C.L. No. 626, *Proceedings of the* 2nd

International Conference on the Peaceful Uses of Atomic Energy, 19, 12-31. Geneva, September 1958.

1959   164.   J. W. SUTHERLAND and J. W. T. SPINKS: Radiolysis of tetrachloroethylene. *Can. J. Chem.* **37**, 79-90. 1959.

165.   D. A. ARMSTRONG and J. W. T. SPINKS. Low temperature irradiation of mixtures of HBr and C_2H_4. *Can. J. Chem.* **37**, 1002-1003. 1959.

166.   J. W. T. SPINKS: Atomic energy in agriculture at the 2nd Geneva Conference. *Bulletin of the University of Saskatchewan Farm and Home Week, 66-74.* January 1959.

167.   A. L. RIEGERT and J. W. T. SPINKS: A 90-curie Co^{60} irradiation unit. *Proceedings of the 7th Hot Laboratories and Equipment Conference, Cleveland, Ohio, 315-324.* 1959. Reprinted in *Gamma Irradiation in Canada,* **2**, 5-12. 1962.

168.   J. W. T. SPINKS: Radiotracer techniques in inorganic chemistry. (Paper given at 41st Annual Conference of the Chemical Institute of Canada, Toronto, May 1958). *Chem. Can.* **11**, 4, 51-56. 1959.

169.   R. F. PLATFORD and J. W. T. SPINKS. Irradiation of aqueous chloral hydrate with $Sr^{90}Y^{90}$ beta rays. *Can. J. Chem.* **37**, 1022-1028. 1959.

170.   D. A. ARMSTRONG and J. W. T. SPINKS: Radiation-induced addition of HBr to C_2H_4 in the gaseous state. *Can. J. Chem.* **37**, 1210-1224. 1959.

171.   H. HEUSINGER, R. J. WOODS, and J. W. T. SPINKS: Study of the radiolysis of bromal hydrate solutions using C^{14}-labelled bromal. *Can. J. Chem.* **37**, 1127-1131. 1959.

172.   J. W. T. SPINKS: Moral implications of atomic energy. *The Rotunda, 7-9.* 1959.

173.   D. A. ARMSTRONG and J. W. T. SPINKS: Low temperature irradiation of mixtures of HBr and C_2H_4. *Proceedings of 4th International Symposium on Free Radical Stabilization, B-II-I.* September 1959.

174.   J. W. T. SPINKS: Education in a world of change—the 4th R. (Talk given to the Canadian Education Association, September 15, 1959.) *School progress 40-42, 59-60.* Oct.-Nov. 1959; *Canadian Education* **15**, 1, 64-69. 1959.

175.   J. W. T. SPINKS: Nuclear fission—Power and problem in a troubled world. *Proceedings of the 16th Annual Conference of the Provincial Ministers of Mines, Regina,* September 1959.

176.   M. L. HAWRYLUK, R. A. OLESKIW, and J. W. T. SPINKS: Isotope separation in surface exchange. In "Crystal imperfections and the chemical reactivity of solids", 134-135, *Faraday Society Discussions,* **28**, 122-135. 1959.

1960   177.   R. J. WOODS and J. W. T. SPINKS: The radiolysis of some organic halogen compounds in aqueous solution. *Can. J. Chem.* **38**, 77-93. 1960.

178.   R. G. McINTOSH, R. L. EAGER, and J. W. T. SPINKS: Mean lifetime of free radical chains determined by a flow technique. *Science* **131**, 3405, 992. 1960.

179.   F. W. MITCHELL, B. C. GREEN, and J. W. T. SPINKS: Electron spin resonance studies of the radiation-induced addition of HBr and C_2H_4 in the solid state. *Can. J. Chem.* **38**, 689-696. 1960.

180.   J. W. T. SPINKS: An atomic automaton. In *Memory, Learning and Language:* The Physical Basis of Mind, J. F. LEDDY, W. FEINDEL, A. HOFFER, W. G. PENFOLD, and J. W. T. SPINKS, University of Toronto Press, Toronto. 1960.

181.   J. W. T. SPINKS: Farming and the fourth "R". *Addresses and Proceedings of the Saskatchewan Agricultural Societies' Association,* University of Saskatchewan Farm and Home Week, Jan. 11-15, 1960. Pub. by the University of Saskatchewan, News and Information Service, 73-80. June 1960.

182. J. W. T. SPINKS: Sulfur isotopes and hydrothermal mineral deposits. *Economic Geology* **55**, 206. 1960.

183. J. W. T. SPINKS: Agricultural research. Text of speech to Saskatchewan Farmers Union. *The Western Producer*, December 29, 1960.

1961 184. J. W. T. SPINKS: Education for a world of change: the next fifty. (Inaugural address at installation as fourth President of the University of Saskatchewan.) *Improving College and University Teaching* **9**, 1, 9. 1961.

185. J. W. T. SPINKS: Trends in university research in science (paper given at Joint Symposium of Sections 3, 4 and 5 of the Royal Society of Canada at Kingston, June 1960). *Canadian Universities Today*, ed. G. STANLEY and G. SYLVESTRE. Pub. for the Society by the Univ. of Toronto Press, Toronto, 38-44. 1961.

186. J. KROH, B. C. GREEN, and J. W. T. SPINKS: Formation of free radicals in tritiated H_2O and D_2O ice. *Science* **133**, 3458, 1082. 1961.

187. J. KROH, B. C. GREEN, and J. W. T. SPINKS: Tritium as a source of radiation in electron spin resonance studies. *Nature* **189**, 655-656. 1961.

188. J. KROH and J. W. T. SPINKS: Tritium as an internal source of radiation in EPR studies of organic materials. *J. Chem. Physics* **34**, 1853, 1961; reprinted in *J. Chem. Physics* **35**, 760. 1961.

189. J. KROH, B. C. GREEN, and J. W. T. SPINKS: Electron paramagnetic resonance studies on the production of free radicals in hydrogen peroxide at liquid nitrogen temperature. *J. Am. Chem. Soc.* **83**, 2201-2202. 1961.

190. J. W. T. SPINKS: Some present problems and changes in higher education. *The Bulletin of the American College of Physicans* **2**, 3, 131-133. 1961.

191. J. W. T. SPINKS: Function and philosophy of pure research. *Agricultural Institute Review*, **16**, 4, 13-16. 1961.

192. J. W. T. SPINKS: Graduate studies and research in the sciences. In *Canada's Universities in a New Age*, ed. DUNTON and PATTERSON (proceedings of a conference held by the National Conference of Canadian Universities and Colleges at Ottawa, Nov. 13-15, 1961), 39-50.

1962 193. J. W. T. SPINKS: The changing face of scientific research in the universities. *Addresses and Proceedings of the Canadian Seed Growers' Association*, University of Saskatchewan Farm and Home Week, Jan. 1962. Pub. by the University of Saskatchewan, News and Information Service, June 1962. 4-10.

194. J. KROH, B. C. GREEN, and J. W. T. SPINKS: Electron paramagnetic resonance studies on free radicals produced by $T\beta$-particles in frozen H_2O D_2O media at liquid nitrogen temperature. *Can. J. Chem.* **40**, 413-425. 1962.

195. F. W. MITCHELL, B. C. GREEN, and J. W. T. SPINKS: Electron spin resonance of irradiated ethyl bromide. *J. Chem. Physics*, **38**, 4, 1095-1096. 1962.

196. J. KROH, B. C. GREEN, and J. W. T. SPINKS: Photolysis of deuterium peroxide at liquid nitrogen temperature. *Roczniki Chemii*, Ann. Soc. Chim. Polonorum **36**, 1337-1340. 1962.

197. J. KROH and J. W. T. SPINKS: The yields of Fe^{++}ion oxidation in H_2O ice irradiated with Co^{60} γ-rays. *Roczniki Chemii*, Ann. Soc. Chim. Polonorum, **36**, 563-564. 1962.

198. J. W. T. SPINKS: Education and employment (an address to the 1962 graduates of the Saskatchewan Technical Institute, Moose Jaw). *The School Trustee*, **15**, 1, 5-8. September 1962.

1963 199. A. SAFARIK, B. C. GREEN, and J. W. T. SPINKS: EPR studies of free radicals produced by irradiation of hydrogen peroxide-water solutions at low temperatures. *Sixth International Free Radical Symposium,* University of Cambridge, AG1-AG8. July 1963.

200. J. W. T. SPINKS: Researching radiation chemistry at Saskatchewan. *Canadian Nuclear Technology* **2**, 1, 31-34. 1963.

201. J. W. T. SPINKS: education for tomorrow's world. *The School Trustee* **15**, 7; 5-6, 16. May 1963.

1964   202. J. W. T. SPINKS: What we've learned from 'Green Cheese' research. *The Furrow,* 2-3. March 1964.

203. J. W. T. SPINKS: Research and resource development. In the report of the Saskatchewan Resources Conference, *Resources for People,* 87-91, Jan. 1964, Saskatoon; and British Columbia Resources Conference June 1964, 15th British Columbia Natural Resources Conference, p. 72.

204. R. J. WOODS and J. W. T. SPINKS: *An Introduction to Radiation Chemistry.* John Wiley & Sons Inc., New York. 1964. pp. xi, 477.

205. R. L. EAGER, R. G. MCINTOSH, and J. W. T. SPINKS: The radiation chemistry of aqueous solutions of chloral hydrate and of bromal hydrate. *Can. J. Chem.* **42**, 2033-2042. 1964.

206. J. W. T. SPINKS: The National Research Council forecast of support needed for basic research in Canadian universities. *Transactions of the Royal Society of Canada,* **II**, 4, 327-337. 1964.

1965   207. J. W. T. SPINKS; *A Decade of Change* (from address to a "State of the University" Banquet, Feb. 1965). Pam. University of Saskatchewan Publications. 1965.

208. J. W. T. SPINKS: Impressions of Russia, 1965. Articles in *Leader-Post,* Regina, Sept. 9 and 10, 1965. Also *The Sheaf,* Sept. 24, 1965.

209. R. G. MCINTOSH, R. L. EAGER, and J. W. T. SPINKS: Mean lifetime of free radical chains in $^{60}Co\gamma$-irradiated chloral hydrate and bromal hydrate solutions. *Can. J. Chem.* **43**, 3490-3495. 1965.

1966   210. J. W. T. SPINKS and R. J. WOODS: Radiation chemistry. *The Encyclopedia of Physics,* 579-581 ed. R. W. BESANCON, Reinhold Publishing Co. 1966.

211. J. W. T. SPINKS: Russia revisited. *Chem. Can.,* 58. March 1966.

212. J. W. T. SPINKS: Canada's changing international image. *The Canadian Mining and Metallurgical Bulletin,* 1-3. Dec. 1966.

213. J. W. T. SPINKS: The changing face of Canada in world affairs. *The Canadian Surveyor,* **20**, 3, 191-197. 1966.

214. J. W. T. SPINKS: The expanding university in a contracting world. *Western Canadian Society for Horticulture, Proceedings of 22nd Annual Meeting,* 30-34. February 1966.

215. J. W. T. SPINKS, G ARLT and F. K. HARE: *Development of Graduate Programs in Ontario Universities.* Report of commission to study the development of graduate programs in Ontario universities submitted to the Committee on University Affairs and the Committee of Presidents of provincially assisted universities. Toronto. 1966.

216. J. W. T. SPINKS: *Annual Report, 1966–67,* University of Saskatchewan. Nov. 1967.

217. J. W. T. SPINKS: The University's commitment to its Graduate Faculty. *Proceedings of 6th Annual Meeting, Council of Graduate Schools in the United States,* pp. 40-53, Denver, Colo. December 1966.

1967   218. J. W. T. SPINKS and R. J. WOODS: *Radiation Chemistry* in Japanese translation. May 1967.

219.   J. W. T. SPINKS and R. J. WOODS: *Radiation Chemistry* in Russian translation (V. Gromov). August 1967.

220.   J. W. T. SPINKS: Campus wildlife. *The Blue Jay*, Vol. 25, No. 3, p. 107. September 1967.

221.   J. W. T. SPINKS: *Bibliography of Publications 1929–1966*. (Published 1967).

222.   J. W. T. SPINKS: Canadas Universitäten und Ihre Aufgaben. *Saskatchewan — Courier*, pp. 28, 29. October 26, 1967.

223.   J. W. T. SPINKS: An operations research approach to education. *Canadian Education Association Convention Proceedings*, Regina, Sask. p. 50. September 1967.

224.   J. W. T. SPINKS: Radiation chemistry, *Science Affairs*, pp. 8-10. January 1967.

1968   225.   J. W. T. SPINKS: Spinks Space Age Primer. *Canadian Research and Development*, p. 52. March/April 1968.

226.   J. W. T. SPINKS: *The University of Saskatchewan in Transition*, pp. 24. U of S publication. March 1968.

227.   J. W. T. SPINKS: The Idea of a University. *The Green & White*, p. 1. Fall, 1968.

228.   J. W. T. SPINKS: E. W. R. Steacie, biography.

229.   J. W. T. SPINKS: *Annual Report, 1967–68*. University of Saskatchewan. November 1968.

1969   230.   J. W. T. SPINKS: Optimization of municipal services: An operations research approach. *SOMA Annual Report*.

231.   J. W. T. SPINKS: Education for change. *Estevan Sun*, March 4, 1969. Also *Melfort Superintendency Intercom*, Vol. Ed. 1. March 1969.

232.   J. W. T. SPINKS: A systems approach to University research. *Science Forum*, Vol. 2, No. 3, p. 19. 1969.

233.   J. W. T. SPINKS: Zero-one. *Computation Centre Newsletter*, p. 1. July 1969.

234.   J. W. T. SPINKS: Ten little Presidents. *The Green & White*, p. 8 Summer, 1969.

235.   J. W. T. SPINKS: Apollo X and Zero-one. *Canadian Research & Development*, p. 35. July 1969.

236.   J. W. T. SPINKS: President as computer. *Fulmerstonian* (Thetford, England), Nov. 1969.

237.   J. W. T. SPINKS: Science Policy. Proceedings of Special Committee on Science Policy, Senate of Canada. No. 48, May 29, 1969, Appendix 89, p. 6167-6186.

238.   J. W. T. SPINKS: Mendeleeff Celebration. *C.I.C. Journal*, Jan. 1970, p. 27; *Science Forum*, Vol. 2, No. 6, p. 24, 1969.

239.   J. W. T. SPINKS: The University President in 1969. *Green & White*, Autumn 1969, p. 8.

240.   J. W. T. SPINKS: Research, the Need & Challenge of our Times. *School Trustees*, Dec. 1969, p. 6.

241.   J. W. T. SPINKS: The Role of the Universities in Regional, National & International Research Programs. *23rd Annual Convention, Sask. Institute of Agrologists*, May 31, 1969.

1970   242.   Human Skeletal Remains Near Bradwell, Sask. Kupsch, McCallum & Spinks. *Sask. Arch. Newsletter* 28, 7-9, 1970.

1971   243.   J. W. T. SPINKS: No Man is an Island. *Canadian Research & Development*. March 1971, pp. 36, 37.

244.   J. W. T. SPINKS: An Operations Research Approach to Decision Making. Seminar on Economic Decision-making. Economic Society of Alberta, March 1971.

245.   J. W. T. SPINKS: A Year in Darmstadt with Dr. Herzberg. *Green & White*, Winter 1971, pp. 11, 12.

1972   246.   J. W. T. SPINKS: An Account of a Year with Herzberg. *Physics in Canada*. Vol. 28, April 1972, pp. 13, 14.

247.   J. W. T. SPINKS: Learning to Count in Seal-Land. *Musk-Ox* No. 10, 1972, p. 69.

248.   J. W. T. SPINKS: A Decade of Change. *Published by the University of Saskatchewan*, 1972. 169 pages.

249.   J. W. T. SPINKS: The View of the Educationist. Paper 72-CNA-505. *Proceedings of the 1972 Annual Conference, Canadian Nuclear Association*. June 11, 1972.

1973   250.   J. W. T. SPINKS: *Space Age Garden of Atomic Verse*. April 1973.

251.   J. W. T. SPINKS: Universities and the North. Society of Chemical Industry. *Chemistry & Industry*, 736, 1973.

1974   252.   R. J. WOODS and J. W. T. SPINKS: Radiation Chemistry in *The Encyclopedia of Physics*, 2nd. ed., 1974, 764-767, ed. R. Besançon.

253.   J. W. T. SPINKS: Forger les maillons d'une chaine. L'enseignement superieure, Vol. 3, No. 1, 19-27, March 1974.

254.   J. W. T. SPINKS: Energy, the A.B.C.'s of the energy crisis. 5 talks on C.T.V., October 1974.

1975   255.   J. W. T. SPINKS: Creativity. *Chemistry in Canada*, May 1975, 21-24.

256.   J. W. T. SPINKS: Ozone depletion. *C. & Eng. News*, June 23, 1975, p. 3.

257.   J. W. T. SPINKS: Alternate energy sources. *Musk-Ox*, No. 15, 1975, 57-64.

1976   258.   J. W. T. SPINKS and R. J. WOODS: *Introduction to Radiation Chemistry*. 2nd Edition. 1976.

1977   259.   J. W. T. SPINKS: Memories of the '30's. *Green and White*. Sixtieth Anniversary issue 1977. p. 4.

260.   R. J. WOODS and J. W. T. SPINKS. Canadian Prospects in Radiation Chemical Industry. *Proceedings of the 17th International Conference of the Canadian Nuclear Association*. June 1977, Montreal.

1978   261.   Montreal Medal address. Science and Social Change, *Chelsea Journal*, Jan. 1978, Vol. 4, No. 1 30-34.

262.   *Publications and Addresses*, 1929-1976. J. W. T. SPINKS, University of Saskatchewan Printing Services, Dec. 1977, 49 pp.

263.   R. J. WOODS and J. W. T. SPINKS. Radiation Synthesis as a Future Source of Organic Chemicals. Abstract No. P28. CHEMRAWN Conference on future sources of organic raw materials. IUPAC Toronto, July 1978.

264.   E. W. R. STEACIE biography. *Dictionary of Scientific Biography*, Vol. 13, p. 6.

265.   Reminiscences of A. J. ALLMAND, 1928-30, photochemist, K. C. L. *Association Newsletter* No. 2, 1978, pp. 13-16.

266.   First steps in green cheese research. J. W. T. SPINKS, 11th ISSS Congress, Edmonton, June 1978, *Proceedings*, Vol. 3, pp. 2-31.

267.   A research strategy for the Canada West Region, *Prairie Forum, III, No. 1*, (1978), 39-43.

268.   After dinner thoughts on the infrastructure of Science. Conference on the study of the History of Canadian Science and Technology. Nov. 1978, Queen's University.

269.   U.S.S.R. once more. J. W. T. SPINKS, *Chemistry in Canada*. Feb. 1979, p. 4.

BOOKS, TRANSLATIONS, AND CHAPTERS OF BOOKS

1937   1.   *Atomic Spectra and Atomic Structure:* G. HERZBERG. Translated from the German of G. HERZBERG by J. W. T. SPINKS. Prentice Hall, New York. 1937.

1939   2.   *Molecular Spectra and Molecular Structure,* Part I. Diatomic Molecules, G. HERZBERG. Translated from the German of G. HERZBERG. by J. W. T. SPINKS. Prentice Hall, New York. 1939.

1951   3.   The Natural Sciences. J. W. T. SPINKS. An essay prepared for the *Royal Commission on National Development in the Arts, Letters and Sciences, 1949-1951,* (The Massey Report), 261-288. 1951.

1957   4.   Radioisotopes in agriculture and silviculture research. J. W. T. SPINKS. Chapter I in *Nuclear Radiation in Food and Agriculture,* ed. Ralph Singleton, 3-71. The Geneva Series on the Peaceful Uses of Atomic Energy. D. Van Nostrand Co., Inc. 1957.

1960   5.   An Atomic Automaton, In *Memory, Learning and Language—The Physical Basis of Mind:* J. F. LEDDY, W. H. FEINDEL, A. HOFFER, J. W. T. SPINKS, and W. G. PENFOLD. University of Toronto Press, 1960.

1964   6.   *Introduction to Radiation Chemistry:* R. J. WOODS and J. W. T. SPINKS, 477 pp. John Wiley & Sons, Inc., New York. 1964. Japanese edition, trans. Toshuhiko Abe, Masao Gotoda, Hiroshi Hotta, Yunosuke Oshima, Toshio Sugiura. Sangyo Tosho Pub. Co. Ltd., 1967. Russian edition, trans. V. Gromov. Moscow, 1967.

1966   7.   *Development of Graduate Programs in Ontario Universities:* J. W. T. SPINKS, G. ARLT, and F. K. HARE. Report of Commission to study the development of graduate programs in Ontario universities, submitted to the Committee on University Affairs and the Committee of Presidents of provincially assisted universities. Toronto 1966.

1972   8.   *A Decade of Change.* J. W. T. SPINKS. University of Saskatchewan, 1972, 172 pp.

1973   9.   *Space Age Garden of Atomic Verse.* J. W. T. SPINKS, Saskatoon, Saskatchewan, 1973.

1976   10.   *An Introduction to Radiation Chemistry.* Second Edition. R. J. WOODS and J. W. T. SPINKS. John Wiley & Sons, Inc., New York, 1976.

Appendix B–A Brief History of the University of Saskatchewan*

The Act establishing the University of Saskatchewan was passed by the Legislative Assembly of the Province on the third of April, 1907. The Senate held its first meeting on the eighth of January, 1908, when elections to the Board of Governors were held. In August of the same year, Professor Walter C. Murray of Dalhousie University, Nova Scotia, was appointed first President of the University, and he continued to hold that office until June 30th, 1937. Other presidents have been J. S. Thomson (1937–49), and W. P. Thompson (1949–59), J. W. T. Spinks (1959–74), and R. W. Begg (1974–80).

The first classes in Arts and Science began on September 28th, 1909, when seventy students were registered. The first building on the campus was opened for the admission of students in October, 1912. The other Colleges and Schools were established as follows: Agriculture 1912; Engineering 1912; Law 1913; Pharmacy 1914; Commerce 1917; Medicine 1926; Education 1927; Home Economics 1928; Nursing 1938; Graduate Studies 1946; Physical Education 1958; Veterinary Medicine 1964; Dentistry 1965; Religious Studies 1973; Physical Therapy 1976.

St. Thomas More College was established by the Fathers of the Order of St. Basil in 1936 and gives classes in most of the Arts subjects on the same footing as the College of Arts and Science, Saskatoon.

In 1934, Regina College became part of the University and continued as a Junior College with a Conservatory of Music. In 1959, a major decision was taken to raise the institution to full degree granting status, making it a

*(reproduced, with permission of the Registrar, from the *University Calendar*, *1977–78*)

second campus of the University of Saskatchewan. On July 1, 1961, the College was renamed the University of Saskatchewan Regina Campus. Dr. W. A. Riddell was appointed first Principal of the Regina Campus in 1962 and held this position until December 31, 1969, at which time he was succeeded by Dr. J. H. Archer. The Regina Campus offered courses leading to the degrees of Bachelor of Arts, Bachelor of Arts Honours, Bachelor of Education, Bachelor of Applied Science, Bachelor of Administration, Bachelor of Music, Bachelor of Science, Bachelor of Science Honours, Bachelor of Fine Arts, Bachelor of Laboratory Technology, Bachelor of Music Education, Bachelor of Social Work, Master of Arts, Master of Education, Master of Science, Doctor of Philosophy. By an Act of Legislation in 1974, the Regina Campus became an independent university, called the University of Regina.

Other Junior Colleges were authorized in 1924 to give work for university credit to the end of the first year in Arts. Those continuing to function are St. Peter's College, Muenster, and St. Joseph's College, Yorkton.

On July 1, 1964 the two Teacher Colleges at Saskatoon and Regina became a part of the University and all teacher training programs were integrated within the University.

Theological Colleges, affiliated with the University and located on or near the campus, began work as follows: Emmanuel College (Anglican) 1909 (now the College of Emmanuel and St. Chad). St. Andrew's College (United Church) 1913. Lutheran Theological Seminary (formerly Lutheran College and Seminary 1920, and Luther Theological Seminary 1949).

A further step in the evolution of a two-campus structure for the university was taken on July 1, 1967, when Dr. R. W. Begg was appointed the first Principal of the Saskatoon Campus. In July 1974, he became the Acting President of the new University of Saskatchewan, and President as of March 17, 1975.

Constitution

The Constitution of the University is determined by the University Act of the Province of Saskatchewan, first passed in 1907 and subsequently amended. The present University Act was assented to on May 10, 1974.

The composition and functions of various bodies making up the University are as follows:

Convocation is composed of the Chancellor, the Senate, the surviving members of the first Convocation and all graduates of the University. It has power to consider all matters affecting the interests and well-being of the University and to make representations thereon to the Senate. Annual meetings are held in May and October for the admission of candidates to degrees.

The Senate is composed as follows: The Chancellor, and all persons who at any time have held the office of Chancellor, the President of the

University, Vice-Presidents of the University, the Minister of Continuing Education, the Deputy Minister of Continuing Education, the Chairman of the Educational Council, the principals of affiliated colleges at the University, Deans or Acting Deans of Colleges, and such other Deans of Academic and Student Affairs and such Directors as nominated by the President and approved by the Senate, six students, fourteen members elected by Convocation from the members thereof and to represent the districts in the Province in which they must reside; representatives of professional societies, groups or organizations in the Province which in the opinion of the Senate contribute in a significant way to the social, economic and cultural welfare of the Province.

The Senate provides for the granting of degrees: authorizes the establishment of colleges, departments, chairs or courses of instruction within the University and considers and determines as to all courses of study; and may make statutes concerning these or other educational matters provided always that statutes dealing with the establishment of colleges, departments, chairs and courses of instruction must be approved by the Board of Governors, and further that the Senate cannot take action on the granting of degrees, the establishment of colleges, departments, chairs and courses of instruction without first having received a report from the Council embodying its recommendations on such matters. The Senate has the duty and power to make recommendations to the Board of Governors and the Council and further, to require the Council to consider and take action upon matters within the authority of the Senate.

The Board of Governors consists of twelve members as follows: The Chancellor, the President of the University, six members appointed by the Lieutenant-Governor-in-Council, two members elected by the Senate, one student, and one faculty member. It elects its own Chairman and Vice-Chairman from among its members.

The management, administration and control of the property, revenues, business and affairs of the University are vested in the Board, which has the duty and power to erect and maintain buildings, to expend money on their maintenance and equipment, to provide for the establishment and maintenance of such faculties, departments, chairs, exhibitions, scholarships and prizes as have been determined by the Senate; to appoint the President of the University, the Vice-Presidents of the University, the librarian, professors, and instructors, and all officers, clerks, employees and servants; to fix their salaries or remuneration, to define their duties and terms of employment, which unless otherwise provided, shall be during the pleasure of the Board; to fix and determine all fees to be paid by students.

There is a Council which consists of the President, the Vice-Presidents of the University, the university secretary, the registrar, the librarian, the assistant librarian, heads of library departments, the professional heads of branch libraries, and the deans, directors, professors, associate professors, assistant professors, full-time lecturers, special lecturers and instructors, who are employed by the University or a federated college, and a number of students.

The Council appoints examiners, conducts and determines the results of examinations, and considers for report to the Senate courses of studies and such matters affecting the educational interests and well-being of the University as it may deem meet; deal with, subject to an appeal to the Senate, all applications and memorials by students and others; and also deal with all matters referred to it by the Senate or Board.

The Faculties of the different Colleges include in each case the President, Dean, Vice-Presidents, University Secretary, Registrar, and professors, associate professors, assistant professors, lecturers, and lecturers who are members of departments which, for administrative purposes are assigned to the Dean of that College, together with certain representatives of other colleges and departments named by the Senate. Each Faculty, subject to the statutes of the Senate and the general control of the Council has charge of all matters of scholarship within its College.

Advisory Councils have been set up for the Colleges of Agriculture, Dentistry, Education, Engineering, Medicine and Veterinary Medicine, to consider and report to the Senate and Board of Governors on general regulations, courses of study and other related matters within the Colleges for which they are appointed, as set forth in the Senate Statutes.

A Board of Teacher Education has been established to advise the Minister of Education and the University concerning teacher training.

High Points of 1959–74, under a one-university system
Overall growth: 4,500 to 13,500 full time students.
Operational budget: $7.25 m. to $49.25 m.
Total capital funds: $112 m.
Fund raising: $2.5 m. + $8.0 million = $10.5 million.

Regina
Development of the Regina Campus from 289 to 3,500 students—budget $0.6 m. to $15.5 m.
Development of Faculties of Arts and Science, Education, Administration, Graduate Studies, Engineering.

Buildings
Classroom, Laboratory, Education, Physical Education, Library, Administration-Humanities, College West (plus Campion and Luther), Student Service Centre.

Other Programs
Development of bilingual program, Canadian Plains Studies, Water Studies.

Saskatoon
Students: 4,200 to 9,500.
New Colleges of Veterinary Medicine and Dentistry.

Buildings

Arts Building, Biology Building, Engineering addition, Physical Education addition, Linear Accelerator, Marquis Hall, Athabasca Hall, Thorvaldson addition, Commerce, Law, Cancer and Medical Research addition, Physics addition, Medical addition, Western College of Veterinary Medicine, College of Education, McEown Park residences, Library addition. (Also additions to St. Andrew's, St. Thomas More, Emmanuel and St. Chad, new buildings Luther and St. Pius X).

Large scale research projects

Linear Accelerator, upper atmosphere (including S.E.D. Systems Ltd.), animal feeding, crop science development, Institute for Northern Studies, Indian and Metis studies.

Select Bibliography

Bonneau, Louis-Philippe, and J. A. Corry. *Quest for the Optimum: Research Policy in the Universities of Canada.* (Report of a Commission to Study the Rationalization of University Research.) Vols. I and II. Ottawa: Association of Universities and Colleges of Canada, 1972, 1973.

Canada: *Royal Commission on National Development in the Arts, Letters, and Sciences.* (The Massey Commission Report.) Ottawa: the King's Printer, 1951.

Cassirer, Ernst. *An Essay on Man: An Introduction to a Philosophy of Human Culture.* New Haven: Yale University Press, 1944.

Conger, D. Stuart, ed. *Methods for Human Resource Development.* Prince Albert: Saskatchewan NewStart, Inc., 1973.

Duff, James (Sir), and Robert O. Berdahl. *Report of a Commission Sponsored by the Canadian Association of University Teachers and the Association of Universities and Colleges of Canada.* Toronto: published for the Associations by the University of Toronto Press, 1966.

Eccles, John Carew (Sir). *Facing Reality: Philosophical Adventures by a Brain Scientist.* New York: Springer-Verlag, 1970.

Eggleston, Wilfrid. *National Research in Canada: the N.R.C., 1916–1966.* Toronto: Clarke, Irwin, 1978.

Gamow, George. *Thirty Years that Shook Physics: The Story of the Quantum Theory.* London: Heinemann Educational, 1972.

Hayes, F. Ronald. *The Chaining of Prometheus: Evolution of a Power Structure for Canadian Science.* Toronto: University of Toronto Press, 1973.

Hume, Robert Ernest, trans. *The Thirteen Principal Upanishads.* 2nd edn. rev. London: Oxford University Press, 1968.

King, Carlyle. *Extending the Boundaries: Scholarship and Research at the University of Saskatchewan, 1909–1966.* [Saskatoon]: the University of Saskatchewan, 1967.

Krebs, Hans A. (Sir), and Julian H. Shelley, eds. *The Creative Process in Science and Medicine.* (Proceedings of the C. H. Boehringer Sohn Symposium held at Kronberg, Taunus, May, 1974) New York: American Elsevier, 1975.

Kuhn, Thomas S. *The Essential Tension: Selected Studies in Scientific Tradition and Change.* Chicago: University of Chicago Press, 1977.

————. *The Structure of Scientific Revolutions.* (Issued as Vol. II, No. 2 of the *International Encyclopedia of Unified Science.*) Chicago: University of Chicago Press, 1962.

Lebel, Maurice. *L'Éducation et l'Humanisme: Essais.* Sherbrooke [Quebec]: Édition Paulines, 1966.

Margenau, Henry. *The Nature of Physical Reality.* New York: McGraw-Hill, 1950.

Newman, John Henry (Cardinal). *The Idea of a University, Defined and Illustrated.* New York: Longmans, Green, 1947.

Northrop, Filmer Stuart Cockow. *The Logic of the Sciences and the Humanities.* New York: MacMillan Co., 1947.

Ortega y Gasset, José. *The Modern Theme.* Trans. James Cleugh. London: the C. W. Daniel Co., 1931.

Parliament of Canada: *Senate Special Committee on Science Policy.* Vols. I, II, III, and IV (The Lamontagne Commission Report.) Ottawa: the Queen's Printer, 1968, 1970, 1973, and 1977.

Poincaré, [Jules] Henri. *The Value of Science. (Le Science et l'Hypothèse.)* Trans. George Bruce Halsted. New York: Dover Publications, 1958.

Swift, Jonathan. *Gulliver's Travels.* Ed. Herbert Davis. Oxford: Blackwell, 1965.

Thompson, Fred G. *Saskatchewan Seminar on Futures Forecasting, Prince Albert, Saskatchewan, 1974.* Ed. Dallas McQuarrie. Regina: Canadian Plains Research Center, 1974.

Werkmeister, William Henry. *A Philosophy of Science.* New York: Harper and brothers, 1940.

Whitehead, Alfred North. *The Aims of Education and Other Essays.* New York: New American Library of World Literature, 1949.

Woodger, Joseph Henry. *Biology and Language: An Introduction to the Methodology of the Biological Sciences, Including Medicine.* (The Tarner Lectures, 1949-1950.) Cambridge: Cambridge University Press, 1952.

Index

Ajawaan, Lake, 46
Allmand, A. J., 15, 19
Alumni, visits to, 110
Anahareo, wife of Grey Owl, 46
Archeology, 10
Archeological Society, 34
Atomic Energy Project, Canadian, 63
A.U.C.C., 158
Auld, H., chancellor, 143

Ballet, 91, 118
Barber, L., Vice-President, 143
Bardwell, John and Millicent, 105
Begg, R., Dean of Medicine, 98
Behrdal, 95
Bentley, J., 46
Blakeney, Alan, Premier, 144
Bone, 101
Bonneau, 95
Brockelbank, J. H., 91, 100
Bronowski, 177

Campbell, Dr. Jim, 56
Camping, 6, 46
Canada Council, 157
Canadian Agricultural Research Council, 166
Canadian Plains Research Center, 170

Carpenter, G. C., 135
Cawley, James, 90
Claxton, Brooke, 157
Cobalt, radioactive, 73
    therapy unit, 167
Cockcroft, John, 63, 99
Colombo, Ceylon, 128
Coastal Command, 55
Commando, 54
Creative process, 185
Culliton, E. M., chancellor, 143
    chairman of the Board, 143
Correy, A., 95
Currie, B. W., 143
Cushing, C. G., 155
C.W.F., 160

Darmstadt, Technisches Hochschule, 35
Dentistry, College of, 97
Deuterium, 39
Dichlorine hexoxide, 24
Dicoumarin, 70
Diefenbaker Center, 101
Diefenbaker, John, chancellor, 143
Douglas, Premier, 99, 100
Defense Research Board, 156
Duff, 95
Duleep Singh, 10

Edmunds, H., 90
Emma Lake, 34
Exhibition, London, 22

Fertilizer, radioactive, 69
Fighter Command, 55
Flying effort, 57
Francis, W. B. 92
Fulmerstone, Sir Richard, 9

Gamow, G., 171
Geneva, U.N. Conference, 124
Geneva, Atoms for Peace
  Conferences,
  first (1955), 77
  second (1958), 88
  third (1964), 82
  fourth (1971), 83
Glinz, L., 46
Grammar School, 8
Green, the Rev. Mr., 10
Green Cheese Research, 72
Goldschmidt, Bertrand, 64
Grey Owl, 46
Grimes Graves, flint mines, 11
Grinyer, C. A., 82
Gustin, Lyell, 33

Hall Commission, 146
Hamilton, Alvin, 100
Harrington, E. L., 34
Haycock, Maurice, 110
Hayes, F. R., 155
Herzberg, G., 35, 43, 45
Herzberg, Louise, 37
Hinshelwood, Cyril, 29
Hitler, 39
Honeymoon, Banff, 48
House, President's, 103
Hutcheon, L., 96

Indian and Metis Studies, 101
Institute for Northern Studies, 100
I.P.C.U.R., 159
Isotopes, radioactive, 69
Israel, 126

Jackson, A. Y., 110
Jamaica, 124
Jane, Dr., 155
Johns, Harold, 73, 168

Katz, Dr., 98, 156
King's College, University of
  London, 14, 15
Klechkowski, 114
Kotelawala, Sir John, 132
Kuhn, T. S., 153
Kupsch, W., 101

Language, 178
Lapp Commission, 146
Leningrad, 119
Lawrence, G. C., 82
Leggatt, C. W., 57
Lepeschinskaya, 92
Leslie, E. C., 143
Levesque, G. H., 157
Lewis, W. B., 82
Lindner, Ernest, 33
Linear Accelerator Laboratory, 98
Lloyd, Woodrow, 100, 156
Lovell, F., 108, 143

MacEwan, Grant, 34
Mackenzie, C. J., 53, 61, 155
Macmillan, Sir Ernest, 157
McMurchy, Minister of Education,
  144
Manning, Roger, 48
Matriculation, Cambridge, 9
Mawdsley, J., 100
M.B.E., 67
McEown, Colb, 94
McFaull, J., 143
McRae, I. F., 82
Medal, Duleep Singh, 10
Mendeleef Centenary, 121
Methwold, 3
Military Science, Dr. of, 67
Mitchell, J., 69
Moisture meter, neutron, 71
Moscow, 113
Moss, H., 106
Murray, Walter, President, 28, 42
Museum, Hermitage, 118
Musk-Ox Journal, 100
  scholarships, 100

National Research Council, 154
Neatby, Hilda, 99
New Delhi, 134
Neutron source, high intensity, 66

Newman, Cardinal, 188
NewStart program, 163
Norrish, R., 29
Northern Studies, Institute of, 99
Nuclear Power, 75

O.E.C.D. meeting, Paris, 126
Oil and Gas Board, 159
Operational Research Center, 54
Operations Research, 163
Optimization, 162

Paine, Tom, 9
Panofsky, 99
Patunak, 108
Peene, Vida, 157
Paradis, A., 157
Photochemical experiment, 21
Phillips, E. K., 143
Pinder, H., 143
Pringle, J., 143
P.O.S., Pilot Plant, 95
President, University, 92
Presidents, Western University, 159
Publication, first scientific, 24

Quantum jungle, 171

Radiation, industrial use of, 74
Radical, free, 25, 73
Radiation chemistry, 187
Rae, S. F., Canadian Ambassador,
    Geneva, 124
Rankin Inlet, 100, 138
Rapeseed, 95
Rowley, Graham, 100
Reaction, chain, 24
Rees, H. C., 143
Regina campus, expansion of, 141
Rénaud, André, 101
Resolute, 135
Resonance, electron spin, 25
Riddell, W., 141
Riga, 121
Russia
    (1960), 113
    (1965), 115
    (1969), 121
    (1978), 121

Santon Downham, 10
Saskatchewan Oil and Gas Board,
    90
Saskatchewan, University of, 28
Saskatoon, 28, 31
Saunders, G., 108, 143
Scholarship, 8, 22
Scientific method, 176
Scouts, 18
Searches for missing aircraft, 59
Semenov, N. N., 114
Shakespear, Inspector, 94
Short-snorter, 55
Sit-in, Saskatoon campus, 145
Smith, E. C., 56
Solandt, O., 156
Spectra, hydrochloric acid, 39
    hydrogen cyanide, 39
    acetylene, 39
Spinks, Mary, 61, 65, 84, 90, 104,
    105, 108, 112, 115
Sports, 17
S.R.C., 156
Steacie, E. W. R., 63, 99, 155
Strelioff, Mary, 47
Strike, general, 26
Systems Study Group, hospital, 162

Taylor, E. P., 157
Tamerlane, tomb of, 117
Tashkent, 115
Tblisi, 121
Tea, instant, 105
Teacher training, 98
Thatcher, Premier, 97
Theatre, Bolshoi, 114
Thetford, 4
Thorvaldson, T., 28, 46
Tracer method, 69
Trueman, A., 157
Trials, bombing, 58
Tubby, A., 143

Unashamed men's club, 48
University, Hamburg, 123

Vanier, General and Madame, 104
Veterinary College, 96
Vidodaya University, 129
Vigfuson, Dr., 34
Vladimirski, Prof., 99

Warden, Qu'Appelle Hall, 42
Wedgwood, J., 143
Wells, K. F., 97
Whiting, 92, 143
Wilkinson, Dr., 99
Williamson, Bob, 100

Woods, R. J., 74, 121

Yamasaki, Minoru, 141

Zagorsk, 120
Zilch, F. O., 59